D1277012

ISBN 0-17-641279-4

Consists of:

Precalculus Mathematics for Calculus, 4th Edition, Stewart/Redlin/Watson

ISBN 0-534-43421-5, © 2002

Contents

· ·

· ·

10. A **logistic model** is a function of the form

$$y = \frac{c}{1 + ae^{-bx}}$$

Logistic functions are appropriate for modeling population growth where the growth is limited by available resources. The table and scatter plot give the population of black flies in a closed laboratory container over an 18-day period.

(a) Use the **Logistic** command on your calculator to find a logistic model for these data.

(b) Use the model to estimate the time when there were 400 flies in the container.

Time (days)	Number of flies
0	10
2	25
4	66
6	144
8	262
10	374
12	446
16	492
18	498

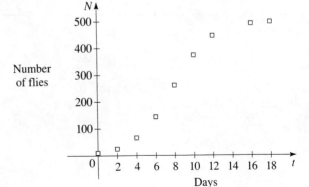

Number of flies

5 Trigonometric Functions of Real Numbers

Trigonometric functions are used to describe periodic phenomena such as the ebb and flow of tides, or the vibrations of a violin string.

Trigonometry contains the science of continually undulating magnitude . . .

Augustus De Morgan

In this chapter and the next, we introduce two different but equivalent ways of viewing the trigonometric functions. One way is to view them as *functions of real numbers* (Chapter 5), the other as *functions of angles* (Chapter 6). The two approaches to trigonometry are independent of each other, so either Chapter 5 or Chapter 6 may be studied first.

The trigonometric functions defined in these two different ways are identical—they assign the same value to a given real number. In the first case, the real number is the length of an arc along the unit circle; in the second case, it is the measure of an angle. We study both approaches because different applications require that we view these functions differently. One approach (Chapter 5) lends itself to dynamic applications such as the modeling of harmonic motion, whereas the other approach (Chapter 6) lends itself to static applications such as the measurement of distance using triangles. The power and versatility of trigonometry stems from the fact that it can be viewed in these different ways. In modern times, trigonometry has found application in such diverse fields as signal processing, coding of music on compact discs, designing guidance systems for the space shuttle, finding distances to stars, producing CAT scans for medical imaging, and many others.

5.1 THE UNIT CIRCLE

In this section we explore some properties of the circle of radius 1 centered at the origin. These properties are used in the next section to define the trigonometric functions.

The Unit Circle

The set of points at a distance 1 from the origin is a circle of radius 1 (see Figure 1). In Section 1.8 we learned that the equation of this circle is $x^2 + y^2 = 1$.

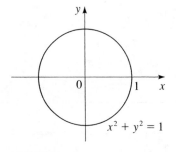

FIGURE 1
The unit circle

> **THE UNIT CIRCLE**
>
> The **unit circle** is the circle of radius 1 centered at the origin in the xy-plane. Its equation is
> $$x^2 + y^2 = 1$$

EXAMPLE 1 ■ A Point on the Unit Circle

Show that the point $P\left(\dfrac{\sqrt{3}}{3}, \dfrac{\sqrt{2}}{\sqrt{3}}\right)$ is on the unit circle.

SOLUTION

We need to show that this point satisfies the equation of the unit circle, that is, $x^2 + y^2 = 1$. Since

$$\left(\frac{\sqrt{3}}{3}\right)^2 + \left(\frac{\sqrt{2}}{\sqrt{3}}\right)^2 = \frac{3}{9} + \frac{2}{3} = \frac{1}{3} + \frac{2}{3} = 1$$

P is on the unit circle.   ∎

EXAMPLE 2 ■ Locating a Point on the Unit Circle

The point $P(\sqrt{3}/2, y)$ is on the unit circle in quadrant IV. Find its y-coordinate.

SOLUTION   Since the point is on the unit circle, we have

$$\left(\frac{\sqrt{3}}{2}\right)^2 + y^2 = 1$$

$$y^2 = 1 - \frac{3}{4} = \frac{1}{4}$$

$$y = \pm\frac{1}{2}$$

Since the point is in quadrant IV, its y-coordinate must be negative, so $y = -\frac{1}{2}$.   ∎

Terminal Points on the Unit Circle

Suppose t is a real number. Let's mark off a distance t along the unit circle, starting at the point $(1, 0)$ and moving in a counterclockwise direction if t is positive or in a clockwise direction if t is negative (Figure 2). In this way we arrive at a point $P(x, y)$ on the unit circle. The point $P(x, y)$ obtained in this way is called the **terminal point** determined by the real number t.

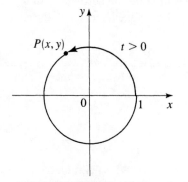

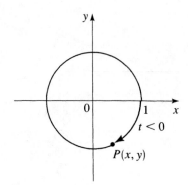

FIGURE 2

(a) Terminal point $P(x, y)$ determined by $t > 0$

(b) Terminal point $P(x, y)$ determined by $t < 0$

The circumference of the unit circle is $C = 2\pi(1) = 2\pi$. So, if a point starts at $(1, 0)$ and moves counterclockwise all the way around the unit circle and returns to $(1, 0)$, it travels a distance of 2π. To move halfway around the circle, it travels a distance of $\frac{1}{2}(2\pi) = \pi$. To move a quarter of the distance around the circle, it travels a distance of $\frac{1}{4}(2\pi) = \pi/2$. Where does the point end up when it travels these distances along the circle? From Figure 3 we see, for example, that when it travels a distance of π starting at $(1, 0)$, its terminal point is $(-1, 0)$.

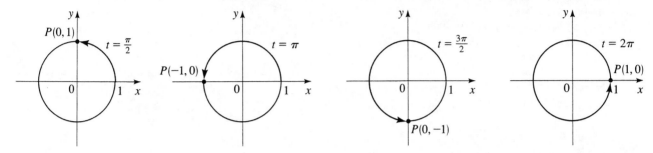

FIGURE 3

Terminal points determined by $t = \frac{\pi}{2}, \pi, \frac{3\pi}{2}$, and 2π

EXAMPLE 3 ■ Finding Terminal Points

Find the terminal point on the unit circle determined by each real number t.

(a) $t = 3\pi$ (b) $t = -\pi$ (c) $t = -\dfrac{\pi}{2}$

SOLUTION

From Figure 4 we get the following.

(a) The terminal point determined by 3π is $(-1, 0)$.

(b) The terminal point determined by $-\pi$ is $(-1, 0)$.

(c) The terminal point determined by $-\pi/2$ is $(0, -1)$.

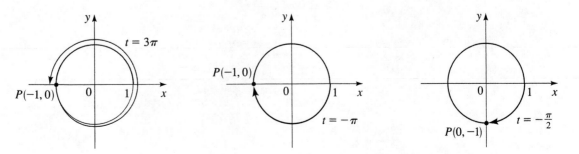

FIGURE 4

Notice that different values of t can determine the same terminal point.   ■

The Value of π

The number π is the ratio of the circumference of a circle to its diameter. It has been known since ancient times that this ratio is the same for all circles. The first systematic effort to find a numerical approximation for π was made by Archimedes (ca. 240 B.C.), who proved that $\frac{22}{7} < \pi < \frac{223}{71}$ by finding the perimeters of regular polygons inscribed in and circumscribed about a circle. (See Problem 4, page 530.)

In about A.D. 480, the Chinese physicist Tsu Ch'ung-chih gave the approximation

$$\pi \approx \frac{355}{113} = 3.141592\ldots$$

which is correct to six decimals. This remained the most accurate estimation of π until the Dutch mathematician Adrianus Romanus (1593) used polygons with more than a billion sides to compute π correct to 15 decimals. In the 17th century, mathematicians began to use infinite series and trigonometric identities in the quest for π. (See Problem 8, page 619.) The Englishman William Shanks spent 15 years (1858–1873) using these methods to compute π to 707 decimals, but in 1946 it was found that his figures were wrong beginning with the 528th decimal. Today, with the aid of computers, mathematicians routinely determine π correct to millions of decimals.

The terminal point $P(x, y)$ determined by $t = \pi/4$ is the same distance from $(1, 0)$ as from $(0, 1)$ along the unit circle (see Figure 5).

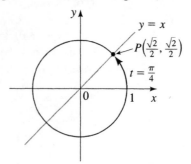

FIGURE 5

Since the unit circle is symmetric with respect to the line $y = x$, it follows that P lies on the line $y = x$. So P is the point of intersection (in the first quadrant) of the circle $x^2 + y^2 = 1$ and the line $y = x$. Substituting x for y in the equation of the circle, we get

$$x^2 + x^2 = 1$$
$$2x^2 = 1 \qquad \text{Combine like terms}$$
$$x^2 = \frac{1}{2} \qquad \text{Divide by 2}$$
$$x = \pm\frac{1}{\sqrt{2}} \qquad \text{Take square roots}$$

Since P is in the first quadrant, $x = 1/\sqrt{2}$ and since $y = x$, we have $y = 1/\sqrt{2}$ also. Thus, the terminal point determined by $\pi/4$ is

$$P\left(\frac{1}{\sqrt{2}}, \frac{1}{\sqrt{2}}\right) = P\left(\frac{\sqrt{2}}{2}, \frac{\sqrt{2}}{2}\right)$$

Similar methods can be used to find the terminal points determined by $t = \pi/6$ and $t = \pi/3$ (see Exercises 47 and 48). Table 1 and Figure 6 give the terminal points for some special values of t.

TABLE 1

t	Terminal point determined by t
0	$(1, 0)$
$\frac{\pi}{6}$	$\left(\frac{\sqrt{3}}{2}, \frac{1}{2}\right)$
$\frac{\pi}{4}$	$\left(\frac{\sqrt{2}}{2}, \frac{\sqrt{2}}{2}\right)$
$\frac{\pi}{3}$	$\left(\frac{1}{2}, \frac{\sqrt{3}}{2}\right)$
$\frac{\pi}{2}$	$(0, 1)$

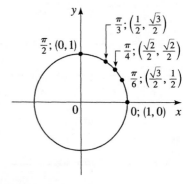

FIGURE 6

EXAMPLE 4 ■ Finding Terminal Points

Find the terminal point determined by each given real number t.

(a) $t = -\dfrac{\pi}{4}$ (b) $t = \dfrac{3\pi}{4}$ (c) $t = -\dfrac{5\pi}{6}$

SOLUTION

(a) Let P be the terminal point determined by $-\pi/4$, and let Q be the terminal point determined by $\pi/4$. From Figure 7(a) we see that the point P has the same coordinates as Q except for sign. Since P is in quadrant IV, its x-coordinate is positive and its y-coordinate is negative. Thus, the terminal point is $P(\sqrt{2}/2, -\sqrt{2}/2)$.

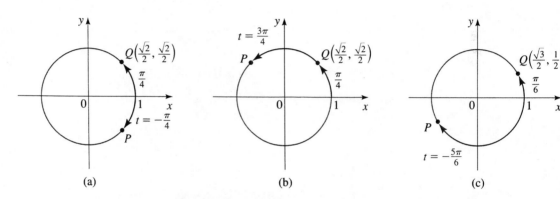

FIGURE 7   (a)   (b)   (c)

(b) Let P be the terminal point determined by $3\pi/4$, and let Q be the terminal point determined by $\pi/4$. From Figure 7(b) we see that the point P has the same coordinates as Q except for sign. Since P is in quadrant II, its x-coordinate is negative and its y-coordinate is positive. Thus, the terminal point is $P(-\sqrt{2}/2, \sqrt{2}/2)$.

(c) Let P be the terminal point determined by $-5\pi/6$, and let Q be the terminal point determined by $\pi/6$. From Figure 7(c) we see that the point P has the same coordinates as Q except for sign. Since P is in quadrant III, its coordinates are both negative. Thus, the terminal point is $P\left(-\sqrt{3}/2, -\tfrac{1}{2}\right)$.   ■

The Reference Number

From Examples 3 and 4, we see that to find a terminal point in any quadrant we need only know the "corresponding" terminal point in the first quadrant. We give a procedure for finding such terminal points using the idea of the *reference number*.

REFERENCE NUMBER

Let t be a real number. The **reference number** $\bar{t}$ associated with t is the shortest distance along the unit circle between the terminal point determined by t and the x-axis.

Figure 8 shows that to find the reference number $\bar{t}$ it's helpful to know the quadrant in which the terminal point determined by t lies.

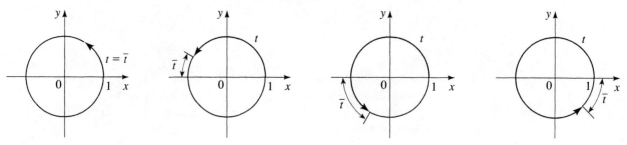

FIGURE 8

The reference number $\bar{t}$ for t

EXAMPLE 5 ■ Finding Reference Numbers

Find the reference number for each value of t.

(a) $t = \dfrac{5\pi}{6}$ (b) $t = \dfrac{7\pi}{4}$ (c) $t = -\dfrac{2\pi}{3}$ (d) $t = 5.80$

SOLUTION

From Figure 9 we find the reference numbers as follows.

(a) $\bar{t} = \pi - \dfrac{5\pi}{6} = \dfrac{\pi}{6}$

(b) $\bar{t} = 2\pi - \dfrac{7\pi}{4} = \dfrac{\pi}{4}$

(c) $\bar{t} = \pi - \dfrac{2\pi}{3} = \dfrac{\pi}{3}$

(d) $\bar{t} = 2\pi - 5.80 \approx 0.48$

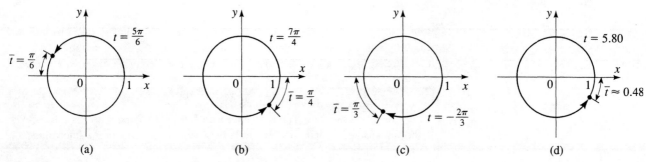

FIGURE 9

■

USING REFERENCE NUMBERS TO FIND TERMINAL POINTS

To find the terminal point P determined by any value of t, we use the following steps:

1. Find the reference number $\bar{t}$.

2. Find the terminal point $Q(a, b)$ determined by $\bar{t}$.

3. The terminal point determined by t is $P(\pm a, \pm b)$, where the signs are chosen according to the quadrant in which this terminal point lies.

EXAMPLE 6 ■ **Using Reference Numbers to Find Terminal Points**

Find the terminal point determined by each given real number t.

(a) $t = \dfrac{5\pi}{6}$ (b) $t = \dfrac{7\pi}{4}$ (c) $t = -\dfrac{2\pi}{3}$

SOLUTION

The reference numbers associated with these values of t were found in Example 5.

(a) The reference number is $\bar{t} = \pi/6$, which determines the terminal point $\left(\sqrt{3}/2, \frac{1}{2}\right)$ from Table 1. Since the terminal point determined by t is in quadrant II, its x-coordinate is negative and its y-coordinate is positive. Thus, the desired terminal point is

$$\left(-\frac{\sqrt{3}}{2}, \frac{1}{2}\right)$$

(b) The reference number is $\bar{t} = \pi/4$, which determines the terminal point $\left(\sqrt{2}/2, \sqrt{2}/2\right)$ from Table 1. Since the terminal point is in quadrant IV, its x-coordinate is positive and its y-coordinate is negative. Thus, the desired terminal point is

$$\left(\frac{\sqrt{2}}{2}, -\frac{\sqrt{2}}{2}\right)$$

(c) The reference number is $\bar{t} = \pi/3$, which determines the terminal point $\left(\frac{1}{2}, \sqrt{3}/2\right)$ from Table 1. Since the terminal point determined by t is in quadrant III, its coordinates are both negative. Thus, the desired terminal point is

$$\left(-\frac{1}{2}, -\frac{\sqrt{3}}{2}\right)$$
■

Since the circumference of the unit circle is 2π, the terminal point determined by t is the same as that determined by $t + 2\pi$ or $t - 2\pi$. In general, we can add or subtract 2π any number of times without changing the terminal point determined by t. We use this observation in the next example to find terminal points for large t.

EXAMPLE 7 ■ **Finding the Terminal Point for Large t**

Find the terminal point determined by $t = \dfrac{29\pi}{6}$.

SOLUTION

Since

$$t = \frac{29\pi}{6} = 4\pi + \frac{5\pi}{6}$$

we see that the terminal point of t is the same as that of $5\pi/6$ (that is, we subtract 4π). So by Example 6(a) the terminal point is $\left(-\sqrt{3}/2, \frac{1}{2}\right)$. ■

5.1   EXERCISES

1–4 ■ Show that the point is on the unit circle.

1. $\left(\frac{3}{5}, \frac{4}{5}\right)$

2. $\left(\frac{5}{13}, -\frac{12}{13}\right)$

3. $\left(-\frac{2}{3}, -\frac{\sqrt{5}}{3}\right)$

4. $\left(\frac{\sqrt{11}}{6}, \frac{5}{6}\right)$

5–10 ■ The point P is on the unit circle. Find $P(x, y)$ from the given information.

5. The x-coordinate of P is $\frac{4}{5}$ and P is in quadrant I.

6. The y-coordinate of P is $-\frac{1}{3}$ and P is in quadrant IV.

7. The y-coordinate of P is $\frac{2}{3}$ and the x-coordinate is negative.

8. The x-coordinate of P is positive and the y-coordinate of P is $-\sqrt{5}/5$.

9. The x-coordinate of P is $-\sqrt{2}/3$ and P is in quadrant III.

10. The x-coordinate of P is $-\frac{2}{5}$ and P is in quadrant II.

11–12 ■ Find t and the terminal point determined by t for each point in the figure. In Exercise 11, t increases in increments of $\pi/4$; in Exercise 12, t increases in increments of $\pi/6$.

11.

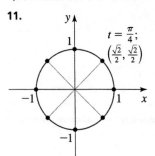

$t = \frac{\pi}{4}$; $\left(\frac{\sqrt{2}}{2}, \frac{\sqrt{2}}{2}\right)$

12.

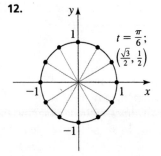

$t = \frac{\pi}{6}$; $\left(\frac{\sqrt{3}}{2}, \frac{1}{2}\right)$

13–22 ■ Find the terminal point $P(x, y)$ on the unit circle determined by the given value of t.

13. $t = \dfrac{\pi}{2}$

14. $t = \dfrac{3\pi}{2}$

15. $t = \dfrac{5\pi}{6}$

16. $t = \dfrac{7\pi}{6}$

17. $t = -\dfrac{\pi}{3}$

18. $t = \dfrac{5\pi}{3}$

19. $t = \dfrac{2\pi}{3}$

20. $t = -\dfrac{\pi}{2}$

21. $t = -\dfrac{3\pi}{4}$

22. $t = \dfrac{11\pi}{6}$

23. Suppose that the terminal point determined by t is the point $\left(\frac{3}{5}, \frac{4}{5}\right)$ on the unit circle. Find the terminal point determined by each of the following.
   (a) $\pi - t$ (b) $-t$ (c) $\pi + t$ (d) $2\pi + t$

24. Suppose that the terminal point determined by t is the point $\left(\frac{3}{4}, \sqrt{7}/4\right)$ on the unit circle. Find the terminal point determined by each of the following.
   (a) $-t$ (b) $4\pi + t$ (c) $\pi - t$ (d) $t - \pi$

25–28 ■ Find the reference number for each value of t.

25. (a) $t = \dfrac{5\pi}{4}$

(b) $t = \dfrac{7\pi}{3}$

(c) $t = -\dfrac{4\pi}{3}$

(d) $t = \dfrac{\pi}{6}$

26. (a) $t = \dfrac{5\pi}{7}$ (b) $t = -\dfrac{9\pi}{8}$

   (c) $t = 3.55$ (d) $t = -2.9$

27. (a) $t = -\dfrac{11\pi}{5}$ (b) $t = \dfrac{13\pi}{6}$

   (c) $t = \dfrac{7\pi}{3}$ (d) $t = -\dfrac{5\pi}{6}$

28. (a) $t = 3$ (b) $t = 6$
    (c) $t = -3$ (d) $t = -6$

29–42 ■ Find (a) the reference number for each value of t, and (b) the terminal point determined by t.

29. $t = \dfrac{2\pi}{3}$ **30.** $t = \dfrac{4\pi}{3}$

31. $t = \dfrac{3\pi}{4}$ **32.** $t = \dfrac{7\pi}{3}$

33. $t = -\dfrac{2\pi}{3}$ **34.** $t = -\dfrac{7\pi}{6}$

35. $t = \dfrac{13\pi}{4}$ **36.** $t = \dfrac{13\pi}{6}$

37. $t = \dfrac{7\pi}{6}$ **38.** $t = \dfrac{17\pi}{4}$

39. $t = -\dfrac{11\pi}{3}$ **40.** $t = \dfrac{31\pi}{6}$

41. $t = \dfrac{16\pi}{3}$ **42.** $t = -\dfrac{41\pi}{4}$

43–46 ■ Use the figure to find the terminal point determined by the real number t, with coordinates correct to one decimal place.

43. $t = 1$

44. $t = 2.5$

45. $t = -1.1$

46. $t = 4.2$

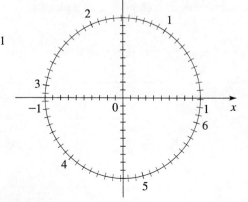

DISCOVERY • DISCUSSION

47. Finding the Terminal Point for $\pi/6$ Suppose the terminal point determined by $t = \pi/6$ is $P(x, y)$ and the points Q and R are as shown in the figure. Why are the distances PQ and PR the same? Use this fact, together with the Distance Formula, to show that the coordinates of P satisfy the equation $2y = \sqrt{x^2 + (y - 1)^2}$. Simplify this equation using the fact that $x^2 + y^2 = 1$. Solve the simplified equation to find $P(x, y)$.

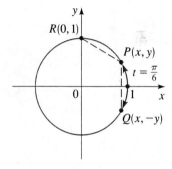

48. Finding the Terminal Point for $\pi/3$ Now that you know the terminal point determined by $t = \pi/6$, use symmetry to find the terminal point determined by $t = \pi/3$ (see the figure). Explain your reasoning.

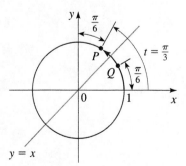

5.2 TRIGONOMETRIC FUNCTIONS OF REAL NUMBERS

A function is a rule that assigns to each real number another real number. In this section we use properties of the unit circle from the preceding section to define certain functions of real numbers, the trigonometric functions.

▪ The Trigonometric Functions

Recall that to find the terminal point $P(x, y)$ for a given real number t, we move a distance t along the unit circle, starting at the point $(1, 0)$. We move in a counterclockwise direction if t is positive and in a clockwise direction if t is negative (see Figure 1). We now use the x- and y-coordinates of the point $P(x, y)$ to define several functions. For instance, we define the function called *sine* by assigning to each real number t the y-coordinate of the terminal point $P(x, y)$ determined by t. The functions *cosine, tangent, cosecant, secant,* and *cotangent* are also defined using the coordinates of $P(x, y)$.

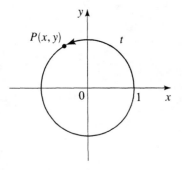

FIGURE 1

DEFINITION OF THE TRIGONOMETRIC FUNCTIONS

Let t be any real number and let $P(x, y)$ be the terminal point on the unit circle determined by t. We define

$$\sin t = y \qquad \cos t = x \qquad \tan t = \frac{y}{x} \quad (x \neq 0)$$

$$\csc t = \frac{1}{y} \quad (y \neq 0) \qquad \sec t = \frac{1}{x} \quad (x \neq 0) \qquad \cot t = \frac{x}{y} \quad (y \neq 0)$$

Because the trigonometric functions can be defined in terms of the unit circle, they are sometimes called the **circular functions**.

EXAMPLE 1 ▪ **Evaluating Trigonometric Functions**

Find the six trigonometric functions of each given real number t.

(a) $t = \dfrac{\pi}{3}$ (b) $t = \dfrac{\pi}{2}$

SOLUTION

(a) The terminal point determined by $t = \pi/3$ is $P\left(\frac{1}{2}, \sqrt{3}/2\right)$. Since the coordinates are $x = \frac{1}{2}$ and $y = \sqrt{3}/2$, we have

$$\sin \frac{\pi}{3} = \frac{\sqrt{3}}{2} \qquad \cos \frac{\pi}{3} = \frac{1}{2} \qquad \tan \frac{\pi}{3} = \frac{\sqrt{3}/2}{1/2} = \sqrt{3}$$

$$\csc \frac{\pi}{3} = \frac{2\sqrt{3}}{3} \qquad \sec \frac{\pi}{3} = 2 \qquad \cot \frac{\pi}{4} = \frac{1/2}{\sqrt{3}/2} = \frac{\sqrt{3}}{3}$$

Relationship to the Trigonometric Functions of Angles

If you have previously studied trigonometry of right triangles (Chapter 6), you are probably wondering how the sine and cosine of an *angle* relate to those of this section. To see how, let's start with a right triangle, $\triangle OPQ$.

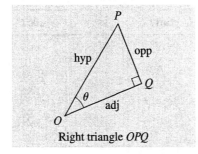

Right triangle OPQ

Place the triangle in the coordinate plane as shown, with angle θ in standard position.

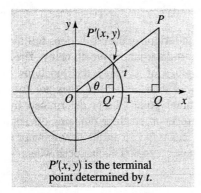

$P'(x, y)$ is the terminal point determined by t.

The point $P'(x, y)$ in the figure is the terminal point determined by the arc t. Note that triangle OPQ is similar to the small triangle $OP'Q'$ whose legs have lengths x and y.

Now, by the definition of the trigonometric functions of the *angle* θ we have

$$\sin \theta = \frac{\text{opp}}{\text{hyp}} = \frac{PQ}{OP} = \frac{P'Q'}{OP'}$$

$$= \frac{y}{1} = y$$

$$\cos \theta = \frac{\text{adj}}{\text{hyp}} = \frac{OQ}{OP} = \frac{OQ'}{OP'}$$

$$= \frac{x}{1} = x$$

By the definition of the trigonometric functions of the *real number t*, we have

$$\sin t = y$$

$$\cos t = x$$

Now, if θ is measured in radians, then $\theta = t$ (see the figure). So the trigonometric functions of the angle with radian measure θ are exactly the same as the trigonometric functions defined in terms of the terminal point determined by the real number t.

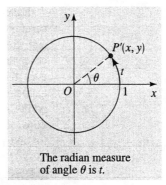

The radian measure of angle θ is t.

Why then study trigonometry in two different ways? Because different applications require that we view the trigonometric functions differently. (See *Focus on Modeling*, page 455, and Sections 6.2, 6.4, and 6.5.)

(b) The terminal point determined by $\pi/2$ is $P(0, 1)$. So

$$\sin\frac{\pi}{2} = 1 \qquad \cos\frac{\pi}{2} = 0 \qquad \csc\frac{\pi}{2} = \frac{1}{1} = 1 \qquad \cot\frac{\pi}{2} = \frac{0}{1} = 0$$

But $\tan \pi/2$ and $\sec \pi/2$ are undefined because $x = 0$ appears in the denominator in each of their definitions. ■

Some special values of the trigonometric functions are listed in Table 1. This table is easily obtained from Table 1 of Section 5.1, together with the definitions of the trigonometric functions.

TABLE 1 Special values of the trigonometric functions

t	$\sin t$	$\cos t$	$\tan t$	$\csc t$	$\sec t$	$\cot t$
0	0	1	0	—	1	—
$\dfrac{\pi}{6}$	$\dfrac{1}{2}$	$\dfrac{\sqrt{3}}{2}$	$\dfrac{\sqrt{3}}{3}$	2	$\dfrac{2\sqrt{3}}{3}$	$\sqrt{3}$
$\dfrac{\pi}{4}$	$\dfrac{\sqrt{2}}{2}$	$\dfrac{\sqrt{2}}{2}$	1	$\sqrt{2}$	$\sqrt{2}$	1
$\dfrac{\pi}{3}$	$\dfrac{\sqrt{3}}{2}$	$\dfrac{1}{2}$	$\sqrt{3}$	$\dfrac{2\sqrt{3}}{3}$	2	$\dfrac{\sqrt{3}}{3}$
$\dfrac{\pi}{2}$	1	0	—	1	—	0

Example 1 shows that some of the trigonometric functions fail to be defined for certain real numbers. So we need to determine their domains. The functions sine and cosine are defined for all values of t. Since the functions cotangent and cosecant have y in the denominator of their definitions, they are not defined whenever the y-coordinate of the terminal point $P(x, y)$ determined by t is 0. This happens when $t = n\pi$ for any integer n, so their domains do not include these points. The functions tangent and secant have x in the denominator in their definitions, so they are not defined whenever $x = 0$. This happens when $t = (\pi/2) + n\pi$ for any integer n.

DOMAINS OF THE TRIGONOMETRIC FUNCTIONS

Function	Domain
sin, cos	All real numbers
tan, sec	All real numbers other than $\dfrac{\pi}{2} + n\pi$ for any integer n
cot, csc	All real numbers other than $n\pi$ for any integer n

Values of the Trigonometric Functions

To compute other values of the trigonometric functions, we first determine their signs. The signs of the trigonometric functions depend on the quadrant in which the terminal point of t lies. For example, if the terminal point $P(x, y)$ determined by t lies in quadrant III, then its coordinates are both negative. So $\sin t$, $\cos t$, $\csc t$, and $\sec t$ are all negative, while $\tan t$ and $\cot t$ are positive. You can check the other entries in the following box.

The following mnemonic device can be used to remember which trigonometric functions are positive in each quadrant: All of them, Sine, Tangent, or Cosine.

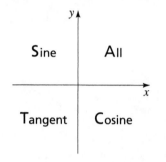

You can remember this as "All Students Take Calculus."

SIGNS OF THE TRIGONOMETRIC FUNCTIONS		
Quadrant	Positive Functions	Negative functions
I	all	none
II	sin, csc	cos, sec, tan, cot
III	tan, cot	sin, csc, cos, sec
IV	cos, sec	sin, csc, tan, cot

EXAMPLE 2 ■ Determining the Sign of a Trigonometric Function

(a) $\cos \dfrac{\pi}{3} > 0$, since the terminal point of $t = \dfrac{\pi}{3}$ is in quadrant I.

(b) $\tan 4 > 0$, since the terminal point of $t = 4$ is in quadrant III.

(c) If $\cos t < 0$ and $\sin t > 0$, then the terminal point of t must be in quadrant II. ■

In Section 5.1 we used the reference number to find the terminal point determined by a real number t. Since the trigonometric functions are defined in terms of the coordinates of terminal points, we can use the reference number to find values of the trigonometric functions. Suppose that $\bar{t}$ is the reference number for t. Then the terminal point of $\bar{t}$ has the same coordinates, except possibly for sign, as the terminal point of t. So the values of the trigonometric functions at t are the same, except possibly for sign, as their values at $\bar{t}$. We illustrate the procedure in the next example.

EXAMPLE 3 ■ Evaluating Trigonometric Functions

Find each value.

(a) $\cos \dfrac{2\pi}{3}$ (b) $\tan\left(-\dfrac{\pi}{3}\right)$ (c) $\sin \dfrac{19\pi}{4}$

SOLUTION

(a) The reference number for $2\pi/3$ is $\pi/3$. Since the terminal point of $2\pi/3$ is in quadrant II, $\cos(2\pi/3)$ is negative. Thus

$$\cos \frac{2\pi}{3} = -\cos \frac{\pi}{3} = -\frac{1}{2}$$

$$\underset{\text{sign}}{\uparrow} \quad \underset{\substack{\text{reference} \\ \text{number}}}{\uparrow} \quad \underset{\substack{\text{from} \\ \text{Table 1}}}{\uparrow}$$

(b) The reference number for $-\pi/3$ is $\pi/3$. Since the terminal point of $-\pi/3$ is in quadrant IV, $\tan(-\pi/3)$ is negative. Thus

$$\tan\left(-\frac{\pi}{3}\right) = -\tan\frac{\pi}{3} = -\sqrt{3}$$

$$\uparrow \qquad \uparrow \qquad\qquad \uparrow$$

sign   reference   from
number   Table 1

(c) Since $(19\pi/4) - 4\pi = 3\pi/4$, the terminal points determined by $19\pi/4$ and $3\pi/4$ are the same. The reference number for $3\pi/4$ is $\pi/4$. Since the terminal point of $3\pi/4$ is in quadrant II, $\sin(3\pi/4)$ is positive. Thus

$$\sin\frac{19\pi}{4} = \sin\frac{3\pi}{4} = +\sin\frac{\pi}{4} = \frac{\sqrt{2}}{2}$$

$$\uparrow \qquad\qquad \uparrow \quad \uparrow \qquad \nwarrow$$

subtract 4π sign   reference   from
number   Table 1   ∎

So far we have been able to compute the values of the trigonometric functions only for certain values of t. In fact, we can compute the values of the trigonometric functions whenever t is a multiple of $\pi/6$, $\pi/4$, $\pi/3$, and $\pi/2$. How can we compute the trigonometric functions for other values of t? For example, how can we find $\sin 1.5$? One way is to carefully sketch a diagram and read the value (see Exercises 35–42); however, this method is not very accurate. Fortunately, programmed directly into scientific calculators are mathematical procedures (see the margin) that find the values of *sine, cosine,* and *tangent* correct to the number of digits in the display. The calculator must be put in *radian mode* to evaluate these functions. To find values of cosecant, secant, and cotangent using a calculator, we need to use the following *reciprocal relations:*

$$\csc t = \frac{1}{\sin t} \qquad \sec t = \frac{1}{\cos t} \qquad \cot t = \frac{1}{\tan t}$$

These identities follow from the definitions of the trigonometric functions. For instance, since $\sin t = y$ and $\csc t = 1/y$, we have $\csc t = 1/y = 1/(\sin t)$. The others follow similarly.

EXAMPLE 4 ∎ Using a Calculator to Evaluate Trigonometric Functions

Making sure our calculator is set to radian mode and rounding the results to six decimal places, we get

(a) $\sin 2.2 \approx 0.808496$

(b) $\cos 1.1 \approx 0.453596$

(c) $\cot 28 = \dfrac{1}{\tan 28} \approx -3.553286$

(d) $\csc 0.98 = \dfrac{1}{\sin 0.98} \approx 1.204098$ ■

Let's consider the relationship between the trigonometric functions of t and those of $-t$. From Figure 2 we see that

$$\sin(-t) = -y = -\sin t$$

$$\cos(-t) = x = \cos t$$

$$\tan(-t) = \frac{-y}{x} = -\frac{y}{x} = -\tan t$$

These equations show that sine and tangent are odd functions, whereas cosine is an even function. It's easy to see that the reciprocal of an even function is even and the reciprocal of an odd function is odd (see Section 2.5). This fact, together with the reciprocal relations, completes our knowledge of the even-odd properties for all the trigonometric functions.

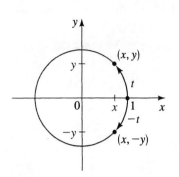

FIGURE 2

EVEN-ODD PROPERTIES

Sine, cosecant, tangent, and cotangent are odd functions; cosine and secant are even functions.

$$\sin(-t) = -\sin t \qquad \cos(-t) = \cos t \qquad \tan(-t) = -\tan t$$

$$\csc(-t) = -\csc t \qquad \sec(-t) = \sec t \qquad \cot(-t) = -\cot t$$

EXAMPLE 5 ■ Even and Odd Trigonometric Functions

Use the even-odd properties of the trigonometric functions to determine each value.

(a) $\sin\left(-\dfrac{\pi}{6}\right)$ (b) $\cos\left(-\dfrac{\pi}{4}\right)$

SOLUTION

By the even-odd properties and Table 1, we have

(a) $\sin\left(-\dfrac{\pi}{6}\right) = -\sin\dfrac{\pi}{6} = -\dfrac{1}{2}$ Sine is odd

(b) $\cos\left(-\dfrac{\pi}{4}\right) = \cos\dfrac{\pi}{4} = \dfrac{\sqrt{2}}{2}$ Cosine is even   ■

Fundamental Identities

The trigonometric functions are related to each other through equations called **trigonometric identities**. We give the most important ones in the following box.*

FUNDAMENTAL IDENTITIES

Reciprocal Identities

$$\csc t = \frac{1}{\sin t} \qquad \sec t = \frac{1}{\cos t} \qquad \cot t = \frac{1}{\tan t}$$

$$\tan t = \frac{\sin t}{\cos t} \qquad \cot t = \frac{\cos t}{\sin t}$$

Pythagorean Identities

$$\sin^2 t + \cos^2 t = 1 \qquad \tan^2 t + 1 = \sec^2 t \qquad 1 + \cot^2 t = \csc^2 t$$

■ **Proof** The reciprocal identities follow immediately from the definition on page 418. We now prove the Pythagorean identities. By definition, $\cos t = x$ and $\sin t = y$, where x and y are the coordinates of a point $P(x, y)$ on the unit circle. Since $P(x, y)$ is on the unit circle, we have $x^2 + y^2 = 1$. Thus

$$\sin^2 t + \cos^2 t = 1$$

Dividing both sides by $\cos^2 t$ (provided $\cos t \neq 0$), we get

$$\frac{\sin^2 t}{\cos^2 t} + \frac{\cos^2 t}{\cos^2 t} = \frac{1}{\cos^2 t}$$

$$\left(\frac{\sin t}{\cos t}\right)^2 + 1 = \left(\frac{1}{\cos t}\right)^2$$

$$\tan^2 t + 1 = \sec^2 t$$

We have used the reciprocal identities $\sin t/\cos t = \tan t$ and $1/\cos t = \sec t$. Similarly, dividing both sides of the first Pythagorean identity by $\sin^2 t$ (provided $\sin t \neq 0$) gives us $1 + \cot^2 t = \csc^2 t$. □

As their name indicates, the fundamental identities play a central role in trigonometry because we can use them to relate any trigonometric function to any

---

*We follow the usual convention of writing $\sin^2 t$ for $(\sin t)^2$. In general, we write $\sin^n t$ for $(\sin t)^n$ for all integers n except $n = -1$. The exponent $n = -1$ will be assigned another meaning in Section 7.4. Of course, the same convention applies to the other five trigonometric functions.

other. So, if we know the value of any one of the trigonometric functions at t, then we can find the values of all the others at t.

EXAMPLE 6 ■ Finding All Trigonometric Functions from the Value of One

If $\cos t = \frac{3}{5}$ and t is in quadrant IV, find the values of all the trigonometric functions at t.

SOLUTION

From the Pythagorean identities we have

$$\sin^2 t + \cos^2 t = 1$$

$$\sin^2 t + \left(\tfrac{3}{5}\right)^2 = 1 \qquad\qquad \text{Substitute } \cos t = \tfrac{3}{5}$$

$$\sin^2 t = 1 - \tfrac{9}{25} = \tfrac{16}{25} \qquad \text{Solve for } \sin^2 t$$

$$\sin t = \pm\tfrac{4}{5} \qquad\qquad \text{Take square roots}$$

Since this point is in quadrant IV, $\sin t$ is negative, so $\sin t = -\frac{4}{5}$. Now that we know both $\sin t$ and $\cos t$, we can find the values of the other trigonometric functions using the reciprocal identities:

$$\sin t = -\frac{4}{5} \qquad\qquad \cos t = \frac{3}{5} \qquad\qquad \tan t = \frac{\sin t}{\cos t} = \frac{-\frac{4}{5}}{\frac{3}{5}} = -\frac{4}{3}$$

$$\csc t = \frac{1}{\sin t} = -\frac{5}{4} \qquad \sec t = \frac{1}{\cos t} = \frac{5}{3} \qquad \cot t = \frac{1}{\tan t} = -\frac{3}{4} \qquad ■$$

EXAMPLE 7 ■ Writing One Trigonometric Function in Terms of Another

Write $\tan t$ in terms of $\cos t$, where t is in quadrant III.

SOLUTION

Since $\tan t = \sin t / \cos t$, we need to write $\sin t$ in terms of $\cos t$. By the Pythagorean identities we have

$$\sin^2 t + \cos^2 t = 1$$

$$\sin^2 t = 1 - \cos^2 t \qquad \text{Solve for } \sin^2 t$$

$$\sin t = \pm\sqrt{1 - \cos^2 t} \quad \text{Take square roots}$$

Since $\sin t$ is negative in quadrant III, the negative sign applies here. Thus

$$\tan t = \frac{\sin t}{\cos t} = \frac{-\sqrt{1 - \cos^2 t}}{\cos t} \qquad\qquad ■$$

5.2 EXERCISES

1–2 ■ Find $\sin t$ and $\cos t$ for the values of t whose terminal points are shown on the unit circle in the figure. In Exercise 1, t increases in increments of $\pi/4$; in Exercise 2, t increases in increments of $\pi/6$. (See Exercises 11 and 12 in Section 5.1.)

1.

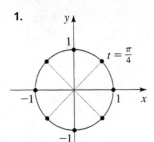

2.

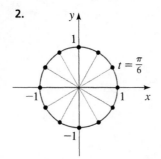

3–22 ■ Find the exact value of the trigonometric function at the given real number.

3. (a) $\sin\left(-\dfrac{\pi}{3}\right)$

   (b) $\cos\left(-\dfrac{\pi}{3}\right)$

4. (a) $\sin \pi$

   (b) $\sin(-\pi)$

5. (a) $\cos \pi$

   (b) $\cos(-\pi)$

6. (a) $\cos \dfrac{\pi}{6}$

   (b) $\cos \dfrac{5\pi}{6}$

7. (a) $\sin \dfrac{\pi}{2}$

   (b) $\sin \dfrac{3\pi}{2}$

8. (a) $\sin \dfrac{7\pi}{6}$

   (b) $\cos \dfrac{7\pi}{6}$

9. (a) $\cos \dfrac{\pi}{2}$

   (b) $\cos \dfrac{5\pi}{2}$

10. (a) $\sin \dfrac{5\pi}{6}$

   (b) $\csc \dfrac{5\pi}{6}$

11. (a) $\cos \dfrac{7\pi}{3}$

   (b) $\sec \dfrac{7\pi}{3}$

12. (a) $\sin \dfrac{3\pi}{4}$

   (b) $\cos \dfrac{3\pi}{4}$

13. (a) $\cos \dfrac{\pi}{3}$

   (b) $\cos\left(-\dfrac{\pi}{3}\right)$

14. (a) $\sin \dfrac{\pi}{6}$

   (b) $\sin\left(-\dfrac{\pi}{6}\right)$

15. (a) $\tan \dfrac{\pi}{6}$

   (b) $\tan\left(-\dfrac{\pi}{6}\right)$

16. (a) $\tan \dfrac{\pi}{3}$

   (b) $\cot \dfrac{\pi}{3}$

17. (a) $\sec \dfrac{11\pi}{3}$

   (b) $\csc \dfrac{11\pi}{3}$

18. (a) $\sec \dfrac{13\pi}{6}$

   (b) $\sec\left(-\dfrac{13\pi}{6}\right)$

19. (a) $\sin \dfrac{9\pi}{4}$

   (b) $\csc \dfrac{9\pi}{4}$

20. (a) $\sec \pi$

   (b) $\csc \dfrac{\pi}{2}$

21. (a) $\tan\left(-\dfrac{\pi}{4}\right)$

   (b) $\cot\left(-\dfrac{\pi}{4}\right)$

22. (a) $\tan \dfrac{3\pi}{4}$

   (b) $\tan \dfrac{11\pi}{4}$

23–26 ■ Find the value of each of the six trigonometric functions (if it is defined) at the given real number t. Use your answers to complete the table.

23. $t = 0$ **24.** $t = \dfrac{\pi}{2}$ **25.** $t = \pi$ **26.** $t = \dfrac{3\pi}{2}$

t	$\sin t$	$\cos t$	$\tan t$	$\csc t$	$\sec t$	$\cot t$
0	0	1		undefined		
$\dfrac{\pi}{2}$						
π		0				undefined
$\dfrac{3\pi}{2}$						

27–34 ■ The terminal point $P(x, y)$ determined by t is given. Find $\sin t$, $\cos t$, and $\tan t$.

27. $\left(\dfrac{3}{5}, \dfrac{4}{5}\right)$

28. $\left(-\dfrac{3}{5}, \dfrac{4}{5}\right)$

29. $\left(\dfrac{\sqrt{5}}{4}, -\dfrac{\sqrt{11}}{4}\right)$

30. $\left(-\dfrac{1}{3}, -\dfrac{2\sqrt{2}}{3}\right)$

31. $\left(\dfrac{40}{41}, \dfrac{9}{41}\right)$

32. $\left(-\dfrac{6}{7}, \dfrac{\sqrt{13}}{7}\right)$

33. $\left(-\dfrac{5}{13}, -\dfrac{12}{13}\right)$

34. $\left(\dfrac{\sqrt{5}}{5}, \dfrac{2\sqrt{5}}{5}\right)$

35–42 ■ Find the approximate value of the given trigonometric function by using (a) the figure and (b) a calculator. Compare the two values.

35. sin 1

36. cos 0.8

37. sin 1.2

38. cos 5

39. tan 0.8

40. tan(−1.3)

41. cos 4.1

42. sin(−5.2)

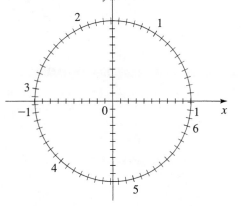

43–46 ■ Find the sign of the expression if the terminal point determined by t is in the given quadrant.

43. sin t cos t,   quadrant II   **44.** tan t sec t,   quadrant IV

45. $\dfrac{\tan t \sin t}{\cot t}$,   quadrant III   **46.** cos t sec t,   any quadrant

47–50 ■ From the information given, find the quadrant in which the terminal point determined by t lies.

47. sin $t > 0$ and cos $t < 0$ **48.** tan $t > 0$ and sin $t < 0$

49. csc $t > 0$ and sec $t < 0$ **50.** cos $t < 0$ and cot $t < 0$

51–60 ■ Write the first expression in terms of the second if the terminal point determined by t is in the given quadrant.

51. sin t, cos t;   quadrant II   **52.** cos t, sin t;   quadrant IV

53. tan t, sin t;   quadrant IV   **54.** tan t, cos t;   quadrant III

55. sec t, tan t;   quadrant II   **56.** csc t, cot t;   quadrant III

57. tan t, sec t;   quadrant III   **58.** sin t, sec t;   quadrant IV

59. tan²t, sin t;   any quadrant

60. sec²t sin²t, cos t;   any quadrant

61–68 ■ Find the values of the trigonometric functions of t from the given information.

61. sin $t = \frac{3}{5}$,   terminal point of t is in quadrant II

62. cos $t = -\frac{4}{5}$,   terminal point of t is in quadrant III

63. sec $t = 3$,   terminal point of t is in quadrant IV

64. tan $t = \frac{1}{4}$,   terminal point of t is in quadrant III

65. tan $t = -\frac{3}{4}$,   cos $t > 0$ **66.** sec $t = 2$,   sin $t < 0$

67. sin $t = -\frac{1}{4}$,   sec $t < 0$ **68.** tan $t = -4$,   csc $t > 0$

69–76 ■ Determine whether the function is even, odd, or neither.

69. $f(x) = x^2 \sin x$ **70.** $f(x) = x^2 \cos 2x$

71. $f(x) = \sin x \cos x$ **72.** $f(x) = e^x \sin x$

73. $f(x) = |x| \cos x$ **74.** $f(x) = x \sin^3 x$

75. $f(x) = x^3 + \cos x$ **76.** $f(x) = \cos(\sin x)$

DISCOVERY · DISCUSSION

77. Reduction Formulas   Explain how the figure shows that the following "reduction formulas" are valid:

$$\sin(t + \pi) = -\sin t \qquad \cos(t + \pi) = -\cos t$$
$$\tan(t + \pi) = \tan t$$

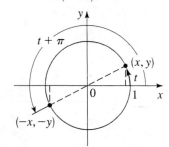

78. More Reduction Formulas   By the "Angle-Side-Angle" theorem from elementary geometry, triangles CDO and AOB in the figure are congruent. Explain how this proves that if B has coordinates (x, y), then D has coordinates $(-y, x)$. Then explain how the figure shows that the following "reduction formulas" are valid:

$$\sin\left(t + \frac{\pi}{2}\right) = \cos t$$
$$\cos\left(t + \frac{\pi}{2}\right) = -\sin t$$
$$\tan\left(t + \frac{\pi}{2}\right) = -\cot t$$

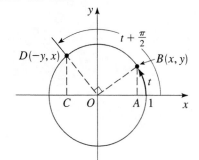

5.3 TRIGONOMETRIC GRAPHS

The graph of a function gives us a better idea of its behavior. So, in this section we graph the sine and cosine functions and certain transformations of these functions. The other trigonometric functions are graphed in the next section.

▓ Graphs of the Sine and Cosine Functions

To help us graph the sine and cosine functions, we first observe that these functions repeat their values in a regular fashion. To see exactly how this happens, recall that the circumference of the unit circle is 2π. It follows that the terminal point $P(x, y)$ determined by the real number t is the same as that determined by $t + 2\pi$. Since the sine and cosine functions are defined in terms of the coordinates of $P(x, y)$, it follows that their values are unchanged by the addition of any integer multiple of 2π. In other words,

$$\sin(t + 2n\pi) = \sin t \qquad \text{for any integer } n$$

$$\cos(t + 2n\pi) = \cos t \qquad \text{for any integer } n$$

Thus, the sine and cosine functions are *periodic* according to the following definition: A function f is **periodic** if there is a positive number p such that $f(t + p) = f(t)$ for every t. The least such positive number (if it exists) is the **period** of f. If f has period p, then the graph of f on any interval of length p is called **one complete period** of f.

PERIODIC PROPERTIES OF SINE AND COSINE

The function sine has period 2π: $\sin(t + 2\pi) = \sin t$

The function cosine has period 2π: $\cos(t + 2\pi) = \cos t$

TABLE 1

t	$\sin t$	$\cos t$
$0 \to \dfrac{\pi}{2}$	$0 \to 1$	$1 \to 0$
$\dfrac{\pi}{2} \to \pi$	$1 \to 0$	$0 \to -1$
$\pi \to \dfrac{3\pi}{2}$	$0 \to -1$	$-1 \to 0$
$\dfrac{3\pi}{2} \to 2\pi$	$-1 \to 0$	$0 \to 1$

So the sine and cosine functions repeat their values in any interval of length 2π. To sketch their graphs, we first graph one period. To sketch the graphs on the interval $0 \le t \le 2\pi$, we could try to make a table of values and use those points to draw the graph. Since no such table can be complete, let's look more closely at the definitions of these functions.

Recall that $\sin t$ is the y-coordinate of the terminal point $P(x, y)$ on the unit circle determined by the real number t. How does the y-coordinate of this point vary as t increases? It's easy to see that the y-coordinate of $P(x, y)$ increases to 1, then decreases to -1 repeatedly as the point $P(x, y)$ travels around the unit circle. (See Figure 1.) In fact, as t increases from 0 to $\pi/2$, $y = \sin t$ increases from 0 to 1. As t increases from $\pi/2$ to π, the value of $y = \sin t$ decreases from 1 to 0. Table 1 shows the variation of the sine and cosine functions for t between 0 and 2π.

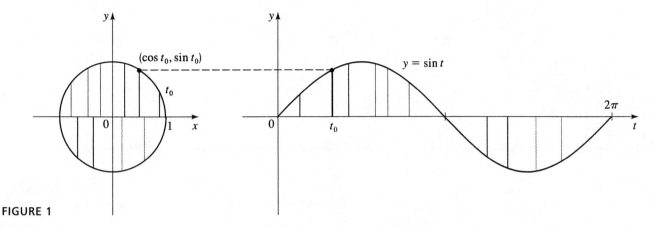

FIGURE 1

To draw the graphs more accurately, we find a few other values of sin t and cos t in Table 2. We could find still other values with the aid of a calculator.

TABLE 2

t	0	$\dfrac{\pi}{6}$	$\dfrac{\pi}{3}$	$\dfrac{\pi}{2}$	$\dfrac{2\pi}{3}$	$\dfrac{5\pi}{6}$	π	$\dfrac{7\pi}{6}$	$\dfrac{4\pi}{3}$	$\dfrac{3\pi}{2}$	$\dfrac{5\pi}{3}$	$\dfrac{11\pi}{6}$	2π
sin t	0	$\dfrac{1}{2}$	$\dfrac{\sqrt{3}}{2}$	1	$\dfrac{\sqrt{3}}{2}$	$\dfrac{1}{2}$	0	$-\dfrac{1}{2}$	$-\dfrac{\sqrt{3}}{2}$	-1	$-\dfrac{\sqrt{3}}{2}$	$-\dfrac{1}{2}$	0
cos t	1	$\dfrac{\sqrt{3}}{2}$	$\dfrac{1}{2}$	0	$-\dfrac{1}{2}$	$-\dfrac{\sqrt{3}}{2}$	-1	$-\dfrac{\sqrt{3}}{2}$	$-\dfrac{1}{2}$	0	$\dfrac{1}{2}$	$\dfrac{\sqrt{3}}{2}$	1

Now we use this information to graph the functions sin t and cos t for t between 0 and 2π in Figures 2 and 3. These are the graphs of one period. Using the fact that these functions are periodic with period 2π, we get their complete graphs by continuing the same pattern to the left and to the right in every successive interval of length 2π.

The graph of the sine function is symmetric with respect to the origin. This is as expected, since sine is an odd function. Since the cosine function is an even function, its graph is symmetric with respect to the y-axis.

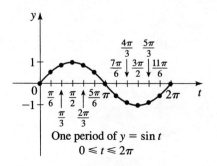

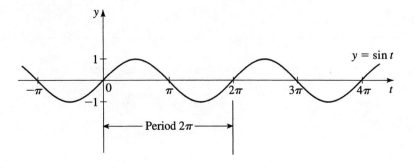

FIGURE 2 Graph of sin t

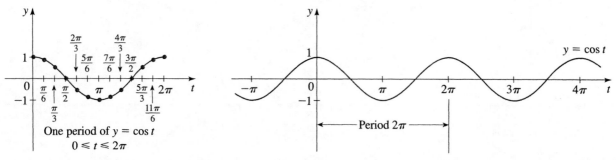

FIGURE 3 Graph of cos *t*

Graphs of Transformations of Sine and Cosine

We now consider graphs of functions that are transformations of the sine and cosine functions. Thus, the graphing techniques of Section 2.5 are very useful here. The graphs we obtain are important for understanding applications to physical situations such as harmonic motion (see *Focus on Modeling,* page 455), but some of them are beautiful graphs that are interesting in their own right.

It's traditional to use the letter *x* to denote the variable in the domain of a function. So, from here on we use the letter *x* and write $y = \sin x$, $y = \cos x$, $y = \tan x$, and so on to denote these functions.

EXAMPLE 1 ■ Cosine Curves

Sketch the graph of each function.

(a) $f(x) = 2 + \cos x$ (b) $g(x) = -\cos x$

SOLUTION

(a) The graph of $y = 2 + \cos x$ is the same as the graph of $y = \cos x$, but shifted up 2 units [see Figure 4(a)].

(b) The graph of $y = -\cos x$ in Figure 4(b) is the reflection of the graph of $y = \cos x$ in the *x*-axis.

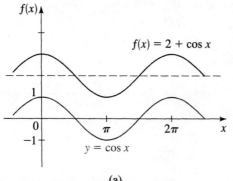

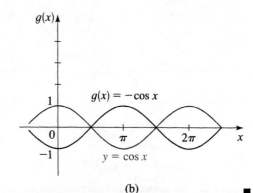

FIGURE 4   (a)   (b) ■

Vertical stretching and shrinking of graphs is discussed in Section 2.5.

Let's graph $y = 2 \sin x$. We start with the graph of $y = \sin x$ and multiply the y-coordinate of each point by 2. This has the effect of stretching the graph vertically by a factor of 2. To graph $y = \frac{1}{2} \sin x$, we start with the graph of $y = \sin x$ and multiply the y-coordinate of each point by $\frac{1}{2}$. This has the effect of shrinking the graph vertically by a factor of $\frac{1}{2}$ (see Figure 5).

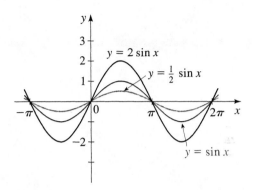

FIGURE 5

In general, for the functions

$$y = a \sin x \quad \text{and} \quad y = a \cos x$$

the number $|a|$ is called the **amplitude** and is the largest value these functions attain. Graphs of $y = a \sin x$ for several values of a are shown in Figure 6.

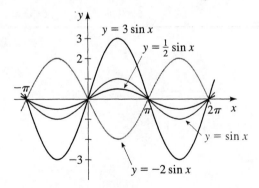

FIGURE 6

EXAMPLE 2 ■ Stretching a Cosine Curve

Find the amplitude of $y = -3 \cos x$ and sketch its graph.

SOLUTION

The amplitude is $|-3| = 3$, so the largest value the graph attains is 3 and the smallest value is -3. To sketch the graph, we begin with the graph of $y = \cos x$, stretch the graph vertically by a factor of 3, and reflect in the x-axis, arriving at the graph in Figure 7.

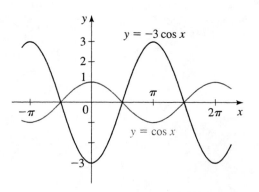

FIGURE 7

Since the sine and cosine functions have period 2π, the functions

$$y = a \sin kx \qquad \text{and} \qquad y = a \cos kx \qquad (k > 0)$$

complete one period as kx varies from 0 to 2π, that is, for $0 \leqslant kx \leqslant 2\pi$ or for $0 \leqslant x \leqslant 2\pi/k$. So these functions complete one period as x varies between 0 and $2\pi/k$ and thus have period $2\pi/k$. The graphs of these functions are called **sine curves** and **cosine curves**, respectively. (Collectively, sine and cosine curves are often referred to as **sinusoidal** curves.)

SINE AND COSINE CURVES

The sine and cosine curves

$$y = a \sin kx \qquad \text{and} \qquad y = a \cos kx \qquad (k > 0)$$

have amplitude $|a|$ and period $2\pi/k$.

An appropriate interval on which to graph one complete period is $[0, 2\pi/k]$.

To see how the value of k affects the graph of $y = \sin kx$, let's graph the sine curve $y = \sin 2x$. Since the period is $2\pi/2 = \pi$, the graph completes one period in the interval $0 \leqslant x \leqslant \pi$ [see Figure 8(a)]. For the sine curve $y = \sin \frac{1}{2}x$, the period is $2\pi \div \frac{1}{2} = 4\pi$, and so the graph completes one period in the interval $0 \leqslant x \leqslant 4\pi$ [see Figure 8(b)]. We see that the effect is to shrink the graph if $k > 1$ or to stretch the graph if $k < 1$.

Horizontal stretching and shrinking of graphs is discussed in Section 2.5.

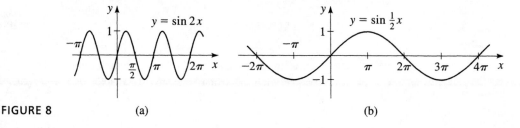

FIGURE 8   (a)   (b)

For comparison, in Figure 9 we show the graphs of one period of the sine curve $y = a \sin kx$ for several values of k.

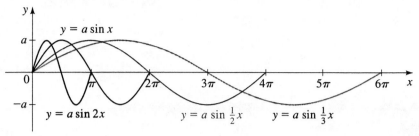

FIGURE 9

EXAMPLE 3 ■ Amplitude and Period

Find the amplitude and period of each function, and sketch its graph.

(a) $y = 4 \cos 3x$ (b) $y = -2 \sin \frac{1}{2}x$

SOLUTION

(a) For $y = 4 \cos 3x$,

$$\text{amplitude} = |a| = 4$$

$$\text{period} = \frac{2\pi}{3}$$

The graph is shown in Figure 10.

(b) For $y = -2 \sin \frac{1}{2}x$,

$$\text{amplitude} = |a| = |-2| = 2$$

$$\text{period} = \frac{2\pi}{\frac{1}{2}} = 4\pi$$

The graph is shown in Figure 11. ■

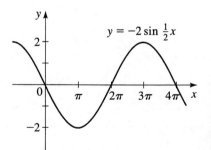

FIGURE 10

The graphs of functions of the form $y = a \sin k(x - b)$ and $y = a \cos k(x - b)$ are simply sine and cosine curves shifted horizontally by an amount $|b|$. They are shifted to the right if $b > 0$ or to the left if $b < 0$. The number b is the **phase shift**. We summarize the properties of these functions in the following box.

y ↑

2

y = -2 sin ½x

0   π   2π 3π 4π   x

-2

FIGURE 11

SHIFTED SINE AND COSINE CURVES

The sine and cosine curves

$$y = a \sin k(x - b) \qquad \text{and} \qquad y = a \cos k(x - b) \qquad (k > 0)$$

have amplitude $|a|$, period $2\pi/k$, and phase shift b.

An appropriate interval on which to graph one complete period is $[b, b + (2\pi/k)]$.

The graphs of $y = \sin\left(x - \dfrac{\pi}{3}\right)$ and $y = \sin\left(x + \dfrac{\pi}{6}\right)$ are shown in Figure 12.

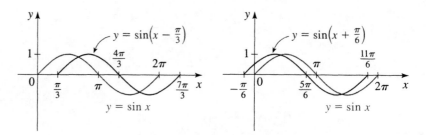

FIGURE 12

EXAMPLE 4 ■ A Shifted Sine Curve

Find the amplitude, period, and phase shift of $y = 3 \sin 2\left(x - \dfrac{\pi}{4}\right)$, and graph one complete period.

SOLUTION

We have

$$\text{amplitude} = |a| = 3$$

$$\text{period} = \frac{2\pi}{2} = \pi$$

$$\text{phase shift} = \frac{\pi}{4} \qquad \text{Shift } \tfrac{\pi}{4} \text{ to the } right$$

Here is another way to find an appropriate interval on which to graph one complete period. Since the period of $y = \sin x$ is 2π, the function $y = 3 \sin 2(x - \tfrac{\pi}{4})$ will go through one complete period as $2(x - \tfrac{\pi}{4})$ varies from 0 to 2π.

Start of period: End of period:

$2\left(x - \tfrac{\pi}{4}\right) = 0$ $2\left(x - \tfrac{\pi}{4}\right) = 2\pi$

$x - \tfrac{\pi}{4} = 0$ $x - \tfrac{\pi}{4} = \pi$

$x = \tfrac{\pi}{4}$ $x = \tfrac{5\pi}{4}$

So we graph one period on the interval $\left[\tfrac{\pi}{4}, \tfrac{5\pi}{4}\right]$.

Since the phase shift is $\pi/4$ and the period is π, one complete period occurs on the interval

$$\left[\frac{\pi}{4}, \frac{\pi}{4} + \pi\right] = \left[\frac{\pi}{4}, \frac{5\pi}{4}\right]$$

As an aid in sketching the graph, we divide this interval into four equal parts, then graph a sine curve with amplitude 3 as in Figure 13.

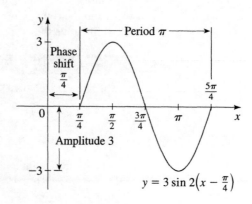

FIGURE 13

EXAMPLE 5 ■ A Shifted Cosine Curve

Find the amplitude, period, and phase shift of

$$y = \frac{3}{4}\cos\left(2x + \frac{2\pi}{3}\right)$$

and graph one complete period.

SOLUTION

We first write this function in the form $y = a\cos k(x - b)$. To do this, we factor 2 from the expression $2x + \dfrac{2\pi}{3}$ to get

$$y = \frac{3}{4}\cos 2\left[x - \left(-\frac{\pi}{3}\right)\right]$$

Thus, we have

$$\text{amplitude} = |a| = \frac{3}{4}$$

$$\text{period} = \frac{2\pi}{k} = \frac{2\pi}{2} = \pi$$

$$\text{phase shift} = b = -\frac{\pi}{3} \qquad \text{Shift } \tfrac{\pi}{3} \text{ to the } \textit{left}$$

From this information it follows that one period of this cosine curve begins at $-\pi/3$ and ends at $(-\pi/3) + \pi = 2\pi/3$. To sketch the graph over the interval $[-\pi/3, 2\pi/3]$, we divide this interval into four equal parts and graph a cosine curve with amplitude $\frac{3}{4}$ as shown in Figure 14.

We can also find one complete period as follows:

Start of period: End of period:

$2x + \frac{2\pi}{3} = 0 \qquad 2x + \frac{2\pi}{3} = 2\pi$

$2x = -\frac{2\pi}{3} \qquad\quad 2x = \frac{4\pi}{3}$

$x = -\frac{\pi}{3} \qquad\qquad x = \frac{2\pi}{3}$

So we graph one period on the interval $\left[-\frac{\pi}{3}, \frac{2\pi}{3}\right]$.

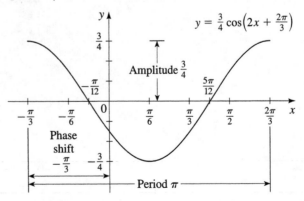

FIGURE 14

Using Graphing Devices to Graph Trigonometric Functions

In Section 1.9 we discussed the use of graphing calculators and computers, and we saw that it's important to choose a viewing rectangle carefully in order to produce a reasonable graph of a function. This is especially true for trigonometric functions; Example 6 shows that, if care is not taken, it's easy to produce a very misleading graph of a trigonometric function.

EXAMPLE 6 ■ Choosing the Viewing Rectangle

Graph the function $f(x) = \sin 50x$ in an appropriate viewing rectangle.

SOLUTION

Figure 15(a) shows the graph of f produced by a graphing calculator using the viewing rectangle $[-12, 12]$ by $[-1.5, 1.5]$. At first glance the graph appears to be reasonable. But if we change the viewing rectangle to the ones shown in Figure 15, the graphs look very different. Something strange is happening.

The appearance of the graphs in Figure 15 depends on the machine used. The graphs you get with your own graphing device might not look like these figures, but they will also be quite inaccurate.

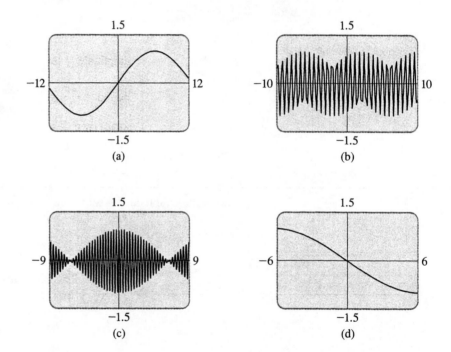

FIGURE 15

Graphs of $f(x) = \sin 50x$ in different viewing rectangles

To explain the big differences in appearance of these graphs and to find an appropriate viewing rectangle, we need to find the period of the function $y = \sin 50x$:

$$\text{period} = \frac{2\pi}{50} = \frac{\pi}{25} \approx 0.126$$

This suggests that we should deal only with small values of x in order to show just a few oscillations of the graph. If we choose the viewing rectangle $[-0.25, 0.25]$ by $[-1.5, 1.5]$, we get the graph shown in Figure 16.

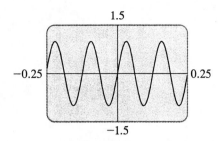

FIGURE 16

$f(x) = \sin 50x$

The function h in Example 7 is **periodic** with period 2π. In general, functions that are sums of functions from the following list

1, $\cos kx$, $\cos 2kx$, $\cos 3kx$, . . .

$\sin kx$, $\sin 2kx$, $\sin 3kx$, . . .

are periodic. Although these functions appear to be special, they are actually fundamental to describing all periodic functions that arise in practice. The French mathematician J. B. J. Fourier (see page 551) discovered that nearly every periodic function can be written as a sum (usually an infinite sum) of these functions (see Section 10.3). This is remarkable because it means that any situation in which periodic variation occurs can be described mathematically using the functions sine and cosine. A modern application of Fourier's discovery is the digital encoding of sound on compact discs.

Now we see what went wrong in Figure 15. The oscillations of $y = \sin 50x$ are so rapid that when the calculator plots points and joins them, it misses most of the maximum and minimum points and therefore gives a very misleading impression of the graph. ■

EXAMPLE 7 ■ **A Sum of Sine and Cosine Curves**

Graph $f(x) = 2\cos x$, $g(x) = \sin 2x$, and $h(x) = 2\cos x + \sin 2x$ on a common screen to illustrate the method of graphical addition.

SOLUTION

Notice that $h = f + g$, so its graph is obtained by adding the corresponding y-coordinates of the graphs of f and g. The graphs of f, g, and h are shown in Figure 17.

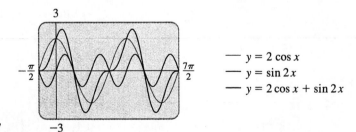

FIGURE 17

— $y = 2\cos x$
— $y = \sin 2x$
— $y = 2\cos x + \sin 2x$

■

EXAMPLE 8 ■ **A Cosine Curve with Exponential Amplitude**

Graph the functions $y = e^{-x}$, $y = -e^{-x}$, and $y = e^{-x}\cos 6\pi x$ on a common screen. Comment on and explain the relationship among the graphs.

SOLUTION

Figure 18 shows all three graphs in the viewing rectangle $[-1, 2]$ by $[-3, 3]$. It appears that the graph of $y = e^{-x}\cos 6\pi x$ lies between the graphs of the exponential functions $y = e^{-x}$ and $y = -e^{-x}$.

To understand this, recall that the values of $\cos 6\pi x$ lie between -1 and 1, that is,

$$-1 \le \cos 6\pi x \le 1$$

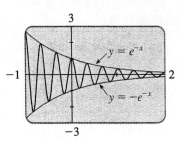

FIGURE 18

$y = e^{-x}\cos 6\pi x$

for all values of x. Multiplying the inequalities by e^{-x}, and noting that $e^{-x} \geq 0$, we get

$$-e^{-x} \leq e^{-x} \cos 6\pi x \leq e^{-x}$$

This explains why the exponential functions form a boundary for the graph of $y = e^{-x} \cos 6\pi x$. (Note that the graphs touch when $\cos 6\pi x = \pm 1$.) ∎

Example 8 shows that the function $y = e^{-x}$ controls the amplitude of the graph of $y = e^{-x} \cos 6\pi x$. In general, if $f(x) = a(x) \sin kx$ or $a(x) \cos kx$, the function a determines how the amplitude of f varies, and the graph of f lies between the graphs of $y = -a(x)$ and $y = a(x)$. Here is another example.

EXAMPLE 9 ■ A Cosine Curve with Variable Amplitude

Graph the function $f(x) = \cos 2\pi x \cos 16\pi x$.

SOLUTION

The graph is shown in Figure 19. Although it was drawn by a computer, we could have drawn it by hand, by first sketching the boundary curves $y = \cos 2\pi x$ and $y = -\cos 2\pi x$. The graph of f is a cosine curve that lies between the graphs of these two functions.

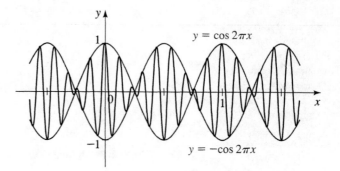

FIGURE 19

$f(x) = \cos 2\pi x \cos 16\pi x$

∎

EXAMPLE 10 ■ A Sine Curve with Decaying Amplitude

The function $f(x) = \dfrac{\sin x}{x}$ is important in calculus. Graph this function and comment on its behavior when x is close to 0.

SOLUTION

The viewing rectangle $[-15, 15]$ by $[-0.5, 1.5]$ shown in Figure 20(a) gives a good global view of the graph of f. The viewing rectangle $[-1, 1]$ by $[-0.5, 1.5]$ in Figure 20(b) focuses on the behavior of f when $x \approx 0$. Notice that although $f(x)$

is not defined when $x = 0$ (in other words, 0 is not in the domain of f), the values of f seem to approach 1 when x gets close to 0. This fact is crucial in calculus.

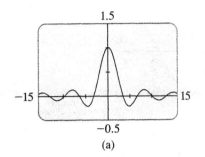

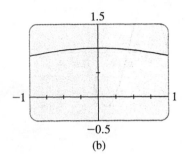

FIGURE 20

$f(x) = \dfrac{\sin x}{x}$

(a)   (b)   ■

The function in Example 10 can be written as

$$f(x) = \left(\frac{1}{x}\right) \cdot \sin x$$

and may thus be viewed as a sine function whose amplitude is controlled by the function $a(x) = 1/x$.

5.3 EXERCISES

1–10 ■ Graph the function.

1. $y = 1 + \sin x$

2. $y = -\sin x$

3. $y = 1 - \cos x$

4. $y = -2 + \cos x$

5. $y = -2 \sin x$

6. $y = 3 \cos x$

7. $y = 4 - 2 \cos x$

8. $y = 3 + 3 \sin x$

9. $y = |\cos x|$

10. $y = |\sin x|$

11–20 ■ Find the amplitude and period of the function, and sketch its graph.

11. $y = \cos 4x$

12. $y = -\sin 2x$

13. $y = 3 \sin 3x$

14. $y = -2 \sin 2\pi x$

15. $y = 10 \sin \frac{1}{2}x$

16. $y = \cos 10\pi x$

17. $y = -\cos \frac{1}{3}x$

18. $y = \sin(-2x)$

19. $y = 3 \cos 3\pi x$

20. $y = 5 - 2 \sin 2x$

21–34 ■ Find the amplitude, period, and phase shift of the function, and graph one complete period.

21. $y = \cos\left(x - \dfrac{\pi}{2}\right)$

22. $y = 2 \sin\left(x - \dfrac{\pi}{3}\right)$

23. $y = -2 \sin\left(x - \dfrac{\pi}{6}\right)$

24. $y = 3 \cos\left(x + \dfrac{\pi}{4}\right)$

25. $y = 5 \cos\left(3x - \dfrac{\pi}{4}\right)$

26. $y = -4 \sin 2\left(x + \dfrac{\pi}{2}\right)$

27. $y = 2 \sin\left(\dfrac{2}{3}x - \dfrac{\pi}{6}\right)$

28. $y = \sin \dfrac{1}{2}\left(x + \dfrac{\pi}{4}\right)$

29. $y = 3 \cos \pi\left(x + \tfrac{1}{2}\right)$

30. $y = 1 + \cos\left(3x + \dfrac{\pi}{2}\right)$

31. $y = -\tfrac{1}{2}\cos\left(2x - \dfrac{\pi}{3}\right)$

32. $y = 3 + 2 \sin 3(x + 1)$

33. $y = \sin(3x + \pi)$

34. $y = \cos\left(\dfrac{\pi}{2} - x\right)$

35–40 ■ The graph of one complete period of a sine or cosine curve is given.

(a) Find the amplitude, period, and phase shift.

(b) Write an equation that represents the curve in the form

$$y = a \sin k(x - b) \quad \text{or} \quad y = a \cos k(x - b)$$

35.

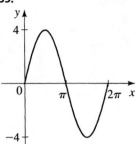

36.

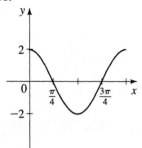

37.

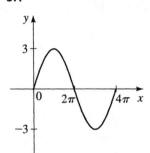

38.

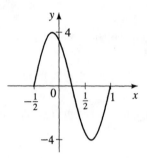

39.

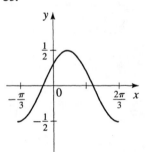

40.

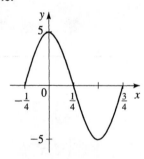

41–48 ■ Determine an appropriate viewing rectangle for each function, and use it to draw the graph.

41. $f(x) = \cos 100x$

42. $f(x) = 3 \sin 120x$

43. $f(x) = \sin(x/40)$

44. $f(x) = \cos(x/80)$

45. $y = \tan 25x$

46. $y = \csc 40x$

47. $y = e^{\sin 20x}$

48. $y = \sqrt{\tan 10\pi x}$

49. As a wave passes by an offshore piling, the height of the water is modeled by the function

$$h(t) = 3 \cos\left(\frac{\pi}{10}t\right)$$

where $h(t)$ is the height in feet above mean sea level at time t seconds.

(a) Find the period of the wave.

(b) Find the wave height, that is, the vertical distance between the trough and the crest of the wave.

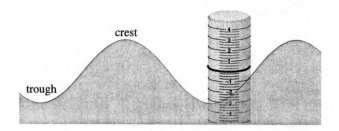

50. A tuning fork is struck, producing a pure tone as its tines vibrate. The vibrations are modeled by the function

$$v(t) = 0.7 \sin(880\pi t)$$

where $v(t)$ is the displacement of the tines in millimeters at time t seconds.

(a) Find the period of the vibration.

(b) Find the frequency of the vibration, that is, the number of times the fork vibrates per second.

(c) Graph the function v.

51. Each time your heart beats, your blood pressure first increases and then decreases as the heart rests between beats. The maximum and minimum blood pressures are called the *systolic* and *diastolic* pressures, respectively. Your *blood pressure reading* is written as systolic/diastolic. A reading of 120/80 is considered normal.

A certain person's blood pressure is modeled by the function

$$p(t) = 115 + 25 \sin(160\pi t)$$

where $p(t)$ is the pressure in mmHg, at time t measured in minutes.

(a) Find the period of p.

(b) Find the number of heartbeats per minute.

(c) Graph the function p.

(d) Find the blood pressure reading. How does this compare to normal blood pressure?

52. Variable stars are ones whose brightness varies periodically. One of the most visible is R Leonis; its brightness is modeled by the function

$$b(t) = 7.9 - 2.1 \cos\left(\frac{\pi}{156}t\right)$$

where t is measured in days.

(a) Find the period of R Leonis.

(b) Find the maximum and minimum brightness.
(c) Graph the function b.

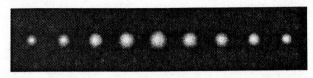

53–54 ■ Graph f, g, and $f + g$ on a common screen to illustrate graphical addition.

53. $f(x) = x$, $g(x) = \sin x$

54. $f(x) = \sin x$, $g(x) = \sin 2x$

55–60 ■ Graph the three functions on a common screen. How are the graphs related?

55. $y = x^2$, $y = -x^2$, $y = x^2 \sin x$

56. $y = x$, $y = -x$, $y = x \cos x$

57. $y = e^x$, $y = -e^x$, $y = e^x \sin 5\pi x$

58. $y = \dfrac{1}{1 + x^2}$, $y = -\dfrac{1}{1 + x^2}$, $y = \dfrac{\cos 2\pi x}{1 + x^2}$

59. $y = \cos 3\pi x$, $y = -\cos 3\pi x$, $y = \cos 3\pi x \cos 21\pi x$

60. $y = \sin 2\pi x$, $y = -\sin 2\pi x$, $y = \sin 2\pi x \sin 10\pi x$

61–64 ■ Find the maximum and minimum values of the function.

61. $y = \sin x + \sin 2x$

62. $y = x - 2 \sin x$, $0 \leqslant x \leqslant 2\pi$

63. $y = 2 \sin x + \sin^2 x$ **64.** $y = \dfrac{\cos x}{2 + \sin x}$

65–68 ■ Find all solutions of the equation that lie in the interval $[0, \pi]$. State each answer correct to two decimal places.

65. $\cos x = 0.4$ **66.** $\tan x = 2$

67. $\csc x = 3$ **68.** $\cos x = x$

69. Let $f(x) = \dfrac{1 - \cos x}{x}$.

(a) Is the function f even, odd, or neither?
(b) Find the x-intercepts of the graph of f.
(c) Graph f in an appropriate viewing rectangle.
(d) Describe the behavior of the function as $x \to \infty$ and as $x \to -\infty$.
(e) Notice that $f(x)$ is not defined when $x = 0$. What happens as $x \to 0$?

DISCOVERY · DISCUSSION

70. Compositions Involving Trigonometric Functions
This exercise explores the effect of the inner function g on a composite function $y = f(g(x))$.
(a) Graph the function $y = \sin(\sqrt{x})$ using the viewing rectangle $[0, 400]$ by $[-1.5, 1.5]$. In what ways does this graph differ from the graph of the sine function?
(b) Graph the function $y = \sin(x^2)$ using the viewing rectangle $[-5, 5]$ by $[-1.5, 1.5]$. In what ways does this graph differ from the graph of the sine function?

71. Periodic Functions I Recall that a function f is *periodic* if there is a positive number p such that $f(t + p) = f(t)$ for every t, and the least such p (if it exists) is the *period* of f. The graph of a function of period p looks the same on each interval of length p, so we can easily determine the period from the graph. Determine whether the function whose graph is shown is periodic; if it is periodic, find the period.

(a)
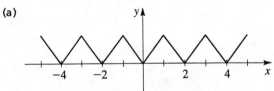

(b)
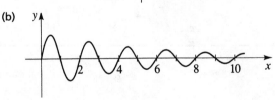

(c)
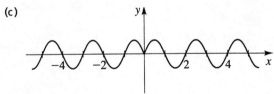

(d)
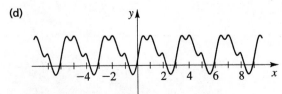

72. Periodic Functions II Use a graphing device to graph the following functions. From the graph, determine whether the function is periodic; if it is periodic find the period.
(a) $y = |\sin x|$ (b) $y = \sin|x|$
(c) $y = 2^{\cos x}$ (d) $y = x - [\![x]\!]$

73. Sinusoidal Curves   The graph of $y = \sin x$ is the same as
the graph of $y = \cos x$ shifted to the right $\pi/2$ units. So the
sine curve $y = \sin x$ is also at the same time a cosine
curve: $y = \cos(x - \pi/2)$. In fact, any sine curve is also a
cosine curve with a different phase shift, and any cosine
curve is also a sine curve. Sine and cosine curves are collectively referred to as *sinusoidal*. Find all possible ways of
expressing the curve whose graph is shown as a sine curve
$y = a \sin(x - b)$ and as a cosine curve $y = a \cos(x - b)$.
Explain why you think you have found all possible choices
for a and b in each case.

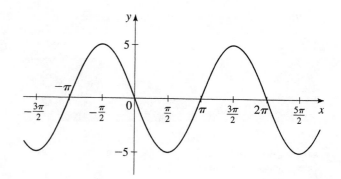

Discovery Project

Predator/Prey Models

Sine and cosine functions are used primarily in physics and engineering to model
oscillatory behavior, such as the motion of a pendulum or the current in an AC
electrical circuit. (See *Focus on Modeling*, pages 455–471.) But these functions
also arise in the other sciences. In this project, we consider an application to biology—we use sine functions to model the population of a predator and its prey.

    An isolated island is inhabited by two species of mammals: lynx and hares.
The lynx are *predators* who feed on the hares, their *prey*. The lynx and hare populations change cyclically, as graphed in Figure 1. In part A of the graph, hares
are abundant, so the lynx have plenty to eat and their population increases. By
the time portrayed in part B, so many lynx are feeding on the hares that the hare
population declines. In part C, the hare population has declined so much that
there is not enough food for the lynx, so the lynx population starts to decrease. In
part D, so many lynx have died that the hares have few enemies and their population increases again. This takes us back where we started, and the cycle repeats
over and over again.

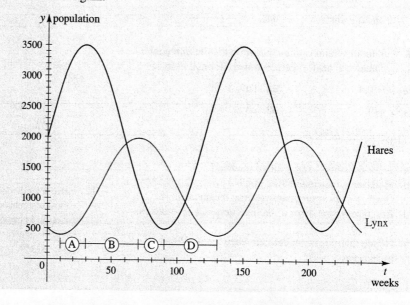

FIGURE 1

The graphs in Figure 1 are sine curves that have been shifted upward, so they are graphs of functions of the form

$$y = a \sin k(t - b) + c$$

Here c is the amount by which the sine curve has been shifted vertically (see Section 2.5). Note that c is the average value of the function, halfway between the highest and lowest values on the graph. The amplitude $|a|$ is the amount by which the graph varies above and below the average value (see Figure 2).

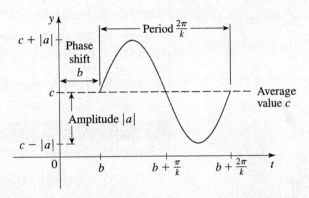

FIGURE 2

$y = a \sin k(t - b) + c$

1. Find functions of the form $y = a \sin k(t - b) + c$ that model the lynx and hare populations graphed in Figure 1. Graph both functions on your calculator and compare to Figure 1 to verify that your functions are the right ones.

2. Add the lynx and hare population functions to get a new function that models the total *mammal* population on this island. Graph this function on your calculator, and find its average value, amplitude, period, and phase shift. How are the average value and period of the mammal population function related to the average value and period of the lynx and hare population functions?

3. A small lake on the island contains two species of fish: hake and redfish. The hake are predators that eat the redfish. The fish population in the lake varies periodically with period 180 days. The number of hake varies between 500 and 1500, and the number of redfish varies between 1000 and 3000. The hake reach their maximum population 30 days after the redfish have reached *their* maximum population in the cycle.

   (a) Sketch a graph (like the one in Figure 1) that shows two complete periods of the population cycle for these species of fish. Assume that $t = 0$ corresponds to a time when the redfish population is at a maximum.

   (b) Find cosine functions of the form $y = a \cos k(t - b) + c$ that model the hake and redfish populations in the lake.

4. In real life, most predator/prey populations do not behave as simply as the examples we have described here. In most cases, the populations of predator and prey oscillate, but the amplitude of the oscillations gets smaller and smaller, so that eventually both populations stabilize near a constant value.

   (a) Sketch a graph that illustrates how the populations of predator and prey might behave in this case.

   (b) What form of function could we use to model the populations in this case?

5.4 MORE TRIGONOMETRIC GRAPHS

In this section we graph the tangent, cotangent, secant, and cosecant functions, and transformations of these functions.

Graphs of the Tangent, Cotangent, Secant, and Cosecant Function

We begin by stating the periodic properties of these functions. Recall that sine and cosine have period 2π. Since cosecant and secant are the reciprocals of sine and cosine, respectively, they also have period 2π (see Exercise 47). Tangent and cotangent, however, have period π (see Exercise 77 of Section 5.2).

> **PERIODIC PROPERTIES**
>
> The functions tangent and cotangent have period π:
>
> $$\tan(x + \pi) = \tan x \qquad \cot(x + \pi) = \cot x$$
>
> The functions cosecant and secant have period 2π:
>
> $$\csc(x + 2\pi) = \csc x \qquad \sec(x + 2\pi) = \sec x$$

x	$\tan x$
0	0
$\dfrac{\pi}{6}$	0.58
$\dfrac{\pi}{4}$	1.00
$\dfrac{\pi}{3}$	1.73
1.4	5.80
1.5	14.10
1.55	48.08
1.57	1,255.77
1.5707	10,381.33

We first sketch the graph of tangent. Since it has period π, we need only sketch the graph on any interval of length π and then repeat the pattern to the left and to the right. We sketch the graph on the interval $(-\pi/2, \pi/2)$. Since $\tan \pi/2$ and $\tan(-\pi/2)$ aren't defined, we need to be careful in sketching the graph at points near $\pi/2$ and $-\pi/2$. As x gets near $\pi/2$ through values less than $\pi/2$, the value of $\tan x$ becomes large. To see this, notice that as x gets close to $\pi/2$, $\cos x$ approaches 0 and $\sin x$ approaches 1 and so $\tan x = \sin x/\cos x$ is large. A table of values of $\tan x$ for x close to $\pi/2$ (≈ 1.570796) is shown in the margin.

Thus, by choosing x close enough to $\pi/2$ through values less than $\pi/2$, we can make the value of $\tan x$ larger than any given positive number. In a similar way, by choosing x close to $-\pi/2$ through values greater than $-\pi/2$, we can make $\tan x$ smaller than any given negative number. In the notation of Section 3.6 we have

$$\tan x \to \infty \qquad \text{as} \qquad x \to \frac{\pi^-}{2}$$

$$\tan x \to -\infty \qquad \text{as} \qquad x \to -\frac{\pi^+}{2}$$

Thus, $x = \pi/2$ and $x = -\pi/2$ are vertical asymptotes (see Section 3.6). With the information we have so far, we sketch the graph of $\tan x$ for $-\pi/2 < x < \pi/2$ in

Figure 1. The complete graph of tangent [see Figure 5(a) on page 446] is now obtained using the fact that tangent is periodic with period π.

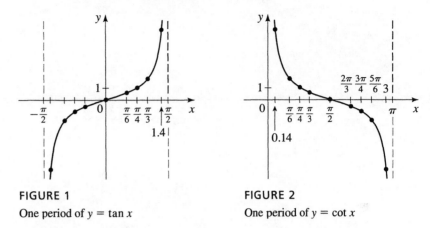

FIGURE 1

One period of $y = \tan x$

FIGURE 2

One period of $y = \cot x$

The function $y = \cot x$ is graphed on the interval $(0, \pi)$ by a similar analysis (see Figure 2). Since $\cot x$ is undefined for $x = n\pi$ with n an integer, its complete graph [in Figure 5(b)] has vertical asymptotes at these values.

To graph the cosecant and secant functions, we use the reciprocal identities

$$\csc x = \frac{1}{\sin x} \quad \text{and} \quad \sec x = \frac{1}{\cos x}$$

So, to graph $y = \csc x$, we take the reciprocals of the y-coordinates of the points of the graph of $y = \sin x$. (See Figure 3.) Similarly, to graph $y = \sec x$, we take the reciprocals of the y-coordinates of the points of the graph of $y = \cos x$. (See Figure 4.)

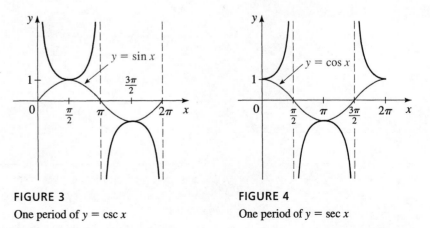

FIGURE 3

One period of $y = \csc x$

FIGURE 4

One period of $y = \sec x$

Let's consider more closely the graph of the function $y = \csc x$ on the interval $0 < x < \pi$. We need to examine the values of the function near 0 and π since at these values $\sin x = 0$, and $\csc x$ is thus undefined. We see that

$$\csc x \to \infty \qquad \text{as} \qquad x \to 0^+$$

$$\csc x \to \infty \qquad \text{as} \qquad x \to \pi^-$$

Thus, the lines $x = 0$ and $x = \pi$ are vertical asymptotes. In the interval $\pi < x < 2\pi$ the graph is sketched in the same way. The values of $\csc x$ in that interval are the same as those in the interval $0 < x < \pi$ except for sign (see Figure 3). The complete graph in Figure 5(c) is now obtained from the fact that the function cosecant is periodic with period 2π. Note that the graph has vertical asymptotes at the points where $\sin x = 0$, that is, at $x = n\pi$, for n an integer.

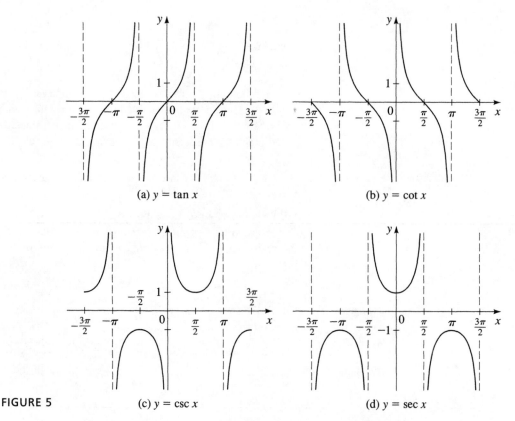

(a) $y = \tan x$

(b) $y = \cot x$

(c) $y = \csc x$

(d) $y = \sec x$

FIGURE 5

The graph of $y = \sec x$ is sketched in a similar manner. Observe that the domain of $\sec x$ is the set of all real numbers other than $x = (\pi/2) + n\pi$, for n an integer, so the graph has vertical asymptotes at those points. The complete graph is shown in Figure 5(d).

It is apparent that the graphs of $y = \tan x$, $y = \cot x$, and $y = \csc x$ are symmetric about the origin, whereas that of $y = \sec x$ is symmetric about the y-axis. This is because tangent, cotangent, and cosecant are odd functions, whereas secant is an even function.

Graphs Involving Tangent and Cotangent Functions

We now consider graphs of transformations of the tangent and cotangent functions.

EXAMPLE 1 ■ Graphing Tangent Curves

Graph each function.

(a) $y = 2 \tan x$ (b) $y = -\tan x$

SOLUTION

We first graph $y = \tan x$ and then transform it as required.

(a) To graph $y = 2 \tan x$, we multiply the y-coordinate of each point on the graph of $y = \tan x$ by 2. The resulting graph is shown in Figure 6(a).

(b) The graph of $y = -\tan x$ in Figure 6(b) is obtained from that of $y = \tan x$ by reflecting in the x-axis.

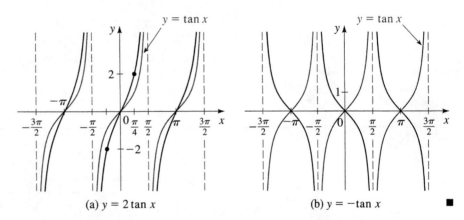

FIGURE 6   (a) $y = 2 \tan x$ (b) $y = -\tan x$ ■

Since the tangent and cotangent functions have period π, the functions

$$y = a \tan kx \quad \text{and} \quad y = a \cot kx \quad (k > 0)$$

complete one period as kx varies from 0 to π, that is, for $0 \leq kx \leq \pi$. Solving this inequality, we get $0 \leq x \leq \pi/k$. So they each have period π/k.

TANGENT AND COTANGENT CURVES

The functions

$$y = a \tan kx \quad \text{and} \quad y = a \cot kx \quad (k > 0)$$

have period π/k.

Thus, one complete period of the graphs of these functions occurs on any interval of length π/k. To sketch a complete period of these graphs, it's convenient to select an interval between vertical asymptotes:

To graph one period of $y = a \tan kx$, an appropriate interval is $\left(-\dfrac{\pi}{2k}, \dfrac{\pi}{2k}\right)$.

To graph one period of $y = a \cot kx$, an appropriate interval is $\left(0, \dfrac{\pi}{k}\right)$.

EXAMPLE 2 ■ Graphing Tangent Curves

Graph each function.

(a) $y = \tan 2x$

(b) $y = \tan 2\left(x - \dfrac{\pi}{4}\right)$

SOLUTION

(a) The period is $\pi/2$ and an appropriate interval is $(-\pi/4, \pi/4)$. The endpoints $x = -\pi/4$ and $x = \pi/4$ are vertical asymptotes. Thus, we graph one complete period of the function on $(-\pi/4, \pi/4)$. The graph has the same shape as that of the tangent function, but is shrunk horizontally by a factor of $\frac{1}{2}$. We then repeat that portion of the graph to the left and to the right. See Figure 7(a).

(b) The graph is the same as that in part (a), but it is shifted to the right $\pi/4$, as shown in Figure 7(b).

Since $y = \tan x$ completes one period between $x = -\frac{\pi}{2}$ and $x = \frac{\pi}{2}$, the function $y = \tan 2\left(x - \frac{\pi}{4}\right)$ completes one period as $2\left(x - \frac{\pi}{4}\right)$ varies from $-\frac{\pi}{2}$ to $\frac{\pi}{2}$.

Start of period: End of period:

$2\left(x - \frac{\pi}{4}\right) = -\frac{\pi}{2}$ $2\left(x - \frac{\pi}{4}\right) = \frac{\pi}{2}$

$x - \frac{\pi}{4} = -\frac{\pi}{4}$ $x - \frac{\pi}{4} = \frac{\pi}{4}$

$x = 0$ $x = \frac{\pi}{2}$

So we graph one period on the interval $\left(0, \frac{\pi}{2}\right)$.

FIGURE 7

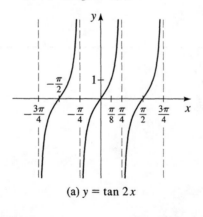

(a) $y = \tan 2x$

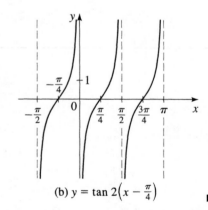

(b) $y = \tan 2\left(x - \frac{\pi}{4}\right)$

EXAMPLE 3 ■ A Shifted Cotangent Curve

Graph $y = 2 \cot\left(3x - \dfrac{\pi}{2}\right)$.

SOLUTION

We first put this in the form $y = a \cot k(x - b)$ by factoring 3 from the expression $3x - \dfrac{\pi}{2}$:

$$y = 2 \cot\left(3x - \frac{\pi}{2}\right) = 2 \cot 3\left(x - \frac{\pi}{6}\right)$$

Since $y = \cot x$ completes one period between $x = 0$ and $x = \pi$, the function $y = 2 \cot\left(3x - \frac{\pi}{2}\right)$ completes one period as $3x - \frac{\pi}{2}$ varies from 0 to π.

Start of period: End of period:

$$3x - \frac{\pi}{2} = 0 \qquad 3x - \frac{\pi}{2} = \pi$$

$$3x = \frac{\pi}{2} \qquad\qquad 3x = \frac{3\pi}{2}$$

$$x = \frac{\pi}{6} \qquad\qquad\quad x = \frac{\pi}{2}$$

So we graph one period on the interval $\left(\frac{\pi}{6}, \frac{\pi}{2}\right)$.

Thus, the graph is the same as that of $y = 2 \cot 3x$, but is shifted to the right $\pi/6$. The period of $y = 2 \cot 3x$ is $\pi/3$, and an appropriate interval is $(0, \pi/3)$. To get the corresponding interval for the desired graph, we shift this interval to the right $\pi/6$. This gives

$$\left(0 + \frac{\pi}{6}, \frac{\pi}{3} + \frac{\pi}{6}\right) = \left(\frac{\pi}{6}, \frac{\pi}{2}\right)$$

Finally, we graph one period in the shape of cotangent on the interval $(\pi/6, \pi/2)$ and repeat that portion of the graph to the left and to the right. See Figure 8.

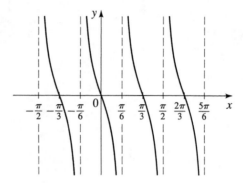

FIGURE 8

$y = 2 \cot\left(3x - \frac{\pi}{2}\right)$

■

Graphs Involving the Cosecant and Secant Functions

We have already observed that the cosecant and secant functions are the reciprocals of the sine and cosine functions. Thus, the following result is the counterpart of the result for sine and cosine curves in Section 5.3.

> **COSECANT AND SECANT CURVES**
>
> The functions
>
> $$y = a \csc kx \qquad \text{and} \qquad y = a \sec kx \qquad (k > 0)$$
>
> have period $2\pi/k$.

An appropriate interval on which to graph one complete period is $[0, 2\pi/k]$.

EXAMPLE 4 ■ **Graphing Cosecant Curves**

Graph each function.

(a) $y = \dfrac{1}{2} \csc 2x$ (b) $y = \dfrac{1}{2} \csc\left(2x + \dfrac{\pi}{2}\right)$

SOLUTION

(a) The period is $2\pi/2 = \pi$. An appropriate interval is $[0, \pi]$, and the asymptotes occur in this interval whenever $\sin 2x = 0$. So the asymptotes in this interval are $x = 0$, $x = \pi/2$, and $x = \pi$. With this information we sketch on the interval $[0, \pi]$ a graph with the same general shape as that of one period of the cosecant function. The complete graph in Figure 9(a) is obtained by repeating this portion of the graph to the left and to the right.

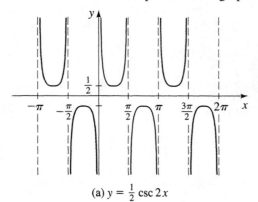

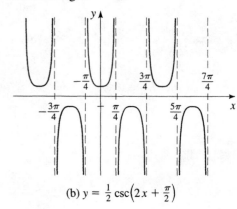

FIGURE 9

(a) $y = \frac{1}{2} \csc 2x$

(b) $y = \frac{1}{2} \csc\left(2x + \frac{\pi}{2}\right)$

Since $y = \csc x$ completes one period between $x = 0$ and $x = 2\pi$, the function $y = \frac{1}{2} \csc\left(2x + \frac{\pi}{2}\right)$ completes one period as $2x + \frac{\pi}{2}$ varies from 0 to 2π.

Start of period: End of period:

$2x + \frac{\pi}{2} = 0$ $2x + \frac{\pi}{2} = 2\pi$

$2x = -\frac{\pi}{2}$ $2x = \frac{3\pi}{2}$

$x = -\frac{\pi}{4}$ $x = \frac{3\pi}{4}$

So we graph one period on the interval $\left(-\frac{\pi}{4}, \frac{3\pi}{4}\right)$.

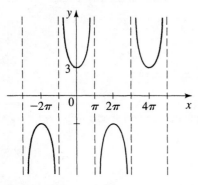

FIGURE 10

$y = 3 \sec \frac{1}{2} x$

(b) We first write

$$y = \frac{1}{2} \csc\left(2x + \frac{\pi}{2}\right) = \frac{1}{2} \csc 2\left(x + \frac{\pi}{4}\right)$$

From this we see that the graph is the same as that in part (a), but shifted to the left $\pi/4$. The graph is shown in Figure 9(b). ■

EXAMPLE 5 ■ Graphing a Secant Curve

Graph $y = 3 \sec \frac{1}{2} x$.

SOLUTION

The period is $2\pi \div \frac{1}{2} = 4\pi$. An appropriate interval is $[0, 4\pi]$, and the asymptotes occur in this interval wherever $\cos \frac{1}{2} x = 0$. Thus, the asymptotes in this interval are $x = \pi$, $x = 3\pi$. With this information we sketch on the interval $[0, 4\pi]$ a graph with the same general shape as that of one period of the secant function. The complete graph in Figure 10 is obtained by repeating this portion of the graph to the left and to the right. ■

5.4 EXERCISES

1–46 ■ Find the period and graph the function.

1. $y = 4 \tan x$

2. $y = -4 \tan x$

3. $y = -\frac{1}{2} \tan x$

4. $y = \frac{1}{2} \tan x$

5. $y = -\cot x$

6. $y = 2 \cot x$

7. $y = 2 \csc x$

8. $y = \frac{1}{2} \csc x$

9. $y = 3 \sec x$

10. $y = -3 \sec x$

11. $y = \tan\left(x + \frac{\pi}{2}\right)$

12. $y = \tan\left(x - \frac{\pi}{4}\right)$

13. $y = \csc\left(x - \frac{\pi}{2}\right)$

14. $y = \sec\left(x + \frac{\pi}{4}\right)$

15. $y = \cot\left(x + \frac{\pi}{4}\right)$

16. $y = 2 \csc\left(x - \frac{\pi}{3}\right)$

17. $y = \frac{1}{2} \sec\left(x - \frac{\pi}{6}\right)$

18. $y = 3 \csc\left(x + \frac{\pi}{2}\right)$

19. $y = \tan 2x$

20. $y = \tan \frac{1}{2} x$

21. $y = \tan \pi x$

22. $y = \cot \frac{\pi}{2} x$

23. $y = \sec 2x$

24. $y = 5 \csc 3x$

25. $y = \csc 2x$

26. $y = \csc \frac{1}{2} x$

27. $y = 2 \tan 3x$

28. $y = 2 \tan \frac{\pi}{2} x$

29. $y = 5 \csc 3x$

30. $y = 5 \sec 2\pi x$

31. $y = \tan 2\left(x + \frac{\pi}{2}\right)$

32. $y = \csc 2\left(x + \frac{\pi}{2}\right)$

33. $y = \tan 2(x - \pi)$

34. $y = \sec 2\left(x - \frac{\pi}{2}\right)$

35. $y = \cot\left(2x - \frac{\pi}{2}\right)$

36. $y = \frac{1}{2} \tan(\pi x - \pi)$

37. $y = 2 \csc\left(\pi x - \frac{\pi}{3}\right)$

38. $y = 2 \sec\left(\frac{1}{2} x - \frac{\pi}{3}\right)$

39. $y = 5 \sec\left(3x - \frac{\pi}{2}\right)$

40. $y = \frac{1}{2} \sec(2\pi x - \pi)$

41. $y = \tan\left(\frac{2}{3} x - \frac{\pi}{6}\right)$

42. $y = \tan \frac{1}{2}\left(x + \frac{\pi}{4}\right)$

43. $y = 3 \sec \pi\left(x + \frac{1}{2}\right)$

44. $y = \sec\left(3x + \frac{\pi}{2}\right)$

45. $y = -2 \tan\left(2x - \frac{\pi}{3}\right)$

46. $y = 2 \csc(3x + 3)$

47. (a) Prove that if f is periodic with period p, then $1/f$ is also periodic with period p.
   (b) Prove that cosecant and secant each have period 2π.

DISCOVERY · DISCUSSION

48. Reduction Formulas   Use the graphs in Figure 5 to explain why the following formulas are true.

$$\tan\left(x - \frac{\pi}{2}\right) = -\cot x$$

$$\sec\left(x - \frac{\pi}{2}\right) = \csc x$$

5 REVIEW

CONCEPT CHECK

1. (a) What is the unit circle?
   (b) Use a diagram to explain what is meant by the terminal point determined by a real number t.
   (c) What is the reference number $\bar{t}$ associated with t?
   (d) If t is a real number and $P(x, y)$ is the terminal point determined by t, write equations that define $\sin t$, $\cos t$, $\tan t$, $\cot t$, $\sec t$, and $\csc t$.
   (e) What are the domains of the six functions that you defined in part (d)?
   (f) Which trigonometric functions are positive in quadrants I, II, III, and IV?

2. (a) What is an even function?
   (b) Which trigonometric functions are even?
   (c) What is an odd function?
   (d) Which trigonometric functions are odd?

3. (a) State the reciprocal identities.
   (b) State the Pythagorean identities.

4. (a) What is a periodic function?
   (b) What are the periods of the six trigonometric functions?

5. Graph the sine and cosine functions. How is the graph of cosine related to the graph of sine?

6. Write expressions for the amplitude, period, and phase shift of the sine curve $y = a \sin k(x - b)$ and the cosine curve $y = a \cos k(x - b)$.

7. (a) Graph the tangent and contangent functions.
   (b) State the periods of the tangent curve $y = a \tan kx$ and the cotangent curve $y = a \cot kx$.

8. (a) Graph the secant and cosecant functions.
   (b) State the periods of the secant curve $y = a \sec kx$ and the cosecant curve $y = a \csc kx$.

EXERCISES

1–2 ■ A point $P(x, y)$ is given.
(a) Show that P is on the unit circle.
(b) Suppose that P is the terminal point determined by t. Find $\sin t$, $\cos t$, and $\tan t$.

1. $P\left(-\dfrac{\sqrt{3}}{2}, \dfrac{1}{2}\right)$

2. $P\left(\dfrac{3}{5}, -\dfrac{4}{5}\right)$

3–6 ■ A real number t is given.
(a) Find the reference number for t.
(b) Find the terminal point $P(x, y)$ on the unit circle determined by t.
(c) Find the six trigonometric functions of t.

3. $t = \dfrac{2\pi}{3}$

4. $t = \dfrac{5\pi}{3}$

5. $t = -\dfrac{11\pi}{4}$

6. $t = -\dfrac{7\pi}{6}$

7–16 ■ Find the value of the trigonometric function. If possible, give the exact value; otherwise, use a calculator to find an approximate value correct to five decimal places.

7. (a) $\sin \dfrac{3\pi}{4}$ **(b)** $\cos \dfrac{3\pi}{4}$

8. (a) $\tan \dfrac{\pi}{3}$ **(b)** $\tan\left(-\dfrac{\pi}{3}\right)$

9. (a) $\sin 1.1$ **(b)** $\cos 1.1$

10. (a) $\cos \dfrac{\pi}{5}$ **(b)** $\cos\left(-\dfrac{\pi}{5}\right)$

11. (a) $\cos \dfrac{9\pi}{2}$ **(b)** $\sec \dfrac{9\pi}{2}$

12. (a) $\sin \dfrac{\pi}{7}$ **(b)** $\csc \dfrac{\pi}{7}$

13. (a) $\tan \dfrac{5\pi}{2}$ **(b)** $\cot \dfrac{5\pi}{2}$

14. (a) $\sin 2\pi$ **(b)** $\csc 2\pi$

15. (a) $\tan \dfrac{5\pi}{6}$ **(b)** $\cot \dfrac{5\pi}{6}$

16. (a) $\cos \dfrac{\pi}{3}$ **(b)** $\sin \dfrac{\pi}{6}$

17–20 ■ Use the fundamental identities to write the first expression in terms of the second.

17. $\dfrac{\tan t}{\cos t}$, $\sin t$ **18.** $\tan^2 t \sec t$, $\cos t$

19. $\tan t$, $\sin t$; t in quadrant IV

20. $\sec t$, $\sin t$; t in quadrant II

21–24 ■ Find the values of the remaining trigonometric functions at t from the given information.

21. $\sin t = \frac{5}{13}$, $\cos t = -\frac{12}{13}$

22. $\sin t = -\frac{1}{2}$, $\cos t > 0$

23. $\cot t = -\frac{1}{2}$, $\csc t = \sqrt{5}/2$

24. $\cos t = -\frac{3}{5}$, $\tan t < 0$

25. If $\tan t = \frac{1}{4}$ and the terminal point for t is in quadrant III, find $\sec t + \cot t$.

26. If $\sin t = -\frac{8}{17}$ and the terminal point for t is in quadrant IV, find $\csc t + \sec t$.

27. If $\cos t = \frac{3}{5}$ and the terminal point for t is in quadrant I, find $\tan t + \sec t$.

28. If $\sec t = -5$ and the terminal point for t is in quadrant II, find $\sin^2 t + \cos^2 t$.

29–36 ■ **(a)** Find the amplitude, period, and phase shift of the function, and **(b)** sketch the graph.

29. $y = 10 \cos \frac{1}{2}x$ **30.** $y = 4 \sin 2\pi x$

31. $y = -\sin \frac{1}{2}x$

32. $y = 2\sin\left(x - \frac{\pi}{4}\right)$

33. $y = 3\sin(2x - 2)$

34. $y = \cos 2\left(x - \frac{\pi}{2}\right)$

35. $y = -\cos\left(\frac{\pi}{2}x + \frac{\pi}{6}\right)$

36. $y = 10\sin\left(2x - \frac{\pi}{2}\right)$

37–40 ■ The graph of one period of a function of the form $y = a\sin k(x - b)$ or $y = a\cos k(x - b)$ is shown. Determine the function.

37.

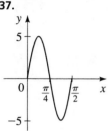

38.

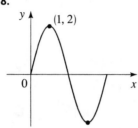

39.

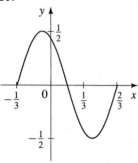

40.

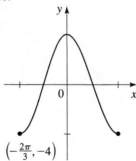

41–48 ■ Find the period, and sketch the graph.

41. $y = 3\tan x$

42. $y = \tan \pi x$

43. $y = 2\cot\left(x - \frac{\pi}{2}\right)$

44. $y = \sec\left(\frac{1}{2}x - \frac{\pi}{2}\right)$

45. $y = 4\csc(2x + \pi)$

46. $y = \tan\left(x + \frac{\pi}{6}\right)$

47. $y = \tan\left(\frac{1}{2}x - \frac{\pi}{8}\right)$

48. $y = -4\sec 4\pi x$

49–54 ■ A function is given.
(a) Use a graphing device to graph the function.
(b) Determine from the graph whether the function is periodic and, if so, determine the period.
(c) Determine from the graph whether the function is odd, even, or neither.

49. $y = |\cos x|$

50. $y = \sin(\cos x)$

51. $y = \cos(2^{0.1x})$

52. $y = 1 + 2^{\cos x}$

53. $y = e^{-|x|}\cos 3x$

54. $y = \ln x \sin 3x \quad (x > 0)$

55–58 ■ Graph the three functions on a common screen. How are the graphs related?

55. $y = x, \quad y = -x, \quad y = x\sin x$

56. $y = 2^{-x}, \quad y = -2^{-x}, \quad y = 2^{-x}\cos 4\pi x$

57. $y = x, \quad y = \sin 4x, \quad y = x + \sin 4x$

58. $y = \sin^2 x, \quad y = \cos^2 x, \quad y = \sin^2 x + \cos^2 x$

59–60 ■ Find the maximum and minimum values of the function.

59. $y = \cos x + \sin 2x$

60. $y = \cos x + \sin^2 x$

61. Find the solutions of $\sin x = 0.3$ in the interval $[0, 2\pi]$.

62. Find the solutions of $\cos 3x = x$ in the interval $[0, \pi]$.

63. Let $f(x) = \dfrac{\sin^2 x}{x}$.
(a) Is the function f even, odd, or neither?
(b) Find the x-intercepts of the graph of f.
(c) Graph f in an appropriate viewing rectangle.
(d) Describe the behavior of the function as $x \to \infty$ and as $x \to -\infty$.
(e) Notice that $f(x)$ is not defined when $x = 0$. What happens as $x \to 0$?

64. Let $y_1 = \cos(\sin x)$ and $y_2 = \sin(\cos x)$.
(a) Graph y_1 and y_2 in the same viewing rectangle.
(b) Determine the period of each of these functions from its graph.
(c) Find an inequality between $\sin(\cos x)$ and $\cos(\sin x)$ that is valid for all x.

5 TEST

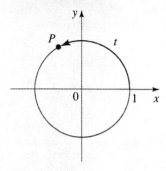

1. The point $P(x, y)$ is on the unit circle in quadrant IV. If $x = \sqrt{11}/6$, find y.

2. The point P in the figure at the left has y-coordinate $\frac{4}{5}$. Find each of the following.
   (a) $\sin t$ (b) $\cos t$
   (c) $\tan t$ (d) $\sec t$

3. Find the exact value of each of the following.
   (a) $\sin \dfrac{7\pi}{6}$ (b) $\cos \dfrac{13\pi}{4}$
   (c) $\tan\left(-\dfrac{5\pi}{3}\right)$ (d) $\csc \dfrac{3\pi}{2}$

4. Express $\tan t$ in terms of $\sin t$, if the terminal point determined by t is in quadrant II.

5. If $\cos t = -\frac{8}{17}$ and if the terminal point determined by t is in quadrant III, find $\tan t \cot t + \csc t$.

6–7 ■ A trigonometric function is given.
(a) Find the amplitude, period, and phase shift of the function.
(b) Sketch the graph.

6. $y = -5 \cos 4x$ 7. $y = 2 \sin\left(\dfrac{1}{2}x - \dfrac{\pi}{6}\right)$

8–9 ■ Find the period, and graph the function.

8. $y = -\csc 2x$ 9. $y = \tan\left(2x - \dfrac{\pi}{2}\right)$

10. The graph shown is one period of a function of the form $y = a \sin k(x - b)$. Determine the function.

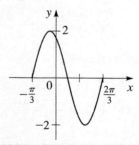

11. (a) Use a graphing device to graph the function in an appropriate viewing rectangle.
    (b) Determine from the graph if the function is even, odd, or neither.
    (c) Find the minimum and maximum values of the function.

$$y = \frac{\cos x}{1 + x^2}$$

Focus on Modeling
Harmonic Motion

Periodic behavior—behavior that repeats over and over again—is common in nature. Perhaps the most familiar example is the daily rising and setting of the sun, which results in the repetitive pattern of day, night, day, night, ... Another example is the daily variation of tide levels at the beach, which results in the repetitive pattern of high tide, low tide, high tide, low tide, ... Certain animal populations increase and decrease in a predictable periodic pattern: A large population exhausts the food supply, which causes the population to dwindle; this in turn results in a more plentiful food supply, which makes it possible for the population to increase; and the pattern then repeats over and over (see pages 442–443).

Other common examples of periodic behavior involve motion that is caused by vibration or oscillation. A mass suspended from a spring that has been compressed and then allowed to vibrate vertically is a simple example. This same "back and forth" motion also occurs in such diverse phenomena as sound waves, light waves, alternating electrical current, and pulsating stars, to name a few. In this section we consider the problem of modeling periodic behavior.

Modeling Periodic Behavior

The trigonometric functions are ideally suited for modeling periodic behavior. A glance at the graphs of the sine and cosine functions, for instance, shows that these functions themselves exhibit periodic behavior. Figure 1 shows the graph of $y = \sin t$. If we think of t as time, we see that as time goes on, $y = \sin t$ increases and decreases over and over again. Figure 2 shows that the motion of a vibrating mass on a spring is modeled very accurately by $y = \sin t$.

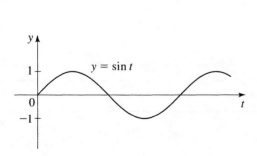

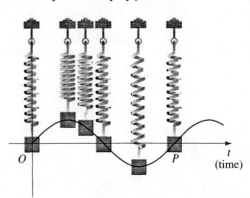

FIGURE 1

$y = \sin t$

FIGURE 2

Motion of a vibrating spring is modeled by $y = \sin t$.

Notice that the mass returns to its original position over and over again. A **cycle** is one complete vibration of an object, so the mass in Figure 2 completes one cycle of its motion between O and P. Our observations about how the sine and cosine functions model periodic behavior are summarized in the following box.

The main difference between the two equations describing simple harmonic motion is the starting point. At $t = 0$, we get

$$y = a \sin \omega \cdot 0 = 0$$

or

$$y = a \cos \omega \cdot 0 = a$$

In other words, in the first case the motion "starts" with zero displacement, while in the second case the motion "starts" with the displacement at maximum (at the amplitude a).

SIMPLE HARMONIC MOTION

If the equation describing the displacement y of an object at time t is

$$y = a \sin \omega t \qquad \text{or} \qquad y = a \cos \omega t$$

then the object is in **simple harmonic motion**. In this case,

amplitude $= |a|$ Maximum displacement of the object

period $= \dfrac{2\pi}{\omega}$ Time required to complete one cycle

frequency $= \dfrac{\omega}{2\pi}$ Number of cycles per unit of time

Notice that the functions

$$y = a \sin 2\pi\nu t \qquad \text{and} \qquad y = a \cos 2\pi\nu t$$

have frequency ν, because $2\pi\nu/(2\pi) = \nu$. Since we can immediately read the frequency from these equations, we often write equations of simple harmonic motion in this form.

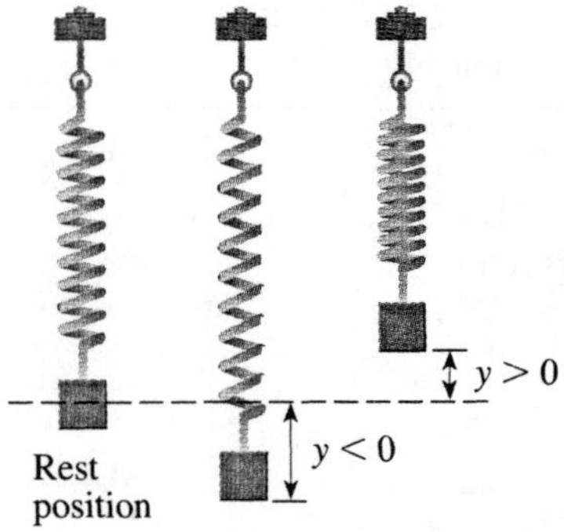

EXAMPLE 1 ■ A Vibrating Spring

The displacement of a mass suspended by a spring is modeled by the function

$$y = 10 \sin 4\pi t$$

where y is measured in inches and t in seconds (see Figure 3).

(a) Find the amplitude, period, and frequency of the motion of the mass.
(b) Sketch the graph of the displacement of the mass.

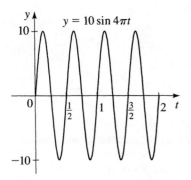

Rest position

FIGURE 3

SOLUTION

(a) From the formulas for amplitude, period, and frequency, we get

$$\text{amplitude} = |a| = 10 \text{ in.}$$

$$\text{period} = \frac{2\pi}{\omega} = \frac{2\pi}{4\pi} = \frac{1}{2} \text{ s}$$

$$\text{frequency} = \frac{\omega}{2\pi} = \frac{4\pi}{2\pi} = 2 \text{ Hz}$$

(b) The graph of the displacement of the mass at time t is shown in Figure 4. ■

An important situation where simple harmonic motion occurs is in the production of sound. Sound is produced by a regular variation in air pressure from the nor-

FIGURE 4

mal pressure. If the pressure varies in simple harmonic motion, then a pure sound is produced. The tone of the sound depends on the frequency and the loudness depends on the amplitude.

EXAMPLE 2 ■ Vibrations of a Musical Note

A tuba player plays the note E and sustains the sound for some time. For a pure E the variation in pressure from normal air pressure is given by

$$V(t) = 0.2 \sin 80\pi t$$

where V is measured in pounds per square inch and t in seconds.

(a) Find the amplitude, period, and frequency of V.
(b) Sketch a graph of V.
(c) If the tuba player increases the loudness of the note, how does the equation for V change?
(d) If the player is playing the note incorrectly and it is a little flat, how does the equation for V change?

SOLUTION

(a) From the formulas for amplitude, period, and frequency, we get

$$\text{amplitude} = |0.2| = 0.2$$

$$\text{period} = \frac{2\pi}{80\pi} = \frac{1}{40}$$

$$\text{frequency} = \frac{80\pi}{2\pi} = 40$$

(b) The graph of V is shown in Figure 5.

(c) If the player increases the loudness the amplitude increases. So the number 0.2 is replaced by a larger number.

(d) If the note is flat, then the frequency is decreased. Thus, the coefficient of t is less than 80π. ■

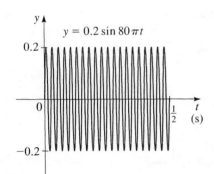

$y = 0.2 \sin 80\pi t$

0.2

0

$\frac{1}{2}$ t (s)

−0.2

FIGURE 5

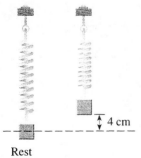

4 cm

Rest position

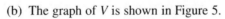

EXAMPLE 3 ■ Modeling a Vibrating Spring

A mass is suspended from a spring. The spring is compressed a distance of 4 cm and then released. It is observed that the mass returns to the compressed position after $\frac{1}{3}$ s.

(a) Find a function that models the displacement of the mass.
(b) Sketch the graph of the displacement of the mass.

SOLUTION

(a) The motion of the mass is given by one of the equations for simple harmonic motion. The amplitude of the motion is 4 cm. Since this amplitude is reached at time $t = 0$, an appropriate function that models the displacement is of the form

$$y = a \cos \omega t$$

Since the period is $p = \frac{1}{3}$, we can find ω from the following equation:

$$\text{period} = \frac{2\pi}{\omega}$$

$$\frac{1}{3} = \frac{2\pi}{\omega} \qquad \text{Period} = \frac{1}{3}$$

$$\omega = 6\pi \qquad \text{Solve for } \omega$$

So, the motion of the mass is modeled by the function

$$y = 4 \cos 6\pi t$$

where y is the displacement from the rest position at time t. Notice that when $t = 0$, the displacement is $y = 4$, as we expect.

(b) The graph of the displacement of the mass at time t is shown in Figure 6. ■

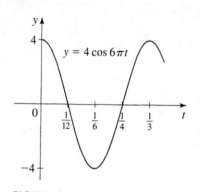

FIGURE 6

In general, the sine or cosine functions representing harmonic motion may be shifted horizontally or vertically. In this case, the equations take the form

$$y = a \sin(\omega(t - c)) + b \qquad \text{or} \qquad y = a \cos(\omega(t - c)) + b$$

The vertical shift b indicates that the variation occurs around an average value b. The horizontal shift c indicates the position of the object at $t = 0$. (See Figure 7.)

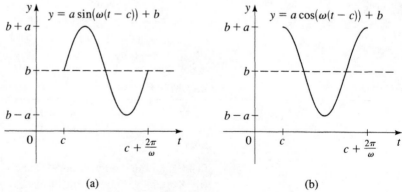

FIGURE 7   (a)   (b)

EXAMPLE 4 ■ Modeling the Brightness of a Variable Star

A variable star is one whose brightness alternately increases and decreases. For the variable star Delta Cephei, the time between periods of maximum brightness is 5.4

days. The average brightness (or magnitude) of the star is 4.0, and its brightness varies by ±0.35 magnitude.

(a) Find a function that models the brightness of Delta Cephei as a function of time.

(b) Sketch a graph of the brightness of Delta Cephei as a function of time.

SOLUTION

(a) Let's find a function in the form

$$y = a \cos(\omega(t - c)) + b$$

The amplitude is the maximum variation from average brightness, so the amplitude is $a = 0.35$ magnitude. We are given that the period is 5.4 days, so

$$\omega = \frac{2\pi}{5.4} \approx 1.164$$

Since the brightness varies from an average value of 4.0 magnitudes, the graph is shifted upward by $b = 4.0$. If we take $t = 0$ to be a time when the star is at maximum brightness, there is no horizontal shift, so $c = 0$ (this is because a cosine curve achieves its maximum at $t = 0$). Thus, the function we want is

$$y = 0.35 \cos(1.16t) + 4.0$$

where t is the number of days from a time when the star is at maximum brightness.

(b) The graph is sketched in Figure 8.

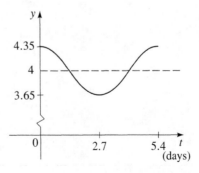

FIGURE 8

The number of hours of daylight varies throughout the course of a year. In the Northern Hemisphere, the longest day is June 21, and the shortest is December 21. The average length of daylight is 12 h, and the variation from this average depends on the latitude. (For example, Fairbanks, Alaska, experiences more than 20 h of daylight on the longest day and less than 4 h on the shortest day!) The graph in Figure 9 shows the number of hours of daylight at different times of the year for various latitudes. It's apparent from the graph that the variation in hours of daylight is simple harmonic.

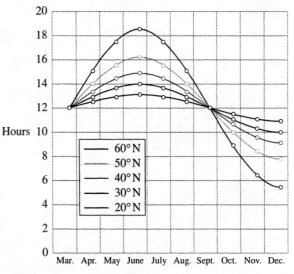

Source: Lucia C. Harrison, *Daylight, Twilight, Darkness and Time* (New York: Silver, Burdett, 1935) page 40.

FIGURE 9

Graph of the length of daylight from March 21 through December 21 at various latitudes

EXAMPLE 5 ■ Modeling the Number of Hours of Daylight

In Philadelphia (40° N latitude), the longest day of the year has 14 h 50 min of daylight and the shortest day has 9 h 10 min of daylight.

(a) Find a function L that models the length of daylight as a function of t, the number of days from January 1.

(b) An astronomer needs at least 11 hours of darkness for a long exposure astronomical photograph. During which days of the year can he do this?

SOLUTION

(a) We need to find a function in the form

$$y = a \sin(\omega(t - c)) + b$$

whose graph is the 40° N latitude curve in Figure 9. From the information given, we see that the amplitude is

$$a = \tfrac{1}{2}\left(14\tfrac{5}{6} - 9\tfrac{1}{6}\right) \approx 2.83 \text{ h}$$

Since there are 365 days in a year, the period is 365, so

$$\omega = \frac{2\pi}{365} \approx 0.0172$$

Since the average length of daylight is 12 h, the graph is shifted upward by 12, so $b = 12$. Since the curve attains the average value (12) on March 21, the

80th day of the year, the curve is shifted 80 units to the right. Thus, $c = 80$. So a function that models the number of hours of daylight is

$$y = 2.83 \sin(0.0172(t - 80)) + 12$$

where t is the number of days from January 1.

(b) Since a day has 24 h, 11 h of night correspond to 13 h of daylight. So we need to solve the inequality $y \leq 13$. To solve this inequality graphically, we graph $y = 2.83 \sin 0.0172(t - 80) + 12$ and $y = 13$ on the same graph. From the graph in Figure 10 we see that there are fewer than 13 h of daylight between day 1 (January 1) and day 101 (April 11) and from day 241 (August 29) to day 365 (December 31). ∎

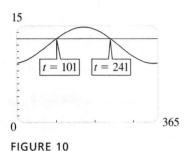

FIGURE 10

Modeling Periodic Behavior from Data

To determine what type of function to use in modeling data, we first draw a scatter plot of the data. The shape of the graph often suggests the appropriate function (see page 394). If the scatter plot has the shape of a sine or cosine curve, then we might try to model the data with a sine or cosine function. The next example illustrates the process.

EXAMPLE 6 ■ Modeling the Height of a Tide

The water depth in a narrow channel varies with the tides. Table 1 shows the water depth over a 12-hour period.

(a) Make a scatter plot of the data in Table 1.
(b) Find a function that models the water depth with respect to time.
(c) Graph the function you found and compare with the data.
(d) If a boat needs at least 11 ft of water to cross the channel, during which times can it safely do so?

SOLUTION

(a) The scatter plot is shown in Figure 11. The scatter plot helps us visualize the data; we see that the data appear to lie on a sine or cosine curve.

TABLE 1

Time	Depth (ft)
12:00 A.M.	9.8
1:00 A.M.	11.4
2:00 A.M.	11.6
3:00 A.M.	11.2
4:00 A.M.	9.6
5:00 A.M.	8.5
6:00 A.M.	6.5
7:00 A.M.	5.7
8:00 A.M.	5.4
9:00 A.M.	6.0
10:00 A.M.	7.0
11:00 A.M.	8.6
12:00 P.M.	10.0

FIGURE 11

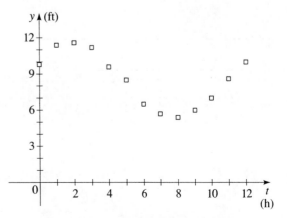

(b) We find a function that models the data in the form

$$y = a \cos \omega(t - c) + b$$

First, we need to find the amplitude a. We have

amplitude $= \frac{1}{2}$(maximum value $-$ minimum value) $= \frac{1}{2}(11.6 - 5.4) = 3.1$

To find the period, we note that the time between consecutive maximum and minimum values represents half of one period. Thus

period $= 2$(time of maximum value $-$ time of minimum value) $= 2(8 - 2) = 12$

Thus, $\omega = 2\pi/12 = 0.52$. The vertical shift is the average of the maximum and minimum values

vertical shift $= \frac{1}{2}$(maximum value $+$ minimum value) $= \frac{1}{2}(11.6 + 5.4) = 8.5$

From the graph we see that the cosine curve is shifted 2 h to the right (because the maximum value occurs at approximately $t = 2.0$), so $c = 2.0$. Thus, a function that models the tides over the given time period is given by

$$y = 3.1 \cos 0.52(t - 2.0) + 8.5$$

(c) A graph of the function and the scatter plot are shown in Figure 12. It appears that the model we found is a good approximation to the data.

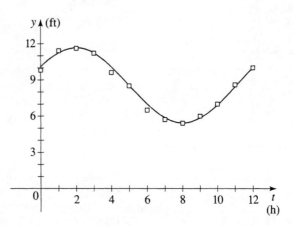

FIGURE 12

(d) We need to solve the inequality $y \geq 11$. We solve this inequality graphically by graphing $y = 3.1 \cos 0.52(t - 2.0) + 8.5$ and $y = 11$ on the same graph. From the graph in Figure 13 we see the water depth is higher than 11 ft between $t \approx 0.8$ and $t \approx 3.2$. This corresponds to the times 12:48 A.M. to 3:12 A.M.

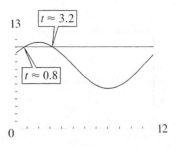

FIGURE 13

For the TI-83 and TI-86 the command **SinReg** (for sine regression) finds the sine curve that best fits the given data.

In Example 6 we used the scatter plot to guide us in finding a cosine curve that gives an approximate model of the data. Some graphing calculators are capable of finding a sine or cosine curve that best fits a given set of data points. The method the calculator uses is similar to the method of finding a line of best fit, as explained on pages 247–248.

EXAMPLE 7 ■ Fitting a Sine Curve to Data

(a) Use a graphing device to find the sine curve that best fits the depth of water data in Table 1 on page 461.
(b) Compare the result to the model found in Example 6.

SOLUTION

(a) Using the data in Table 1 and the **SinReg** command on the TI-83 calculator, we get a function of the form

$$y = a \sin(bt + c) + d$$

where

$$a = 3.1 \qquad b = 0.53$$
$$c = 0.55 \qquad d = 8.42$$

So, the sine function that best fits the data is

$$y = 3.1 \sin(0.53t + 0.55) + 8.42$$

```
SinReg
 y=a*sin(bx+c)+d
 a=3.097877596
 b=.5268322697
 c=.5493035195
 d=8.424021899
```

Output of the **SinReg** function on the TI-83.

(b) To compare this with the function in Example 6, we change the sine function to a cosine function by using the reduction formula $\sin u = \cos\left(u - \frac{\pi}{2}\right)$.

$$y = 3.1 \sin(0.53t + 0.55) + 8.42$$

$$= 3.1 \cos\left(0.53t + 0.55 - \frac{\pi}{2}\right) + 8.42 \qquad \text{Reduction formula}$$

$$= 3.1 \cos(0.53t - 1.02) + 8.42$$

$$= 3.1 \cos 0.53(t - 1.92) + 8.42 \qquad \text{Factor } 0.53$$

Comparing this with the function we obtained in Example 6, we see that there are small differences in the coefficients. In Figure 14 we graph a scatter plot of the data together with the sine function of best fit.

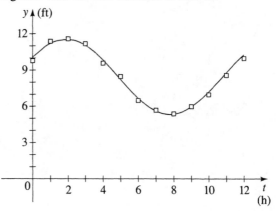

FIGURE 14

In Example 6 we estimated the values of the amplitude, period, and shifts from the data. In Example 7 the calculator computed the sine curve that best fits the data (that is, the curve that deviates least from the data as explained on page 248). The different ways of obtaining the model account for the differences in the functions.

Damped Harmonic Motion

The spring in Figure 2 is assumed to oscillate in a frictionless environment. In this hypothetical case, the amplitude of the oscillation will not change. In the presence of friction, however, the motion of the spring eventually "dies down"; that is, the amplitude of the motion decreases with time. Motion of this type is called *damped harmonic motion*.

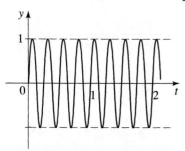

(a) Harmonic motion: $y = \sin 8\pi t$

DAMPED HARMONIC MOTION

If the equation describing the displacement y of an object at time t is

$$y = ke^{-ct} \sin \omega t \quad \text{or} \quad y = ke^{-ct} \cos \omega t \quad (c > 0)$$

then the object is in **damped harmonic motion**. The constant c is the **damping constant**.

Damped harmonic motion is simply harmonic motion for which the amplitude is governed by the function $a(t) = ke^{-ct}$. Figure 15 shows the difference between harmonic motion and damped harmonic motion.

The larger the damping constant c, the quicker the oscillation dies down. When a guitar string is plucked and then allowed to vibrate freely, a point on that string undergoes damped harmonic motion. We can hear the damping of the motion as the sound produced by the vibration of the string fades. How fast the damping of the string occurs (as measured by the size of the constant c) is a property of the size of

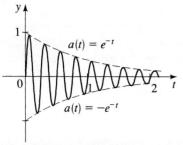

(b) Damped harmonic motion:
$y = e^{-t} \sin 8\pi t$

FIGURE 15

AM and FM Radio

Radio transmissions consist of sound waves superimposed on a harmonic electromagnetic wave form called the **carrier signal**.

Sound wave

Carrier signal

There are two types of radio transmission, called **amplitude modulation (AM)** and **frequency modulation (FM)**. In AM broadcasting the sound wave changes, or **modulates**, the amplitude of the carrier, but the frequency remains unchanged.

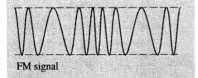

AM signal

In FM broadcasting the sound wave modulates the frequency, but the amplitude remains the same.

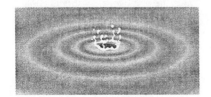

FM signal

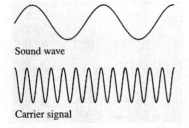

the string and the material it is made of. Another example of damped harmonic motion is the motion that a shock absorber on a car undergoes when the car hits a bump in the road. In this case, the shock absorber is engineered to damp the motion as quickly as possible (large c) and to have the frequency as small as possible (small ω). On the other hand, the sound produced by a tuba player playing a note is undamped as long as the player can maintain the loudness of the note. The electromagnetic waves that produce light move in simple harmonic motion that is not damped.

EXAMPLE 8 ■ A Vibrating Violin String

The G-string on a violin is pulled a distance of 0.5 cm above its rest position, then released and allowed to vibrate. The damping constant c for this string is determined to be 1.4. Suppose that the note produced is a pure G (frequency = 200 cycles per second). Find an equation that describes the motion of the point at which the string was plucked.

SOLUTION

Let P be the point at which the string was plucked. We will find a function $f(t)$ that gives the distance at time t of the point P from its original rest position. Since the maximum displacement occurs at $t = 0$, we find an equation in the form

$$y = ke^{-ct} \cos \omega t$$

From this equation, we see that $f(0) = k$. But we know that the original displacement of the string is 0.5 cm. Thus, $k = 0.5$. Since the frequency of the vibration is 200, we have $\omega/(2\pi) = 200$ or $\omega = (200)(2\pi)$. Finally, since we know that the damping constant is 1.4, we get

$$f(t) = 0.5e^{-1.4t} \cos 400\pi t \qquad ■$$

EXAMPLE 9 ■ Ripples on a Pond

A stone is dropped in a calm lake, causing waves to form. The up-and-down motion of a point on the surface of the water is modeled by damped harmonic motion. At some time the amplitude of the wave is measured, and 20 s later it is found that the amplitude has dropped to $\frac{1}{10}$ of this value. Find the damping constant c.

SOLUTION

The amplitude is governed by the coefficient ke^{-ct} in the equations for damped harmonic motion. Thus, the amplitude at time t is ke^{-ct}, and 20 s later, it is $ke^{-c(t+20)}$. So, from the given information

$$\frac{ke^{-ct}}{ke^{-c(t+20)}} = 10$$

$$ke^{-c(t+20)} = \frac{1}{10} ke^{-ct}$$

We now solve this equation for c. Canceling k and using the Laws of Exponents, we get

$$e^{-ct} \cdot e^{-20c} = \tfrac{1}{10}e^{-ct}$$

$$e^{-20c} = \tfrac{1}{10} \qquad \text{Cancel } e^{-ct}$$

$$e^{20c} = 10 \qquad \text{Take reciprocals}$$

Taking the natural logarithm of each side gives

$$20c = \ln(10)$$

$$c = \tfrac{1}{20}\ln(10) \approx \tfrac{1}{20}(2.30) \approx 0.12$$

Thus, the damping constant is $c \approx 0.12$.   ■

Problems

1–4 ■ A mass suspended from a spring vibrates in simple harmonic motion. The given function models the displacement of the mass from its rest position.
(a) Find the amplitude, period, and frequency of the motion of the mass.
(b) Sketch a graph of the displacement of the mass over one complete period.

1. $y = 2 \sin 3t$ **2.** $y = 3 \cos \tfrac{1}{2}t$

3. $y = -0.25 \cos\left(1.5t - \tfrac{\pi}{3}\right)$ **4.** $y = -\tfrac{3}{2}\sin(0.2t + 1.4)$

5. A cork floating in a lake is bobbing in simple harmonic motion. Its displacement above the bottom of the lake is modeled by

$$y = 0.2 \cos 20\pi t + 8$$

where y is measured in meters and t is measured in minutes.
(a) Find the frequency of the motion of the cork.
(b) Sketch a graph of y.
(c) Find the maximum displacement of the cork above the lake bottom.

6. The carrier wave for an FM radio signal is modeled by the function

$$y = a \sin(2\pi(9.15 \times 10^7)t)$$

where t is measured in seconds. Find the period and frequency of the carrier wave.

7. In a predator/prey model (see page 442), the predator population is modeled by the function

$$y = 900 \cos 2t + 8000$$

where t is measured in years.
(a) What is the maximum population?
(b) Find the length of time between successive periods of maximum population.

8. Each time your heart beats, your blood pressure increases, then decreases as the heart rests between beats. A certain person's blood pressure is modeled by the function

$$p(t) = 115 + 25 \sin(160\pi t)$$

where $p(t)$ is the pressure in mmHg, at time t measured in minutes.
(a) Find the amplitude, period, and frequency of p.
(b) Sketch a graph of p.
(c) If a person is exercising, his heart beats faster. How does this affect the period and frequency of p?

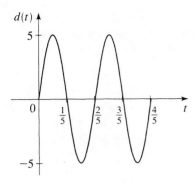

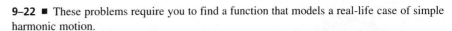

9–22 ■ These problems require you to find a function that models a real-life case of simple harmonic motion.

9. A mass attached to a spring is moving up and down in simple harmonic motion. The graph at the left gives its displacement $d(t)$ from equilibrium at time t. Express the function d in the form $d(t) = a \sin \omega t$.

10. The graph shows the variation of the water level relative to mean sea level in Commencement Bay at Tacoma, Washington, for a particular 24-hour period. Assuming that this variation is modeled by simple harmonic motion, find an equation of the form $y = a \sin \omega t$ that describes the variation in water level as a function of the number of hours after midnight.

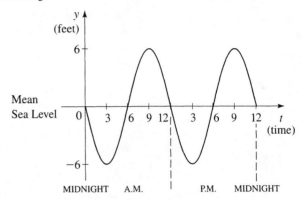

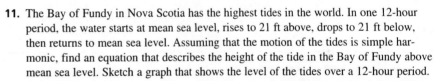

11. The Bay of Fundy in Nova Scotia has the highest tides in the world. In one 12-hour period, the water starts at mean sea level, rises to 21 ft above, drops to 21 ft below, then returns to mean sea level. Assuming that the motion of the tides is simple harmonic, find an equation that describes the height of the tide in the Bay of Fundy above mean sea level. Sketch a graph that shows the level of the tides over a 12-hour period.

12. A mass suspended from a spring is pulled down a distance of 2 ft from its rest position, as shown in the figure at the left. The mass is released at time $t = 0$ and allowed to oscillate. If the mass returns to this position after 1 s, find an equation that describes its motion.

13. A mass is suspended on a spring. The spring is compressed so that the mass is located 5 cm above its rest position. The mass is released at time $t = 0$ and allowed to oscillate. It is observed that the mass reaches its lowest point $\frac{1}{2}$ s after it is released. Find an equation that describes the motion of the mass.

14. The frequency of oscillation of an object suspended on a spring depends on the stiffness k of the spring (called the *spring constant*) and the mass m of the object. If the spring is compressed a distance a and then allowed to oscillate, its displacement is given by

$$f(t) = a \cos \sqrt{k/m}\, t$$

(a) A 10-g mass is suspended from a spring with stiffness $k = 3$. If the spring is compressed a distance 5 cm and then released, find the equation that describes the oscillation of the spring.

(b) Find a general formula for the frequency (in terms of k and m).

(c) How is the frequency affected if the mass is increased? Is the oscillation faster or slower?

(d) How is the frequency affected if a stiffer spring is used (larger k)? Is the oscillation faster or slower?

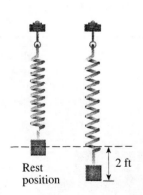

Rest position

2 ft

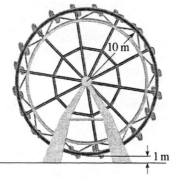

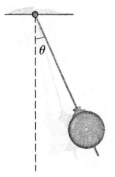

15. A ferris wheel has a radius of 10 m, and the bottom of the wheel passes 1 m above the ground. If the ferris wheel makes one complete revolution every 20 s, find an equation that gives the height above the ground of a person on the ferris wheel as a function of time.

16. The pendulum in a grandfather clock makes one complete swing every 2 s. The maximum angle that the pendulum makes with respect to its rest position is 10°. We know from physical principles that the angle θ between the pendulum and its rest position changes in simple harmonic fashion. Find an equation that describes the size of the angle θ as a function of time. (Take $t = 0$ to be a time when the pendulum is vertical.)

17. The variable star Zeta Gemini has a period of 10 days. The average brightness of the star is 3.8 magnitudes, and the maximum variation from the average is 0.2 magnitude. Assuming that the variation in brightness is simple harmonic, find an equation that gives the brightness of the star as a function of time.

18. Astronomers believe that the radius of a variable star increases and decreases with the brightness of the star. The variable star Delta Cephei (Example 4) has an average radius of 20 million miles and changes by a maximum of 1.5 million miles from this average during a single pulsation. Find an equation that describes the radius of this star as a function of time.

19. An *alternator*, or alternating current (AC) generator, produces an electrical current by rotating an *armature* (or coil) in a magnetic field. The figure represents a simple version of such a generator. As the wire passes through the magnetic field, a voltage E is generated in the wire. It can be shown that the voltage generated is given by

$$E(t) = E_0 \cos \omega t$$

where E_0 is the maximum voltage produced (which depends on the strength of the magnetic field) and $\omega/(2\pi)$ is the number of revolutions per second of the armature (the frequency). Ordinary 110-V household alternating current varies from $+155$ to -155 V with a frequency of 60 Hz (cycles per second). Find an equation that describes this variation in voltage.

Why do we say that household current is 110 V when the maximum voltage produced is 155 V? From the symmetry of the cosine function, we see that the average voltage produced is zero. This average value would be the same for all AC generators and so gives no information about the voltage generated. To obtain a more informative measure of voltage, engineers use the **root-mean-square** (rms) method. It can be shown that the rms voltage is $1/\sqrt{2}$ times the maximum voltage. So, for household current the rms voltage is

$$155 \times \frac{1}{\sqrt{2}} \approx 110 \text{ V}$$

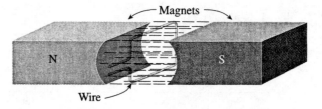

20. The armature in an electric generator is rotating at the rate of 100 revolutions per second (rps). If the maximum voltage produced is 310 V, find an equation that describes this variation in voltage. What is the rms voltage (see the marginal note)?

21. The graph shows an oscilloscope reading of the variation in voltage of an AC current produced by a simple generator.
    (a) Find the maximum voltage produced.
    (b) Find the frequency (cycles per second) of the generator.

(c) How many revolutions per second does the armature in the generator make?
(d) Find a formula that describes the variation in voltage as a function of time.

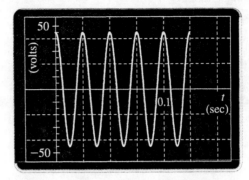

22. A train whistle produces a sharp, pure tone. While the train is moving toward us, the pitch of the whistle increases; it then decreases as the train moves away from us. This phenomenon is known as the *Doppler effect*. Suppose that the maximum change in pressure caused by the whistle is 10 N/m^2 and the frequency is 20 cycles per second.
    (a) Find an equation that describes the variation in pressure as a function of time, and sketch the graph.
    (b) How does the graph in part (a) change as the train moves toward us? Away from us?

23–26 ■ These problems require you to find a function that models simple harmonic motion from data. See Examples 6 and 7.

23. The table gives the average monthly temperature in Montgomery County, Maryland.
    (a) Make a scatter plot of the data.
    (b) Find a cosine curve that models the data (as in Example 6).
    (c) Graph the function you found in part (b) together with the scatter plot.
    (d) Use a graphing calculator to find the sine curve that best fits the data (as in Example 7).

Month	Average temperature (°F)
January	40.0
February	43.1
March	54.6
April	64.2
May	73.8
June	81.8
July	85.8
August	83.9
September	76.9
October	66.8
November	55.5
December	44.5

Time	Body temperature (°F)
0	36.8
2	36.7
4	36.6
6	36.7
8	36.8
10	37.0
12	37.2
14	37.3
16	37.4
18	37.3
20	37.2
22	37.0
24	36.8

 24. Circadian rhythm (from the Latin *circa*—about, and *diem*—day) is the daily biological pattern by which body temperature, blood pressure, and other physiological variables change. The data show typical changes in human body temperature over a 24-hour period ($t = 0$ corresponds to midnight).
(a) Make a scatter plot of the data.
(b) Find a cosine curve that models the data (as in Example 6).
(c) Graph the function you found in part (b) together with the scatter plot.
(d) Use a graphing calculator to find the sine curve that best fits the data (as in Example 7).

 25. When two species interact in a predator/prey relationship (see page 442), the populations of both species tend to vary in a sinusoidal fashion. In a certain midwestern county, the main food source for barn owls consists of field mice and other small mammals. The table gives the population of barn owls in this county every July 1 over a 12-year period.
(a) Make a scatter plot of the data.
(b) Find a sine curve that models the data (as in Example 6).
(c) Graph the function you found in part (b) together with the scatter plot.
(d) Use a graphing calculator to find the sine curve that best fits the data (as in Example 7). Compare to your answer from part (b).

Year	Owl population
0	50
1	62
2	73
3	80
4	71
5	60
6	51
7	43
8	29
9	20
10	28
11	41
12	49

 26. For reasons not yet fully understood, the number of fingerling salmon that survive the trip from their riverbed spawning grounds to the open ocean varies approximately sinusoidally from year to year. The table shows the number of salmon that hatch in a certain British Columbia creek and then make their way to the Strait of Georgia. The data is given in thousands of fingerlings, over a period of 16 years.
(a) Make a scatter plot of the data.
(b) Find a sine curve that models the data (as in Example 6).
(c) Graph the function you found in part (b) together with the scatter plot.

(d) Use a graphing calculator to find the sine curve that best fits the data (as in Example 7). Compare to your answer from part (b).

Year	Salmon (× 1000)	Year	Salmon (× 1000)
1985	43	1993	56
1986	36	1994	63
1987	27	1995	57
1988	23	1996	50
1989	26	1997	44
1990	33	1998	38
1991	43	1999	30
1992	50	2000	22

27–30 ■ These problems deal with modeling damped harmonic motion.

27. A strong gust of wind strikes a tall building, causing it to sway back and forth in damped harmonic motion. The frequency of the oscillation is 0.5 cycle per second and the damping constant is $c = 0.9$. Find an equation that describes the motion of the building. (Assume $k = 1$ and take $t = 0$ to be the instant when the gust of wind strikes the building.)

28. When a car hits a certain bump on the road, a shock absorber on the car is compressed a distance of 6 in., then released (see the figure). The shock absorber vibrates in damped harmonic motion with a frequency of 2 cycles per second. The damping constant for this particular shock absorber is 2.8.
  (a) Find an equation that describes the displacement of the shock absorber from its rest position as a function of time. Take $t = 0$ to be the instant that the shock absorber is released.
  (b) How long does it take for the amplitude of the vibration to decrease to 0.5 in.?

29. A tuning fork is struck and oscillates in damped harmonic motion. The amplitude of the motion is measured, and 3 s later it is found that the amplitude has dropped to $\frac{1}{4}$ of this value. Find the damping constant c for this tuning fork.

30. A guitar string is pulled at point P a distance of 3 cm above its rest position. It is then released and vibrates in damped harmonic motion with a frequency of 165 cycles per second. After 2 s, it is observed that the amplitude of the vibration at point P is 0.6 cm.
  (a) Find the damping constant c.
  (b) Find an equation that describes the position of point P above its rest position as a function of time. Take $t = 0$ to be the instant that the string is released.

6

Trigonometric Functions of Angles

Trigonometric functions are important in surveying, navigation, and astronomy. They are used, for instance, to find heights of mountains or distances to nearby stars.

No one can bypass the science of triangles [trigonometry] and hope to reach a satisfying knowledge of the stars.

The trigonometric functions can be viewed in two different but equivalent ways. One way is to view them as *functions of angles* (Chapter 6), the other as *functions of real numbers* (Chapter 5). The two approaches to trigonometry are independent of each other, so either Chapter 5 or Chapter 6 may be studied first.

The trigonometric functions defined in these two different ways are identical—they assign the same value to a given real number. In the first case, the real number is the measure of an angle; in the second, it is the length of an arc along the unit circle. We study both approaches because different applications require that we view these functions differently. One approach (Chapter 6) lends itself to static applications such as the measurement of distance using triangles. The other approach (Chapter 5) lends itself to dynamic applications such as modeling harmonic motion. The power and versatility of trigonometry stem from the fact that it can be viewed in these different ways. Today, trigonometry is an indispensable tool in physics, engineering, computer science, biology, and in practically all the sciences.

6.1 ANGLE MEASURE

An **angle** AOB consists of two rays R_1 and R_2 with a common vertex O (see Figure 1). We often interpret an angle as a rotation of the ray R_1 onto R_2. In this case, R_1 is called the **initial side**, and R_2 is called the **terminal side** of the angle. If the rotation is counterclockwise, the angle is considered **positive**, and if the rotation is clockwise, the angle is considered **negative**.

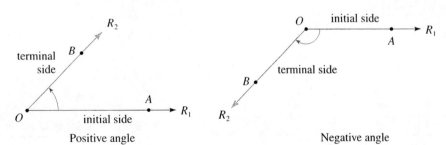

FIGURE 1   Positive angle   Negative angle

Angle Measure

The **measure** of an angle is the amount of rotation about the vertex required to move R_1 onto R_2. Intuitively, this is how much the angle "opens." One unit of measurement for angles is the **degree**. An angle of measure 1 degree is formed by rotating the initial side $\frac{1}{360}$ of a complete revolution. In calculus and other branches of mathematics, a more natural method of measuring angles is used—*radian measure*. The amount an angle opens is measured along the arc of a circle of radius 1 with its center at the vertex of the angle.

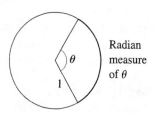

FIGURE 2

> ### DEFINITION OF RADIAN MEASURE
>
> If a circle of radius 1 is drawn with the vertex of an angle at its center, then the measure of this angle in **radians** (abbreviated **rad**) is the length of the arc that subtends the angle (see Figure 2).

The circumference of the circle of radius 1 is 2π and so a complete revolution has measure 2π rad, a straight angle has measure π rad, and a right angle has measure $\pi/2$ rad. An angle that is subtended by an arc of length 2 along the unit circle has radian measure 2 (see Figure 3).

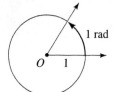 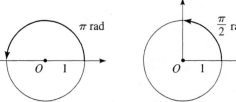 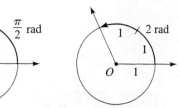

FIGURE 3
Radian measure

Since a complete revolution measured in degrees is $360°$ and measured in radians is 2π rad, we get the following simple relationship between these two methods of angle measurement.

> ### RELATIONSHIP BETWEEN DEGREES AND RADIANS
>
> $$180° = \pi \text{ rad} \qquad 1 \text{ rad} = \left(\frac{180}{\pi}\right)° \qquad 1° = \frac{\pi}{180} \text{ rad}$$
>
> **1.** To convert degrees to radians, multiply by $\dfrac{\pi}{180}$.
>
> **2.** To convert radians to degrees, multiply by $\dfrac{180}{\pi}$.

Measure of $\theta = 1$ rad
Measure of $\theta \approx 57.296°$

FIGURE 4

To get some idea of the size of a radian, notice that

$$1 \text{ rad} \approx 57.296° \qquad \text{and} \qquad 1° \approx 0.01745 \text{ rad}$$

An angle θ of measure 1 rad is shown in Figure 4.

EXAMPLE 1 ■ Converting between Radians and Degrees

(a) Express $60°$ in radians.

(b) Express $\dfrac{\pi}{6}$ rad in degrees.

SOLUTION

The relationship between degrees and radians gives

(a) $60° = 60\left(\dfrac{\pi}{180}\right)$ rad $= \dfrac{\pi}{3}$ rad

(b) $\dfrac{\pi}{6}$ rad $= \left(\dfrac{\pi}{6}\right)\left(\dfrac{180}{\pi}\right) = 30°$ ■

A note on terminology: We often use a phrase such as "a 30° angle" to mean *an angle whose measure is* 30°. Also, for an angle θ, we write $\theta = 30°$ or $\theta = \pi/6$ to mean *the measure of* θ *is* 30° *or* $\pi/6$ *rad.* When no unit is given, the angle is assumed to be measured in radians.

Angles in Standard Position

An angle is in **standard position** if it is drawn in the xy-plane with its vertex at the origin and its initial side on the positive x-axis. Figure 5 gives examples of angles in standard position.

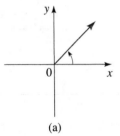

(a)

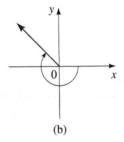

(b)

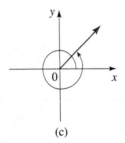

(c)

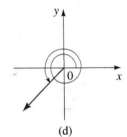

(d)

FIGURE 5
Angles in standard position

Two angles in standard position are **coterminal** if their sides coincide. In Figure 5 the angles in (a) and (c) are coterminal.

EXAMPLE 2 ■ Coterminal Angles

(a) Find angles that are coterminal with the angle $\theta = 30°$ in standard position.

(b) Find angles that are coterminal with the angle $\theta = \dfrac{\pi}{3}$ in standard position.

SOLUTION

(a) To find positive angles that are coterminal with θ, we add any multiple of 360°. Thus

$$30° + 360° = 390° \quad \text{and} \quad 30° + 720° = 750°$$

are coterminal with $\theta = 30°$. To find negative angles that are coterminal with θ, we subtract any multiple of 360°. Thus

$$30° - 360° = -330° \quad \text{and} \quad 30° - 720° = -690°$$

are coterminal with θ. See Figure 6.

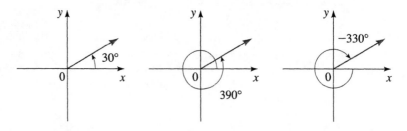

FIGURE 6

(b) To find positive angles that are coterminal with θ, we add any multiple of 2π. Thus

$$\frac{\pi}{3} + 2\pi = \frac{7\pi}{3} \quad \text{and} \quad \frac{\pi}{3} + 4\pi = \frac{13\pi}{3}$$

are coterminal with $\theta = \pi/3$. To find negative angles that are coterminal with θ, we subtract any multiple of 2π. Thus

$$\frac{\pi}{3} - 2\pi = -\frac{5\pi}{3} \quad \text{and} \quad \frac{\pi}{3} - 4\pi = -\frac{11\pi}{3}$$

are coterminal with θ. See Figure 7.

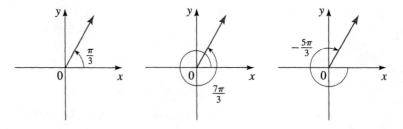

FIGURE 7

EXAMPLE 3 ■ Coterminal Angles

Find an angle with measure between 0° and 360° that is coterminal with the angle of measure 1290° in standard position.

SOLUTION

We can subtract 360° as many times as we wish from 1290°, and the resulting angle will be coterminal with 1290°. Thus, $1290° - 360° = 930°$ is coterminal with 1290°, and so is the angle $1290° - 2(360)° = 570°$.

To find the angle we want between 0° and 360°, we subtract 360° from 1290° as many times as necessary. An efficient way to do this is to determine how many times 360° goes into 1290°, that is, divide 1290 by 360, and the remainder will be the angle we are looking for. We see that 360 goes into 1290 three times with a remainder of 210. Thus, 210° is the desired angle (see Figure 8).

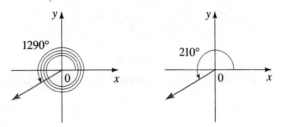

FIGURE 8

Length of a Circular Arc

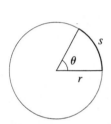

FIGURE 9
$s = \theta r$

An angle whose radian measure is θ is subtended by an arc that is the fraction $\theta/(2\pi)$ of the circumference of a circle. Thus, in a circle of radius r, the length s of an arc that subtends the angle θ (see Figure 9) is

$$s = \frac{\theta}{2\pi} \times \text{circumference of circle}$$

$$= \frac{\theta}{2\pi}(2\pi r) = \theta r$$

LENGTH OF A CIRCULAR ARC

In a circle of radius r, the length s of an arc that subtends a central angle of θ radians is

$$s = r\theta$$

Solving for θ, we get the important formula

$$\theta = \frac{s}{r}$$

This formula allows us to define radian measure using a circle of any radius r: The radian measure of an angle θ is s/r, where s is the length of the circular arc that subtends θ in a circle of radius r (see Figure 10).

FIGURE 10

The radian measure of θ is the number of "radiuses" that can fit in the arc that subtends θ; hence the term *radian*.

EXAMPLE 4 ■ Arc Length and Angle Measure

(a) Find the length of an arc of a circle with radius 10 m that subtends a central angle of 30°.

(b) A central angle θ in a circle of radius 4 m is subtended by an arc of length 6 m. Find the measure of θ in radians.

SOLUTION

(a) From Example 1(b) we see that $30° = \pi/6$ rad. So the length of the arc is

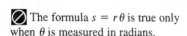
The formula $s = r\theta$ is true only when θ is measured in radians.

$$s = r\theta = (10)\frac{\pi}{6} = \frac{5\pi}{3} \text{ m}$$

(b) By the formula $\theta = s/r$, we have

$$\theta = \frac{s}{r} = \frac{6}{4} = \frac{3}{2} \text{ rad}$$

■

Area of a Circular Sector

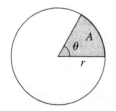

FIGURE 11
$A = \frac{1}{2}r^2\theta$

The area of a circle of radius r is $A = \pi r^2$. A sector of this circle with central angle θ has an area that is the fraction $\theta/(2\pi)$ of the area of the entire circle (see Figure 11). So the area of this sector is

$$A = \frac{\theta}{2\pi} \times \text{area of circle}$$

$$= \frac{\theta}{2\pi}(\pi r^2) = \frac{1}{2}r^2\theta$$

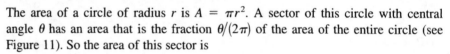

AREA OF A CIRCULAR SECTOR

In a circle of radius r, the area A of a sector with a central angle of θ radians is

$$A = \frac{1}{2}r^2\theta$$

EXAMPLE 5 ■ Area of a Sector

Find the area of a sector of a circle with central angle 60° if the radius of the circle is 3 m.

SOLUTION

To use the formula for the area of a circular sector, we must find the central angle of the sector in radians: $60° = 60(\pi/180)$ rad $= \pi/3$ rad. Thus, the area of the sector is

The formula $A = \frac{1}{2}r^2\theta$ is true only when θ is measured in radians.

$$A = \frac{1}{2}r^2\theta = \frac{1}{2}(3)^2\left(\frac{\pi}{3}\right) = \frac{3\pi}{2} \text{ m}^2$$

■

Circular Motion

Suppose a point moves along a circle as shown in Figure 12. There are two ways to describe the motion of the point—linear speed and angular speed. **Linear speed** is the rate at which the distance traveled is changing, so linear speed is the distance traveled divided by the time elapsed. **Angular speed** is the rate at which the central angle θ is changing, so angular speed is the number of radians this angle changes divided by the time elapsed.

FIGURE 12

LINEAR SPEED AND ANGULAR SPEED

Suppose a point moves along a circle of radius r and the ray from the center of the circle to the point traverses θ radians in time t. Let $s = r\theta$ be the distance the point travels in time t. Then the speed of the object is given by

$$\text{Angular speed} \qquad \omega = \frac{\theta}{t}$$

$$\text{Linear speed} \qquad v = \frac{s}{t}$$

EXAMPLE 6 ■ Finding Linear and Angular Speed

A boy rotates a stone in a 3-ft-long sling at the rate of 15 revolutions every 10 seconds. Find the angular and linear velocities of the stone.

SOLUTION

In 10 s, the angle θ changes by $15 \cdot 2\pi = 30\pi$ radians. So the *angular speed* of the stone is

$$\omega = \frac{\theta}{t} = \frac{30\pi \text{ rad}}{10 \text{ s}} = 3\pi \text{ rad/s}$$

The distance traveled by the stone in 10 s is $s = 15 \cdot 2\pi r = 15 \cdot 2\pi \cdot 3 = 90\pi$ ft. So the *linear speed* of the stone is

$$v = \frac{s}{t} = \frac{90\pi \text{ ft}}{10 \text{ s}} = 9\pi \text{ ft/s} \qquad ■$$

Notice that angular speed does *not* depend on the radius of the circle, but only on the angle θ. However, if we know the angular speed ω and the radius r, we can find linear speed as follows: $v = s/t = r\theta/t = r(\theta/t) = r\omega$.

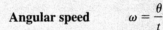
RELATIONSHIP BETWEEN LINEAR AND ANGULAR SPEED

If a point moves along a circle of radius r with angular speed ω, then its linear speed v is given by

$$v = r\omega$$

EXAMPLE 7 ■ Finding Linear Speed from Angular Speed

A woman is riding a bicycle whose wheels are 26 inches in diameter. If the wheels rotate at 125 revolutions per minute (rpm), find the speed at which she is traveling, in mi/h.

SOLUTION

The angular speed of the wheels is $2\pi \cdot 125 = 250\pi$ rad/min. Since the wheels have radius 13 in. (half the diameter), the linear speed is

$$v = r\omega = 13 \cdot 250\pi \approx 10{,}210.2 \text{ in./min}$$

Since there are 12 inches per foot, 5280 feet per mile, and 60 minutes per hour, her speed in miles per hour is

$$\frac{10{,}210.2 \text{ in./min} \times 60 \text{ min/h}}{12 \text{ in./ft} \times 5280 \text{ ft/mi}} \approx 9.7 \text{ mi/h} \qquad ■$$

6.1 EXERCISES

1–8 ■ Find the radian measure of the angle with the given degree measure.

1. 36°

2. 200°

3. −480°

4. −72°

5. 60°

6. 45°

7. −135°

8. 150°

9–16 ■ Find the degree measure of the angle with the given radian measure.

9. $\dfrac{3\pi}{4}$

10. $-\dfrac{7\pi}{2}$

11. $\dfrac{5\pi}{6}$

12. 2

13. −1.5

14. $\dfrac{2\pi}{9}$

15. $-\dfrac{\pi}{12}$

16. $\dfrac{\pi}{18}$

17–22 ■ The measure of an angle in standard position is given. Find two positive angles and two negative angles that are coterminal with the given angle.

17. 50°

18. 135°

19. $\dfrac{3\pi}{4}$

20. $\dfrac{11\pi}{6}$

21. $-\dfrac{\pi}{4}$

22. −45°

23–28 ■ The measures of two angles in standard position are given. Determine whether the angles are coterminal.

23. 70°, 430°

24. −30°, 330°

25. $\dfrac{5\pi}{6}$, $\dfrac{17\pi}{6}$

26. $\dfrac{32\pi}{3}$, $\dfrac{11\pi}{3}$

27. 155°, 875°

28. 50°, 340°

29–34 ■ Find an angle between 0° and 360° that is coterminal with the given angle.

29. 733°

30. 361°

31. 1110°

32. −100°

33. −800°

34. 1270°

35–40 ■ Find an angle between 0 and 2π that is coterminal with the given angle.

35. $\dfrac{17\pi}{6}$

36. $-\dfrac{7\pi}{3}$

37. 87π

38. 10

39. $\dfrac{17\pi}{4}$

40. $\dfrac{51\pi}{2}$

41. Find the length of the arc s in the figure.

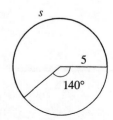

42. Find the angle θ in the figure.

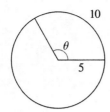

43. Find the radius r of the circle in the figure.

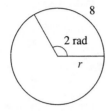

44. Find the length of an arc that subtends a central angle of 45° in a circle of radius 10 m.

45. Find the length of an arc that subtends a central angle of 2 rad in a circle of radius 2 mi.

46. A central angle θ in a circle of radius 5 m is subtended by an arc of length 6 m. Find the measure of θ in degrees and in radians.

47. An arc of length 100 m subtends a central angle θ in a circle of radius 50 m. Find the measure of θ in degrees and in radians.

48. A circular arc of length 3 ft subtends a central angle of 25°. Find the radius of the circle.

49. Find the radius of the circle if an arc of length 6 m on the circle subtends a central angle of $\pi/6$ rad.

50. How many revolutions will a car wheel of diameter 30 in. make as the car travels a distance of one mile?

51. Pittsburgh, Pennsylvania, and Miami, Florida, lie approximately on the same meridian. Pittsburgh has a latitude of 40.5° N and Miami, 25.5° N. Find the distance between these two cities. (The radius of the earth is 3960 mi.)

52. Memphis, Tennessee, and New Orleans, Louisiana, lie approximately on the same meridian. Memphis has latitude 35° N and New Orleans, 30° N. Find the distance between these two cities. (The radius of the earth is 3960 mi.)

53. Find the distance that the earth travels in one day in its path around the sun. Assume that a year has 365 days and that the path of the earth around the sun is a circle of radius 93 million miles. [The path of the earth around the sun is actually an *ellipse* with the sun at one focus (see Section 9.2). This ellipse, however, has very small eccentricity, so it is nearly circular.]

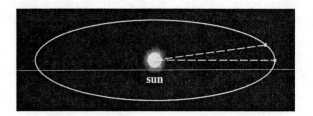

54. The Greek mathematician Eratosthenes (ca. 276–195 B.C.) measured the circumference of the earth from the following observations. He noticed that on a certain day the sun shone directly down a deep well in Syene (modern Aswan). At the same time in Alexandria, 500 miles north (on the same meridian), the rays of the sun shone at an angle of 7.2° to the zenith. Use this information and the figure to find the radius and circumference of the earth. (The data used in this problem are more accurate than those available to Eratosthenes.)

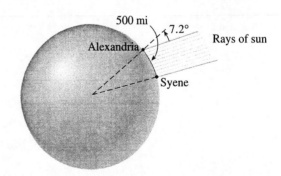

55. Find the distance along an arc on the surface of the earth that subtends a central angle of 1 minute (1 minute = $\frac{1}{60}$ degree). This distance is called a *nautical mile*. (The radius of the earth is 3960 mi.)

56. Find the area of the sector shown in each figure.

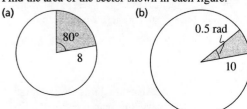

57. Find the area of a sector with central angle 1 rad in a circle of radius 10 m.

58. A sector of a circle has a central angle of 60°. Find the area of the sector if the radius of the circle is 3 mi.

59. The area of a sector of a circle with a central angle of 2 rad is 16 m². Find the radius of the circle.

60. A sector of a circle of radius 24 mi has an area of 288 mi². Find the central angle of the sector.

61. The area of a circle is 72 cm². Find the area of a sector of this circle that subtends a central angle of $\pi/6$ rad.

62. Three circles with radii 1, 2, and 3 ft are externally tangent to one another, as shown in the figure. Find the area of the sector of the circle of radius 1 that is cut off by the line segments joining the center of that circle to the centers of the other two circles.

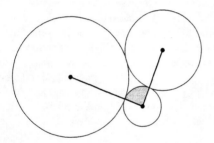

63. A winch of radius 2 ft is used to lift heavy loads. If the winch makes 8 revolutions every 15 s, find the speed at which the load is rising.

64. A ceiling fan with 16-in. blades rotates at 45 rpm.
 (a) Find the angular speed of the fan in rad/min.
 (b) Find the linear speed of the tips of the blades in in/min.

65. A radial saw has a blade with a 6-in. radius. Suppose that the blade spins at 1000 rpm.
 (a) Find the angular speed of the blade in rad/min.
 (b) Find the linear speed of the sawteeth in ft/s.

66. The earth rotates about its axis once every 23 h 56 min 4 s, and the radius of the earth is 3960 mi. Find the linear speed of a point on the equator in mi/h.

67. The wheels of a car have radius 11 in. and are rotating at 600 rpm. Find the speed of the car in mi/h.

68. A truck with 48-in. diameter wheels is traveling at 50 mi/h.
 (a) Find the angular speed of the wheels in rad/min.
 (b) How many revolutions per minute do the wheels make?

69. To measure the speed of a current, scientists place a paddle wheel in the stream and observe the rate at which it rotates. If the paddle wheel has radius 0.20 m and rotates at 100 rpm, find the speed of the current in m/s.

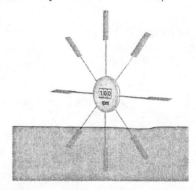

70. The sprockets and chain of a bicycle are shown in the figure. The pedal sprocket has a radius of 4 in, the wheel sprocket a radius of 2 in, and the wheel a radius of 13 in. The cyclist pedals at 40 rpm.
 (a) Find the angular speed of the wheel sprocket.
 (b) Find the speed of the bicycle. (Assume that the wheel turns at the same rate as the wheel sprocket.)

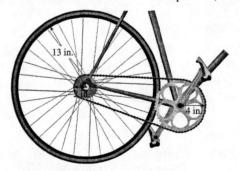

⬤ **DISCOVERY · DISCUSSION**

71. Different Ways of Measuring Angles   The custom of measuring angles using degrees, with 360° in a circle, dates back to the ancient Babylonians, who used a number system based on groups of 60. Another system of measuring angles divides the circle into 400 units, called *grads*. In this system a right angle is 100 grad, so this fits in with our base 10 number system.

Write a short essay comparing the advantages and disadvantages of these two systems and the radian system of measuring angles. Which system do you prefer?

72. Clocks and Angles In one hour, the minute hand on a clock moves through a complete circle, and the hour hand moves through $\frac{1}{12}$ of a circle. Through how many radians do the minute and the hour hand move between 1:00 P.M. and 6:45 P.M. (on the same day)?

6.2 TRIGONOMETRY OF RIGHT TRIANGLES

In this section we study certain ratios of the sides of right triangles, called trigonometric ratios, and give several applications.

▧ Trigonometric Ratios

Consider a right triangle with θ as one of its acute angles. The trigonometric ratios are defined as follows (see Figure 1).

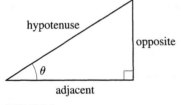

FIGURE 1

THE TRIGONOMETRIC RATIOS		
$\sin\theta = \dfrac{\text{opposite}}{\text{hypotenuse}}$	$\cos\theta = \dfrac{\text{adjacent}}{\text{hypotenuse}}$	$\tan\theta = \dfrac{\text{opposite}}{\text{adjacent}}$
$\csc\theta = \dfrac{\text{hypotenuse}}{\text{opposite}}$	$\sec\theta = \dfrac{\text{hypotenuse}}{\text{adjacent}}$	$\cot\theta = \dfrac{\text{adjacent}}{\text{opposite}}$

The symbols we use for these ratios are abbreviations for their full names: **sine, cosine, tangent, cosecant, secant, cotangent.** Since any two right triangles with angle θ are similar, these ratios are the same, regardless of the size of the triangle; they depend only on the angle θ (see Figure 2).

Hipparchus (circa 140 B.C.) is considered the founder of trigonometry. He constructed tables for a function closely related to the modern sine function and evaluated for angles at half-degree intervals. These are considered the first trigonometric tables. He used his tables mainly to calculate the paths of the planets through the heavens.

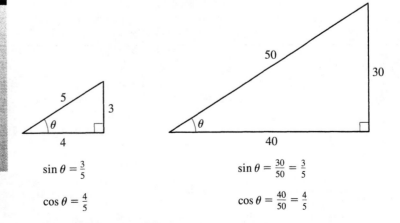

FIGURE 2

$\sin\theta = \frac{3}{5}$

$\cos\theta = \frac{4}{5}$

$\sin\theta = \frac{30}{50} = \frac{3}{5}$

$\cos\theta = \frac{40}{50} = \frac{4}{5}$

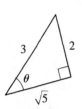

FIGURE 3

EXAMPLE 1 ■ Finding Trigonometric Ratios

Find the six trigonometric ratios of the angle θ in Figure 3.

SOLUTION

$$\sin \theta = \frac{2}{3} \qquad \cos \theta = \frac{\sqrt{5}}{3} \qquad \tan \theta = \frac{2}{\sqrt{5}}$$

$$\csc \theta = \frac{3}{2} \qquad \sec \theta = \frac{3}{\sqrt{5}} \qquad \cot \theta = \frac{\sqrt{5}}{2}$$ ■

EXAMPLE 2 ■ Finding Trigonometric Ratios

If $\cos \alpha = \frac{3}{4}$, sketch a right triangle with acute angle α, and find the other five trigonometric ratios of α.

SOLUTION

Since $\cos \alpha$ is defined as the ratio of the adjacent side to the hypotenuse, we sketch a triangle with hypotenuse of length 4 and a side of length 3 adjacent to α. If the opposite side is x, then by the Pythagorean Theorem, $3^2 + x^2 = 4^2$ or $x^2 = 7$, so $x = \sqrt{7}$. We then use the triangle in Figure 4 to find the ratios.

$$\sin \alpha = \frac{\sqrt{7}}{4} \qquad \cos \alpha = \frac{3}{4} \qquad \tan \alpha = \frac{\sqrt{7}}{3}$$

$$\csc \alpha = \frac{4}{\sqrt{7}} \qquad \sec \alpha = \frac{4}{3} \qquad \cot \alpha = \frac{3}{\sqrt{7}}$$ ■

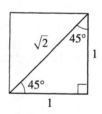

FIGURE 4

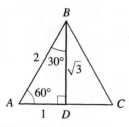

FIGURE 5

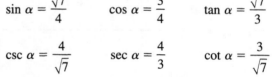

FIGURE 6

Special Triangles

Certain right triangles have ratios that can be calculated easily from the Pythagorean Theorem. Since they are used frequently, we mention them here.

The first triangle is obtained by drawing a diagonal in a square of side 1 (see Figure 5). By the Pythagorean Theorem this diagonal has length $\sqrt{2}$. The resulting triangle has angles 45°, 45°, and 90° (or $\pi/4$, $\pi/4$, and $\pi/2$). To get the second triangle, we start with an equilateral triangle ABC of side 2 and draw the perpendicular bisector DB of the base, as in Figure 6. By the Pythagorean Theorem the length of DB is $\sqrt{3}$. Since DB bisects angle ABC, we obtain a triangle with angles 30°, 60°, and 90° (or $\pi/6$, $\pi/3$, and $\pi/2$).

We can now use the special triangles in Figures 5 and 6 to calculate the trigonometric ratios for angles with measures 30°, 45°, and 60° (or $\pi/6$, $\pi/4$, and $\pi/3$). These are listed in Table 1.

TABLE 1   Values of the trigonometric ratios for special angles

θ in degrees	θ in radians	$\sin\theta$	$\cos\theta$	$\tan\theta$	$\csc\theta$	$\sec\theta$	$\cot\theta$
30°	$\dfrac{\pi}{6}$	$\dfrac{1}{2}$	$\dfrac{\sqrt{3}}{2}$	$\dfrac{\sqrt{3}}{3}$	2	$\dfrac{2\sqrt{3}}{3}$	$\sqrt{3}$
45°	$\dfrac{\pi}{4}$	$\dfrac{\sqrt{2}}{2}$	$\dfrac{\sqrt{2}}{2}$	1	$\sqrt{2}$	$\sqrt{2}$	1
60°	$\dfrac{\pi}{3}$	$\dfrac{\sqrt{3}}{2}$	$\dfrac{1}{2}$	$\sqrt{3}$	$\dfrac{2\sqrt{3}}{3}$	2	$\dfrac{\sqrt{3}}{3}$

It's useful to remember these special trigonometric ratios because they occur often. Of course, they can be recalled easily if we remember the triangles from which they are obtained.

For an explanation of numerical methods, see the marginal note on page 422.

To find the values of the trigonometric ratios for other angles, we use a calculator. Mathematical methods (called *numerical methods*) used in finding the trigonometric ratios are programmed directly into scientific calculators. For instance, when the ⎡SIN⎤ key is pressed, the calculator computes an approximation to the value of the sine of the given angle. Calculators give the values of sine, cosine, and tangent; the other ratios can be easily calculated from these using the following *reciprocal relations:*

$$\csc t = \frac{1}{\sin t} \qquad \sec t = \frac{1}{\cos t} \qquad \cot t = \frac{1}{\tan t}$$

You should check that these relations follow immediately from the definitions of the trigonometric ratios.

We follow the convention that when we write $\sin t$, *we mean the sine of the angle whose radian measure is t.* For instance, $\sin 1$ means the sine of the angle whose radian measure is 1. When using a calculator to find an approximate value for this number, set your calculator to radian mode; you will find that

$$\sin 1 \approx 0.841471$$

If you want to find the sine of the angle whose measure is 1°, set your calculator to degree mode; you will find that

$$\sin 1° \approx 0.0174524$$

Aristarchus of Samos (310–230 B.C.) was a famous Greek scientist, musician, astronomer, and geometer. In his book *On the Sizes and Distances of the Sun and the Moon,* he estimated the distance to the sun by observing that when the moon is exactly half full, the triangle formed by the sun, moon, and the earth has a right angle at the moon. His method was similar to the one described in Exercise 51 in this section. Aristarchus was the first to advance the theory that the earth and planets move around the sun, an idea that did not gain full acceptance until after the time of Copernicus, 1800 years later. For this reason he is often called the "Copernicus of antiquity."

EXAMPLE 3 ■ **Using a Calculator to Find Trigonometric Ratios**

With our calculator in degree mode, and writing the results correct to five decimal places, we find

$$\sin 17° \approx 0.29237 \qquad \sec 88° = \frac{1}{\cos 88°} \approx 28.65371$$

With our calculator in radian mode, and writing the results correct to five decimal places, we find

$$\cos 1.2 \approx 0.36236 \qquad \cot 1.54 = \frac{1}{\tan 1.54} \approx 0.03081$$

■

Applications of Trigonometry of Right Triangles

A triangle has six parts: three angles and three sides. To **solve a triangle** means to determine all of its parts from the information known about the triangle, that is, to determine the lengths of the three sides and the measures of the three angles.

EXAMPLE 4 ■ Solving a Right Triangle

Solve triangle ABC, shown in Figure 7.

SOLUTION

It's clear that $\angle B = 60°$. To find a, we look for an equation that relates a to the lengths and angles we already know. In this case, we have $\sin 30° = a/12$, so

$$a = 12 \sin 30° = 12\left(\tfrac{1}{2}\right) = 6$$

Similarly, $\cos 30° = b/12$, so

$$b = 12 \cos 30° = 12\left(\frac{\sqrt{3}}{2}\right) = 6\sqrt{3}$$

■

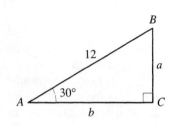

FIGURE 7

It's very useful to know that, using the information given in Figure 8, the lengths of the legs of a right triangle are

$$a = r \sin \theta \qquad \text{and} \qquad b = r \cos \theta$$

The ability to solve right triangles using the trigonometric ratios is fundamental to many problems in navigation, surveying, astronomy, and the measurement of distances. The applications we consider in this section always involve right triangles but, as we will see in the next three sections, trigonometry is also useful in solving triangles that are not right triangles.

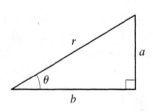

FIGURE 8
$a = r \sin \theta$
$b = r \cos \theta$

To discuss the next examples, we need some terminology. If an observer is looking at an object, then the line from the observer's eye to the object is called the **line of sight** (Figure 9). If the object being observed is above the horizontal, then the angle between the line of sight and the horizontal is called the **angle of elevation**. If the object is below the horizontal, then the angle between the line of sight and the horizontal is called the **angle of depression**. In many of the examples and exercises in this chapter, angles of elevation and depression will be given for a hypothetical observer at ground level. If the line of sight follows a physical object, such as an inclined plane or a hillside, we use the term **angle of inclination**.

Thales of Miletus (circa 625–547 B.C.) is the legendary founder of Greek geometry. It is said that he calculated the height of a Greek column by comparing the length of the shadow of his staff with that of the column. Using properties of similar triangles, he argued that the ratio of the height h of the column to the height h' of his staff was equal to the ratio of the length s of the column's shadow to the length s' of the staff's shadow:

$$\frac{h}{h'} = \frac{s}{s'}$$

Since three of these quantities are known, Thales was able to calculate the height of the column.

According to legend, Thales used a similar method to find the height of the Great Pyramid in Egypt, a feat that impressed Egypt's king. Plutarch wrote that "although he [the king of Egypt] admired you [Thales] for other things, yet he particularly liked the manner by which you measured the height of the pyramid without any trouble or instrument." The principle Thales used, the fact that ratios of corresponding sides of similar triangles are equal, is the foundation of the subject of trigonometry.

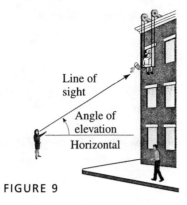 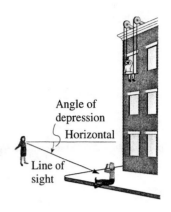

FIGURE 9

The next example gives an important application of trigonometry to the problem of measurement: We measure the height of a tall tree without having to climb it! Although the example is simple, the result is fundamental to the method of applying the trigonometric ratios to such problems.

EXAMPLE 5 ■ Finding the Height of a Tree

A giant redwood tree casts a shadow 532 ft long. Find the height of the tree if the angle of elevation of the sun is 25.7°.

SOLUTION

Let the height of the tree be h. From Figure 10 we see that

$$\frac{h}{532} = \tan 25.7° \qquad \text{Definition of tan}$$

$$h = 532 \tan 25.7° \qquad \text{Multiply by 532}$$

$$\approx 532(0.48127) \approx 256 \qquad \text{Use a calculator}$$

Therefore, the height of the tree is about 256 ft.

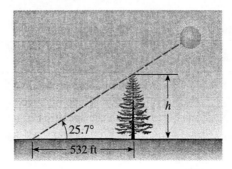

FIGURE 10

EXAMPLE 6 ■ A Problem Involving Right Triangles

From a point on the ground 500 ft from the base of a building, it is observed that the angle of elevation to the top of the building is 24° and the angle of elevation to the top of a flagpole atop the building is 27°. Find the height of the building and the length of the flagpole.

SOLUTION

Figure 11 illustrates the situation. The height of the building is found in the same way that we found the height of the tree in Example 5.

$$\frac{h}{500} = \tan 24° \qquad \text{Definition of tan}$$

$$h = 500 \tan 24° \qquad \text{Multiply by 500}$$

$$\approx 500(0.4452) \approx 223 \qquad \text{Use a calculator}$$

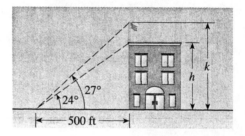

FIGURE 11

The height of the building is approximately 223 ft. To find the length of the flagpole, let's first find the height from the ground to the top of the pole:

$$\frac{k}{500} = \tan 27°$$

$$k = 500 \tan 27° \approx 500(0.5095) \approx 255$$

To find the length of the flagpole, we subtract h from k. So the length of the pole is approximately $255 - 223 = 32$ ft. ■

The key labels $\boxed{\text{SIN}^{-1}}$ or $\boxed{\text{INV}}$ $\boxed{\text{SIN}}$ stand for "inverse sine." The inverse trigonometric functions are studied in Section 7.4.

In some problems we need to find an angle in a right triangle whose sides are given. To do this, we use Table 1 (page 485) "backward"; that is, we find the *angle* with the specified trigonometric ratio. For example, if $\sin \theta = \frac{1}{2}$, what is the angle θ? From Table 1 we can tell that $\theta = 30°$. To find an angle whose sine is not given in the table, we use the $\boxed{\text{SIN}^{-1}}$ or $\boxed{\text{INV}}$ $\boxed{\text{SIN}}$ or $\boxed{\text{ARCSIN}}$ keys on a calculator. For example, if $\sin \theta = 0.8$, we apply the $\boxed{\text{SIN}^{-1}}$ key to get $\theta = 53.13°$ or 0.927 rad. The calculator also gives angles whose cosine or tangent are known, using the $\boxed{\text{COS}^{-1}}$ or $\boxed{\text{TAN}^{-1}}$ key.

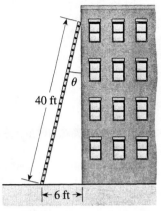

FIGURE 12

EXAMPLE 7 ■ Solving for an Angle in a Right Triangle

A 40-ft ladder leans against a building. If the base of the ladder is 6 ft from the base of the building, what is the angle formed by the ladder and the building?

SOLUTION

First we sketch a diagram as in Figure 12. If θ is the angle between the ladder and the building, then

$$\sin \theta = \tfrac{6}{40} = 0.15$$

So θ is the angle whose sine is 0.15. To find the angle θ, we use a calculator and use the $\boxed{\text{SIN}^{-1}}$ key. With our calculator in degree mode, we get

$$\theta \approx 8.6°$$ ■

6.2 EXERCISES

1–6 ■ Find the exact values of the six trigonometric ratios of the angle θ in the triangle.

1.
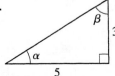

2.
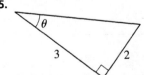

3.
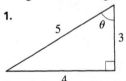

4.
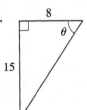

5.
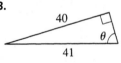

6.
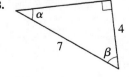

7–8 ■ Find (a) sin α and cos β, (b) tan α and cot β, and (c) sec α and csc β.

7.
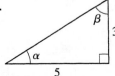

8.
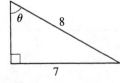

9–14 ■ Find the side labeled x. In Exercises 13 and 14 state your answer correct to five decimal places.

9.
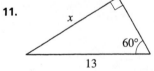

10.
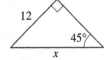

11.
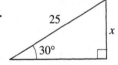

12.
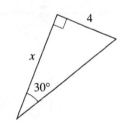

13.
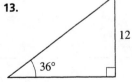

14.
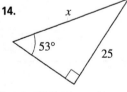

15–16 ■ Express x and y in terms of trigonometric ratios of θ.

15.
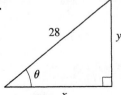

16.
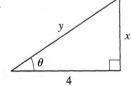

17–22 ■ Sketch a triangle that has acute angle θ, and find the other five trigonometric ratios of θ.

17. $\sin \theta = \frac{3}{5}$

18. $\cos \theta = \frac{9}{40}$

19. $\cot \theta = 1$

20. $\tan \theta = \sqrt{3}$

21. $\sec \theta = \frac{7}{2}$

22. $\csc \theta = \frac{13}{12}$

23–28 ■ Evaluate the expression without using a calculator.

23. $\sin \dfrac{\pi}{6} + \cos \dfrac{\pi}{6}$

24. $\sin 30° \csc 30°$

25. $\sin 30° \cos 60° + \sin 60° \cos 30°$

26. $(\sin 60°)^2 + (\cos 60°)^2$ **27.** $(\cos 30°)^2 - (\sin 30°)^2$

28. $\left(\sin \dfrac{\pi}{3} \cos \dfrac{\pi}{4} - \sin \dfrac{\pi}{4} \cos \dfrac{\pi}{3} \right)^2$

29–32 ■ Solve the right triangle.

29.

30.

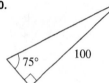

31.

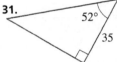

32.

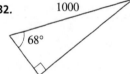

33. Use a ruler to carefully measure the sides of the triangle, and then use your measurements to estimate the six trigonometric ratios of θ.

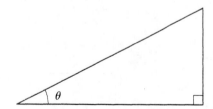

34. Using a protractor, sketch a right triangle that has the acute angle 40°. Measure the sides carefully and use your results to estimate the six trigonometric ratios of 40°.

35. The angle of elevation to the top of the Empire State Building in New York is found to be 11° from the ground at a distance of 1 mi from the base of the building. Using this information, find the height of the Empire State Building.

36. A plane is flying within sight of the Gateway Arch in St. Louis, Missouri, at an elevation of 35,000 ft. The pilot would like to estimate her distance from the Gateway Arch. She finds that the angle of depression to a point on the ground below the arch is 22°.
(a) What is the distance between the plane and the arch?
(b) What is the distance between a point on the ground directly below the plane and the arch?

37. A laser beam is to be directed toward the center of the moon, but the beam strays 0.5° from its intended path.
(a) How far has the beam diverged from its assigned target when it reaches the moon? (The distance from the earth to the moon is 240,000 mi.)
(b) The radius of the moon is about 1000 mi. Will the beam strike the moon?

38. From the top of a 200-ft lighthouse, the angle of depression to a ship in the ocean is 23°. How far is the ship from the base of the lighthouse?

39. A 20-ft ladder leans against a building so that the angle between the ground and the ladder is 72°. How high does the ladder reach on the building?

40. A 20-ft ladder is leaning against a building. If the base of the ladder is 6 ft from the base of the building, what is the angle of elevation of the ladder? How high does the ladder reach on the building?

41. A 96-ft tree casts a shadow that is 120 ft long. What is the angle of elevation of the sun?

42. A 600-ft guy wire is attached to the top of a communication tower. If the wire makes an angle of 65° with the ground, how tall is the communication tower?

43. A man is lying on the beach, flying a kite. He holds the end of the kite string at ground level, and estimates the angle of elevation of the kite to be 50°. If the string is 450 ft long, how high is the kite above the ground?

44. The height of a steep cliff is to be measured from a point on the opposite side of the river. Find the height of the cliff from the information given in the figure.

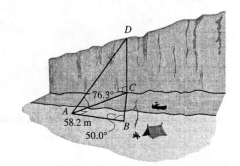

45. A water tower is located 325 ft from a building (see the figure). From a window in the building it is observed that the angle of elevation to the top of the tower is 39° and the angle of depression to the bottom of the tower is 25°. How tall is the tower? How high is the window?

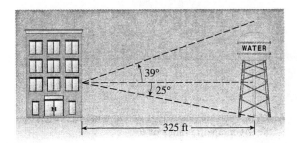

46. An airplane is flying at an elevation of 5150 ft, directly above a straight highway. Two motorists are driving cars on the highway on opposite sides of the plane, and the angle of depression to one car is 35° and to the other is 52°. How far apart are the cars?

47. If both cars in Exercise 46 are on one side of the plane and if the angle of depression to one car is 38° and to the other car is 52°, how far apart are the cars?

48. A hot-air balloon is floating above a straight road. To estimate their height above the ground, the balloonists simultaneously measure the angle of depression to two consecutive mileposts on the road on the same side of the balloon. The angles of depression are found to be 20° and 22°. How high is the balloon?

49. To estimate the height of a mountain above a level plain, the angle of elevation to the top of the mountain is measured to be 32°. One thousand feet closer to the mountain along the plain, it is found that the angle of elevation is 35°. Estimate the height of the mountain.

50. (a) Show that the height h of the mountain in the figure is given by

$$h = d\,\frac{\tan \beta \tan \alpha}{\tan \beta - \tan \alpha} = \frac{d}{\cot \alpha - \cot \beta}$$

(b) Use the formula in part (a) to find the height h of the mountain if $\alpha \approx 25°$, $\beta \approx 29°$, and $d \approx 800$ ft.

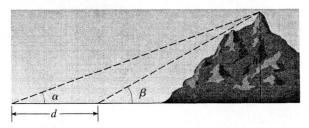

51. When the moon is exactly half full, the earth, moon, and sun form a right angle (see the figure). At that time the angle formed by the sun, earth, and moon is measured to be 89.85°. If the distance from the earth to the moon is 240,000 mi, estimate the distance from the earth to the sun.

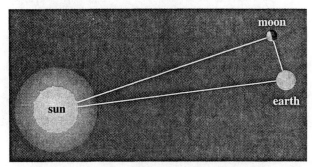

52. To find the distance to the sun as in Exercise 51, we needed to know the distance to the moon. Here is a way to estimate that distance: When the moon is seen at its zenith at a point A on the earth, it is observed to be at the horizon from point B (see the figure). Points A and B are 6155 mi apart, and the radius of the earth is 3960 mi.

(a) Find the angle θ in degrees.
(b) Estimate the distance from point A to the moon.

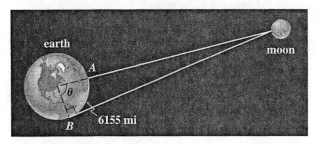

53. In Exercise 54 of Section 6.1 a method was given for finding the radius of the earth. Here is a more modern method: From a satellite 600 mi above the earth, it is observed that the angle formed by the vertical and the line of sight to the horizon is 60.276°. Use this information to find the radius of the earth.

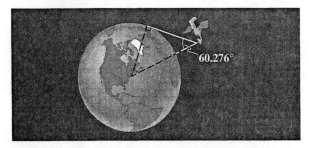

54. To find the distance to nearby stars, the method of parallax is used. The idea is to find a triangle with the star at one vertex and with a base as large as possible. To do this, the star is observed at two different times exactly 6 months apart, and its apparent change in position is recorded. From these two observations, $\angle E_1SE_2$ can be calculated. (The times are chosen so that $\angle E_1SE_2$ is as large as possible, which guarantees that $\angle E_1OS$ is 90°.) The angle E_1SO is called the *parallax* of the star. Alpha Centauri, the star nearest the earth, has a parallax of 0.000211°. Estimate the distance to this star. (Take the distance from the earth to the sun to be 9.3×10^7 mi.)

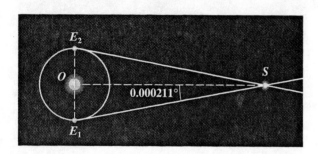

55–58 ■ Find x correct to one decimal place.

55.

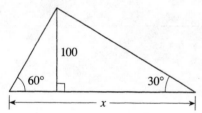

56.

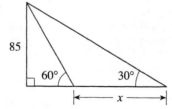

57.

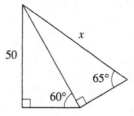

58.

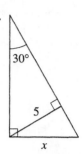

59. Express the lengths a, b, c, and d in the figure in terms of the trigonometric ratios of θ.

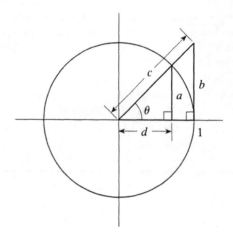

DISCOVERY · DISCUSSION

60. Similar Triangles   If two triangles are similar, what properties do they share? Explain how these properties make it possible to define the trigonometric ratios without regard to the size of the triangle.

6.3 TRIGONOMETRIC FUNCTIONS OF ANGLES

In the preceding section we defined the trigonometric ratios for acute angles. Here we extend the trigonometric ratios to all angles by defining the trigonometric functions of angles. With these functions we can solve practical problems that involve angles which are not necessarily acute.

Trigonometric Functions of Angles

Let POQ be a right triangle with acute angle θ as shown in Figure 1(a). Place θ in standard position as shown in Figure 1(b).

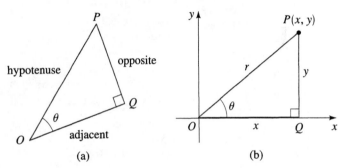

FIGURE 1   (a)   (b)

Then $P = P(x, y)$ is a point on the terminal side of θ. In triangle POQ, the opposite side has length y and the adjacent side has length x. Using the Pythagorean Theorem, we see that the hypotenuse has length $r = \sqrt{x^2 + y^2}$. So

$$\sin \theta = \frac{y}{r}, \qquad \cos \theta = \frac{x}{r}, \qquad \tan \theta = \frac{y}{x}$$

The other trigonometric ratios can be found in the same way.

These observations allow us to extend the trigonometric ratios to any angle. We define the trigonometric functions of angles as follows (see Figure 2).

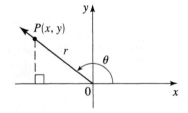

FIGURE 2

DEFINITION OF THE TRIGONOMETRIC FUNCTIONS

Let θ be an angle in standard position and let $P(x, y)$ be a point on the terminal side. If $r = \sqrt{x^2 + y^2}$ is the distance from the origin to the point $P(x, y)$, then

$$\sin \theta = \frac{y}{r} \qquad\qquad \cos \theta = \frac{x}{r} \qquad\qquad \tan \theta = \frac{y}{x} \quad (x \neq 0)$$

$$\csc \theta = \frac{r}{y} \quad (y \neq 0) \qquad \sec \theta = \frac{r}{x} \quad (x \neq 0) \qquad \cot \theta = \frac{x}{y} \quad (y \neq 0)$$

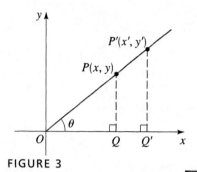

FIGURE 3

The following mnemonic device can be used to remember which trigonometric functions are positive in each quadrant: **A**ll of them, **S**ine, **T**angent, or **C**osine.

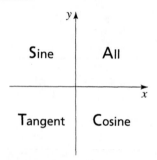

You can remember this as "**A**ll **S**tudents **T**ake **C**alculus."

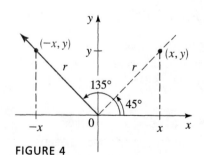

FIGURE 4

FIGURE 5

Since division by 0 is an undefined operation, certain trigonometric functions are not defined for certain angles. For example, $\tan 90° = y/x$ is undefined because $x = 0$. The angles for which the trigonometric functions may be undefined are the angles for which either the x- or y-coordinate of a point on the terminal side of the angle is 0. These are **quadrantal angles**—angles that are coterminal with the coordinate axes.

It is a crucial fact that the values of the trigonometric functions do *not* depend on the choice of the point $P(x, y)$. This is because if $P'(x', y')$ is any other point on the terminal side, as in Figure 3, then triangles POQ and $P'OQ'$ are similar.

Evaluating Trigonometric Functions at Any Angle

From the definition we see that the values of the trigonometric functions are all positive if the angle θ has its terminal side in quadrant I. This is because x and y are positive in this quadrant. [Of course, r is always positive, since it is simply the distance from the origin to the point $P(x, y)$.] If the terminal side of θ is in quadrant II, however, then x is negative and y is positive. Thus, in quadrant II the functions $\sin \theta$ and $\csc \theta$ are positive, and all the other trigonometric functions have negative values. You can check the other entries in the following table.

SIGNS OF THE TRIGONOMETRIC FUNCTIONS		
Quadrant	Positive functions	Negative functions
I	all	none
II	sin, csc	cos, sec, tan, cot
III	tan, cot	sin, csc, cos, sec
IV	cos, sec	sin, csc, tan, cot

We now turn our attention to finding the values of the trigonometric functions for angles that are not acute.

EXAMPLE 1 ■ Finding Trigonometric Functions of Angles

Find (a) $\cos 135°$ and (b) $\tan 390°$.

SOLUTION

(a) From Figure 4 we see that $\cos 135° = -x/r$. But $\cos 45° = x/r$, and since $\cos 45° = \sqrt{2}/2$, we have

$$\cos 135° = -\frac{\sqrt{2}}{2}$$

(b) The angles 390° and 30° are coterminal. From Figure 5 it's clear that $\tan 390° = \tan 30°$ and, since $\tan 30° = \sqrt{3}/3$, we have

$$\tan 390° = \frac{\sqrt{3}}{3}$$

■

Relationship to the Trigonometric Functions of Real Numbers

You may have already studied the trigonometric functions defined using the unit circle (Chapter 5). To see how they relate to the trigonometric functions of an *angle*, let's start with the unit circle in the coordinate plan.

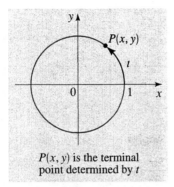

$P(x, y)$ is the terminal point determined by t

Let $P(x, y)$ be the terminal point determined by an arc of length t on the unit circle. Then t subtends an angle θ at the center of the circle. If we drop a perpendicular from P onto the point Q on the x-axis, then triangle $\triangle OPQ$ is a right triangle with legs of length x and y, as shown in the figure.

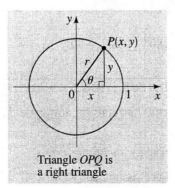

Triangle OPQ is a right triangle

Now, by the definition of the trigonometric functions of the *real number t*, we have

$$\sin t = y$$

$$\cos t = x$$

By the definition of the trigonometric functions of the *angle θ*, we have

$$\sin \theta = \frac{\text{opp}}{\text{hyp}} = \frac{y}{1} = y$$

$$\cos \theta = \frac{\text{adj}}{\text{hyp}} = \frac{x}{1} = x$$

If θ is measured in radians, then $\theta = t$. (See the figure below.) Comparing the two ways of defining the trigonometric functions, we see that they are identical. In other words, as functions, they assign identical values to a given real number (the real number is the radian measure of θ in one case or the length t of an arc in the other).

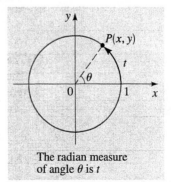

The radian measure of angle θ is t

Why then do we study trigonometry in two different ways? Because different applications require that we view the trigonometric functions differently. (See *Focus on Modeling*, page 455, and Sections 6.2, 6.4, and 6.5.)

From Example 1 we see that the trigonometric functions for angles that aren't acute have the same value, except possibly for sign, as the corresponding trigonometric functions of an acute angle. That acute angle will be called the *reference angle*.

> ### REFERENCE ANGLE
>
> Let θ be an angle in standard position. The **reference angle** $\bar{\theta}$ associated with θ is the acute angle formed by the terminal side of θ and the x-axis.

Figure 6 shows that to find a reference angle it's useful to know the quadrant in which the terminal side of the angle lies.

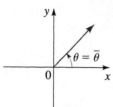 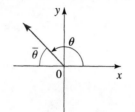 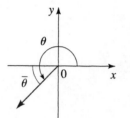 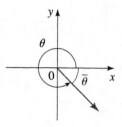

FIGURE 6

The reference angle $\bar{\theta}$ for an angle θ

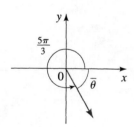

FIGURE 7

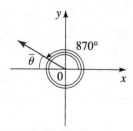

FIGURE 8

EXAMPLE 2 ■ Finding Reference Angles

Find the reference angle for (a) $\theta = \dfrac{5\pi}{3}$ and (b) $\theta = 870°$.

SOLUTION

(a) The reference angle is the acute angle formed by the terminal side of the angle $5\pi/3$ and the x-axis (see Figure 7). Since the terminal side of this angle is in quadrant IV, the reference angle is

$$\bar{\theta} = 2\pi - \frac{5\pi}{3} = \frac{\pi}{3}$$

(b) The angles $870°$ and $150°$ are coterminal [because $870 - 2(360) = 150$]. Thus, the terminal side of this angle is in quadrant II (see Figure 8). So the reference angle is

$$\bar{\theta} = 180° - 150° = 30°$$ ■

EVALUATING TRIGONOMETRIC FUNCTIONS AT ANY ANGLE

To find the values of the trigonometric functions for any angle θ, we carry out the following steps.

1. Find the reference angle $\bar{\theta}$ associated with the angle θ.

2. Determine the sign of the trigonometric function of θ.

3. The value of the trigonometric function of θ is the same, except possibly for sign, as the value of the trigonometric function of $\bar{\theta}$.

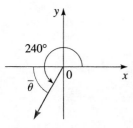

FIGURE 9

$\frac{S|A}{T|C}$　sin 240° *is negative.*

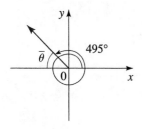

FIGURE 10

$\frac{S|A}{T|C}$　tan 495° *is negative,*
so cot 495° is negative.

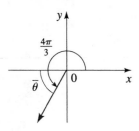

FIGURE 11

$\frac{S|A}{T|C}$　$\sin\frac{16\pi}{3}$ *is negative.*

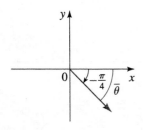

FIGURE 12

$\frac{S|A}{T|C}$　$\cos\left(-\frac{\pi}{4}\right)$ *is positive,*

so $\sec\left(-\frac{\pi}{4}\right)$ *is positive.*

EXAMPLE 3 ■ Using the Reference Angle to Evaluate Trigonometric Functions

Find (a) sin 240° and (b) cot 495°.

SOLUTION

(a) This angle has its terminal side in quadrant III, as shown in Figure 9. The reference angle is therefore 240° − 180° = 60°, and the value of sin 240° is negative. Thus

$$\sin 240° = \underset{\underset{\text{sign}}{\uparrow}}{-}\underset{\underset{\text{reference angle}}{\uparrow}}{\sin 60°} = -\frac{\sqrt{3}}{2}$$

(b) The angle 495° is coterminal with the angle 135°, and the terminal side of this angle is in quadrant II, as shown in Figure 10. So the reference angle is 180° − 135° = 45°, and the value of cot 495° is negative. We have

$$\cot 495° = \underset{\underset{\text{coterminal angles}}{\uparrow}}{\cot 135°} = \underset{\underset{\text{sign}}{\uparrow}}{-}\underset{\underset{\text{reference angle}}{\uparrow}}{\cot 45°} = -1$$

EXAMPLE 4 ■ Using the Reference Angle to Evaluate Trigonometric Functions

Find (a) $\sin\dfrac{16\pi}{3}$ and (b) $\sec\left(-\dfrac{\pi}{4}\right)$.

SOLUTION

(a) The angle 16π/3 is coterminal with 4π/3, and these angles are in quadrant III (see Figure 11). Thus, the reference angle is (4π/3) − π = π/3. Since the value of sine is negative in quadrant III, we have

$$\sin\frac{16\pi}{3} = \underset{\underset{\text{coterminal angles}}{\uparrow}}{\sin\frac{4\pi}{3}} = \underset{\underset{\text{sign}}{\uparrow}}{-}\underset{\underset{\text{reference angle}}{\uparrow}}{\sin\frac{\pi}{3}} = -\frac{\sqrt{3}}{2}$$

(b) The angle −π/4 is in quadrant IV, and its reference angle is π/4 (see Figure 12). Since secant is positive in this quadrant, we get

$$\sec\left(-\frac{\pi}{4}\right) = \underset{\underset{\text{sign}}{\uparrow}}{+}\underset{\underset{\text{reference angle}}{\uparrow}}{\sec\frac{\pi}{4}} = \frac{\sqrt{2}}{2}$$ ■

Trigonometric Identities

The trigonometric functions of angles are related to each other through several important equations called **trigonometric identities**. We've already encountered the reciprocal identities. These identities continue to hold for any angle θ, provided both sides of the equation are defined. The Pythagorean identities are a consequence of the Pythagorean Theorem.*

FUNDAMENTAL IDENTITIES

Reciprocal Identities

$$\csc \theta = \frac{1}{\sin \theta} \qquad \sec \theta = \frac{1}{\cos \theta} \qquad \cot \theta = \frac{1}{\tan \theta}$$

$$\tan \theta = \frac{\sin \theta}{\cos \theta} \qquad \cot \theta = \frac{\cos \theta}{\sin \theta}$$

Pythagorean Identities

$$\sin^2\theta + \cos^2\theta = 1 \qquad \tan^2\theta + 1 = \sec^2\theta \qquad 1 + \cot^2\theta = \csc^2\theta$$

■ **Proof** Let's prove the first Pythagorean identity. Using $x^2 + y^2 = r$ (the Pythagorean Theorem) in Figure 13, we have

$$\sin^2\theta + \cos^2\theta = \left(\frac{y}{r}\right)^2 + \left(\frac{x}{r}\right)^2 = \frac{x^2 + y^2}{r^2} = \frac{r^2}{r^2} = 1$$

Thus, $\sin^2\theta + \cos^2\theta = 1$. (Although the figure indicates an acute angle, you should check that the proof holds for all angles θ.)   □

See Exercises 59 and 60 for the proofs of the other two Pythagorean identities.

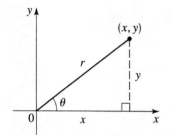

FIGURE 13

EXAMPLE 5 ■ Expressing One Trigonometric Function in Terms of Another

(a) Express $\sin \theta$ in terms of $\cos \theta$.
(b) Express $\tan \theta$ in terms of $\sin \theta$, where θ is in quadrant II.

SOLUTION

(a) From the first Pythagorean identity we get

$$\sin \theta = \pm\sqrt{1 - \cos^2\theta}$$

where the sign depends on the quadrant. If θ is in quadrant I or II, then $\sin \theta$ is positive, and hence

$$\sin \theta = \sqrt{1 - \cos^2\theta}$$

whereas if θ is in quadrant III or IV, $\sin \theta$ is negative and so

$$\sin \theta = -\sqrt{1 - \cos^2\theta}$$

---

*We follow the usual convention of writing $\sin^2\theta$ for $(\sin \theta)^2$. In general, we write $\sin^n\theta$ for $(\sin \theta)^n$ for all integers n except $n = -1$. The exponent $n = -1$ will be assigned another meaning in Section 7.4. Of course, the same convention applies to the other five trigonometric functions.

(b) Since $\tan \theta = \sin \theta / \cos \theta$, we need to write $\cos \theta$ in terms of $\sin \theta$. By part (a)

$$\cos \theta = \pm\sqrt{1 - \sin^2\theta}$$

and since $\cos \theta$ is negative in quadrant II, the negative sign applies here. Thus

$$\tan \theta = \frac{\sin \theta}{\cos \theta} = \frac{\sin \theta}{-\sqrt{1 - \sin^2\theta}} \qquad \blacksquare$$

EXAMPLE 6 ■ Evaluating a Trigonometric Function

If $\tan \theta = \frac{2}{3}$ and θ is in quadrant III, find $\cos \theta$.

SOLUTION 1

We need to write $\cos \theta$ in terms of $\tan \theta$. From the identity $\tan^2\theta + 1 = \sec^2\theta$, we get $\sec \theta = \pm\sqrt{\tan^2\theta + 1}$. In quadrant III, $\sec \theta$ is negative, so

$$\sec \theta = -\sqrt{\tan^2\theta + 1}$$

Thus

$$\cos \theta = \frac{1}{\sec \theta} = \frac{1}{-\sqrt{\tan^2\theta + 1}}$$

$$= \frac{1}{-\sqrt{\left(\frac{2}{3}\right)^2 + 1}} = \frac{1}{-\sqrt{\frac{13}{9}}} = -\frac{3}{\sqrt{13}}$$

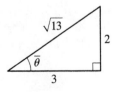

FIGURE 14

SOLUTION 2

This problem can be solved more easily using the method of Example 2 of Section 6.2. Recall that, except for sign, the values of the trigonometric functions of any angle are the same as those of an acute angle (the reference angle). So, ignoring the sign for the moment, let's sketch a right triangle with an acute angle $\bar{\theta}$ satisfying $\tan \bar{\theta} = \frac{2}{3}$ (see Figure 14). By the Pythagorean Theorem the hypotenuse of this triangle has length $\sqrt{13}$. From the triangle in Figure 14 we immediately see that $\cos \bar{\theta} = 3/\sqrt{13}$. Since θ is in quadrant III, $\cos \theta$ is negative and so

$$\cos \theta = -\frac{3}{\sqrt{13}} \qquad \blacksquare$$

EXAMPLE 7 ■ Evaluating Trigonometric Functions

If $\sec \theta = 2$ and θ is in quadrant IV, find the other five trigonometric functions of θ.

SOLUTION

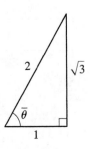

FIGURE 15

We sketch a triangle as in Figure 15 so that $\sec \bar{\theta} = 2$. Taking into account the fact

that θ is in quadrant IV, we get

$$\sin \theta = -\frac{\sqrt{3}}{2} \qquad \cos \theta = \frac{1}{2} \qquad \tan \theta = -\sqrt{3}$$

$$\csc \theta = -\frac{2}{\sqrt{3}} \qquad \sec \theta = 2 \qquad \cot \theta = -\frac{1}{\sqrt{3}}$$ ■

Areas of Triangles

We end this section by giving an application of the trigonometric functions that involves angles that are not necessarily acute. More extensive applications appear in the next two sections.

The area of a triangle is $\mathcal{A} = \frac{1}{2} \times$ base $\times$ height. If we know two sides and the included angle of a triangle, then we can find the height using the trigonometric functions, and from this we can find the area.

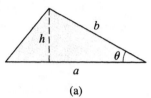

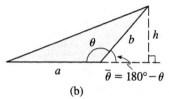

(a)

If θ is an acute angle, then the height of the triangle in Figure 16(a) is given by $h = b \sin \theta$. Thus, the area is

$$\mathcal{A} = \frac{1}{2} \times \text{base} \times \text{height} = \frac{1}{2} ab \sin \theta$$

If the angle θ is not acute, then from Figure 16(b) we see that the height of the triangle is

$$h = b \sin(180° - \theta) = b \sin \theta$$

This is so because the reference angle of θ is the angle $180° - \theta$. Thus, in this case also, the area of the triangle is

$$\mathcal{A} = \frac{1}{2} \times \text{base} \times \text{height} = \frac{1}{2} ab \sin \theta$$

(b)

FIGURE 16

AREA OF A TRIANGLE

The area $\mathcal{A}$ of a triangle with sides of lengths a and b and with included angle θ is

$$\mathcal{A} = \frac{1}{2} ab \sin \theta$$

EXAMPLE 8 ■ Finding the Area of a Triangle

Find the area of triangle ABC shown in Figure 17.

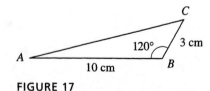

FIGURE 17

SOLUTION

The triangle has sides of length 10 cm and 3 cm, with included angle 120°. Therefore

$$\mathcal{A} = \frac{1}{2} ab \sin \theta$$

$$= \frac{1}{2}(10)(3) \sin 120°$$

$$= 15 \sin 60° \qquad \text{Reference angle}$$

$$= 15 \frac{\sqrt{3}}{2} \approx 13 \text{ cm}^2$$ ■

6.3 EXERCISES

1–6 ■ Find the reference angle for the given angle.

1. (a) 210°   (b) 300°   (c) −120°

2. (a) 225°   (b) 450°   (c) −200°

3. (a) $\dfrac{9\pi}{4}$ (b) $\dfrac{23\pi}{6}$ (c) $-\dfrac{\pi}{3}$

4. (a) $\dfrac{17\pi}{6}$ (b) $\dfrac{31\pi}{4}$ (c) $-\dfrac{4\pi}{3}$

5. (a) $\dfrac{11\pi}{5}$ (b) $\dfrac{11}{5}$ (c) $-\dfrac{4\pi}{7}$

6. (a) 2.3   (b) 2.3π (c) $-\pi$

7–30 ■ Find the exact value of the trigonometric function.

7. $\sin 150°$ **8.** $\sin 225°$ **9.** $\cos 135°$

10. $\cos(-60°)$ **11.** $\tan(-60°)$ **12.** $\sec 300°$

13. $\csc(-630°)$ **14.** $\cot 210°$ **15.** $\cos 570°$

16. $\sec 120°$ **17.** $\tan 750°$ **18.** $\cos 660°$

19. $\sin \dfrac{2\pi}{3}$ **20.** $\sin \dfrac{5\pi}{3}$ **21.** $\sin \dfrac{3\pi}{2}$

22. $\cos \dfrac{7\pi}{3}$ **23.** $\cos\left(-\dfrac{7\pi}{3}\right)$ **24.** $\tan \dfrac{5\pi}{6}$

25. $\sec \dfrac{17\pi}{3}$ **26.** $\csc \dfrac{5\pi}{4}$ **27.** $\cot\left(-\dfrac{\pi}{4}\right)$

28. $\cos \dfrac{7\pi}{4}$ **29.** $\tan \dfrac{5\pi}{2}$ **30.** $\sin \dfrac{11\pi}{6}$

31–34 ■ Find the quadrant in which θ lies from the information given.

31. $\sin \theta < 0$ and $\cos \theta < 0$

32. $\tan \theta < 0$ and $\sin \theta < 0$

33. $\sec \theta > 0$ and $\tan \theta < 0$

34. $\csc \theta > 0$ and $\cos \theta < 0$

35–40 ■ Write the first trigonometric function in terms of the second for θ in the given quadrant.

35. $\tan \theta$, $\cos \theta$; θ in quadrant III

36. $\cot \theta$, $\sin \theta$; θ in quadrant II

37. $\cos \theta$, $\sin \theta$; θ in quadrant IV

38. $\sec \theta$, $\sin \theta$; θ in quadrant I

39. $\sec \theta$, $\tan \theta$; θ in quadrant II

40. $\csc \theta$, $\cot \theta$; θ in quadrant III

41–48 ■ Find the values of the trigonometric functions of θ from the information given.

41. $\sin \theta = \frac{3}{5}$, θ in quadrant II

42. $\cos \theta = -\frac{7}{12}$, θ in quadrant III

43. $\tan \theta = -\frac{3}{4}$, $\cos \theta > 0$

44. $\sec \theta = 5$, $\sin \theta < 0$

45. $\csc \theta = 2$, θ in quadrant I

46. $\cot \theta = \frac{1}{4}$, $\sin \theta < 0$

47. $\cos \theta = -\frac{2}{7}$, $\tan \theta < 0$

48. $\tan \theta = -4$, $\sin \theta > 0$

49. If $\theta = \pi/3$, find the value of each expression.

   (a) $\sin 2\theta$, $2 \sin \theta$ (b) $\sin \frac{1}{2}\theta$, $\dfrac{\sin \theta}{2}$

   (c) $\sin^2\theta$, $\sin(\theta^2)$

50. Find the area of a triangle with sides of length 7 and 9 and included angle 72°.

51. Find the area of a triangle with sides of length 10 and 22 and included angle 10°.

52. Find the area of an equilateral triangle with side of length 10.

53. A triangle has an area of 16 in², and two of the sides of the triangle have lengths 5 in. and 7 in. Find the angle included by these two sides.

54. Find the area of the shaded region in the figure.

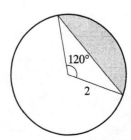

55–58 ■ In the following exercises you are asked to use the trigonometric functions to model real-life situations. See the guidelines in Section 2.7 on modeling with functions.

55. A steel pipe is being carried down a hallway 9 ft wide. At the end of the hall there is a right-angled turn into a narrower hallway 6 ft wide.

(a) Show that the length of the pipe in the figure is modeled by the function

$$L(\theta) = 9 \csc \theta + 6 \sec \theta$$

(b) Graph the function L for $0 < \theta < \pi/2$.
(c) Find the minimum value of the function L.
(d) Explain why the value of L you found in part (c) is the length of the longest pipe that can be carried around the corner.

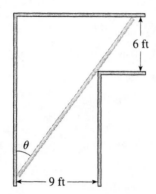

56. A rain gutter is to be constructed from a metal sheet of width 30 cm by bending up one-third of the sheet on each side through an angle θ.

(a) Show that the cross-sectional area of the gutter is modeled by the function

$$A(\theta) = 100 \sin \theta + 100 \sin \theta \cos \theta$$

(b) Graph the function A for $0 \leq \theta \leq \pi/2$.
(c) For what angle θ is the largest cross-sectional area achieved?

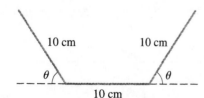
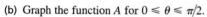

57. A rectangular beam is to be cut from a cylindrical log of diameter 20 cm, as shown in the figure.

(a) Express the cross-sectional area of the beam as a function of the angle θ in the figures.
(b) Graph the function you found in part (a).
(c) Find the dimensions of the beam with largest cross-sectional area.

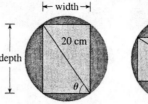

58. The strength of a beam is proportional to the width and the square of the depth. A beam is cut from a log as in Exercise 57. Express the strength of the beam as a function of the angle θ in the figures.

59. Use the first Pythagorean identity to prove the second. [*Hint:* Divide by $\cos^2\theta$.]

60. Use the first Pythagorean identity to prove the third.

▲ DISCOVERY · DISCUSSION

61. Using a Calculator   To solve a certain problem, you need to find the sine of 4 rad. Your study partner uses his calculator and tells you that sin 4 is 0.0697564737. On your calculator you get -0.7568024953. What is wrong? What mistake did your partner make?

62. Viète's Trigonometric Diagram   In the 16th century, the French mathematician François Viète (see page 51) published the following remarkable diagram. Each of the six trigonometric functions of θ is equal to the length of a line segment in the figure. For instance, $\sin \theta = |PR|$, since from $\triangle OPR$ we see that

$$\sin \theta = \frac{\text{opp}}{\text{hyp}} = \frac{|PR|}{|OR|} = \frac{|PR|}{1}$$

For each of the five other trigonometric functions, find a line segment in the figure whose length equals the value of the function at θ. (Note that the radius of the circle is 1, the center is O, segment QS is tangent to the circle at R, and $\angle SOQ$ is a right angle.)

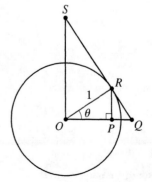

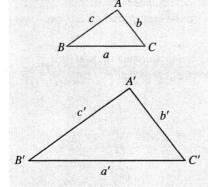

Similarity

In geometry you learned that two triangles are similar if they have the same angles. In this case, the ratios of corresponding sides are equal. Triangles ABC and $A'B'C'$ in the margin are similar, so

$$\frac{a'}{a} = \frac{b'}{b} = \frac{c'}{c}$$

Thales used similar triangles to find the height of a tall column. See page 487.

Similarity is the crucial idea underlying trigonometry. We can define $\sin\theta$ as the ratio of the opposite side to the hypotenuse in *any* right triangle with an angle θ, because all such right triangles are similar. So the ratio represented by $\sin\theta$ does not depend on the size of the right triangle but only on the angle θ. This is a powerful idea because angles are often easier to measure than distances. For example, the angle formed by the sun, earth, and moon can be measured from the earth. The secret to finding the distance to the sun is that the trigonometric ratios are the same for the huge triangle formed by the sun, earth, and moon as for any other similar triangle (see Exercise 51 in Section 6.2).

In general, two objects are **similar** if they have the same shape even though they may not be the same size.* For example, we recognize the following as representations of the letter A because they are all similar.

If two figures are similar, then the distances between corresponding points in the figures are proportional. The blue and red A's above are similar—the ratio of distances between corresponding points is $\frac{3}{2}$. We say that the **similarity ratio** is $s = \frac{3}{2}$. To obtain the distance d' between any two points in the blue A, we multiply the corresponding distance d in the red A by $\frac{3}{2}$. So

$$d' = sd \qquad \text{or} \qquad d' = \tfrac{3}{2}d$$

Likewise, the similarity ratio between the first and last letters is $s = 5$, so $x' = 5x$.

1. Write a short paragraph explaining how the concept of similarity is used to define the trigonometric ratios.

---

*If they have the same shape *and* size, they are congruent, which is a special case of similarity.

2. How is similarity used in map making? How are distances on a city road map related to actual distances?

3. How is your yearbook photograph similar to you? Compare distances between different points on your face (such as distance between ears, length of nose, distance between eyes, and so on) to the corresponding distances in a photograph. What is the similarity ratio?

4. The figure illustrates a method for drawing an apple twice the size of a given apple. Use the method to draw a tie 3 times the size (similarity ratio 3) of the blue tie.

5. Give conditions under which two rectangles are similar to each other. Do the same for two isosceles triangles.

6. Suppose that two similar triangles have similarity ratio s.
   (a) How are the perimeters of the triangles related?
   (b) How are the areas of the triangles related?

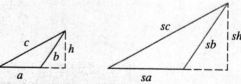

7. (a) If two squares have similarity ratio s, show that their areas A_1 and A_2 have the property that $A_2 = s^2 A_1$.
   (b) If the side of a square is tripled, its area is multiplied by what factor?
   (c) A plane figure can be approximated by squares (as shown). Explain how we can conclude that for any two plane figures with similarity ratio s, their areas satisfy $A_2 = s^2 A_1$. [Use part (a).]

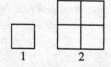

1   2

If the side of a square is doubled, its area is multiplied by 2^2.

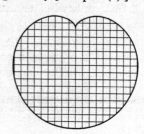

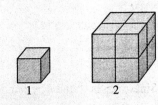

If the side of a cube is doubled, its volume is multiplied by 2^3.

8. (a) If two cubes have similarity ratio s, show that their volumes V_1 and V_2 have the property that $V_2 = s^3 V_1$.

(b) If the side of a cube is multiplied by 10, by what factor is the volume multiplied?

(c) How can we use the fact that a solid object can be "filled" by little cubes to show that for any two solids with similarity ratio s, the volumes satisfy $V_2 = s^3 V_1$?

9. King Kong is 10 times as tall as Joe, a normal-sized 300-lb gorilla. Assuming that King Kong and Joe are similar, use the results from Problems 7 and 8 to answer the following questions.

(a) How much does King Kong weigh?

(b) If Joe's hand is 13 in. long, how long is King Kong's hand?

(c) If it takes 2 square yards of material to make a shirt for Joe, how much material would a shirt for King Kong require?

6.4 THE LAW OF SINES

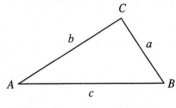

FIGURE 1

In Section 6.2 we used the trigonometric ratios to solve right triangles. The trigonometric functions can also be used to solve *oblique triangles*, that is, triangles with no right angles. To do this, we first study the Law of Sines here and then the Law of Cosines in the next section. To state these laws (or formulas) more easily, we follow the convention of labeling the angles of a triangle as A, B, C, and the lengths of the corresponding opposite sides as a, b, c, as in Figure 1.

To solve a triangle, we need to know certain information about its sides and angles. To decide whether we have enough information, it's often helpful to make a sketch. For instance, if we are given two angles and the included side, then it's clear that one and only one triangle can be formed [see Figure 2(a)]. Similarly, if two sides and the included angle are known, then a unique triangle is determined [Figure 2(c)]. But if we know all three angles and no sides, we cannot uniquely determine the triangle because many triangles can have the same three angles. (All these triangles would be similar, of course.) So we won't consider this last case.

(a) ASA or SAA

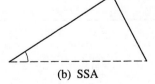

(b) SSA

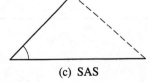

(c) SAS

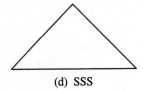

(d) SSS

FIGURE 2

In general, a triangle is determined by three of its six parts (angles and sides) as long as at least one of these three parts is a side. So, the possibilities, illustrated in Figure 2, are as follows:

Case 1   One side and two angles (ASA or SAA)

Case 2   Two sides and the angle opposite one of those sides (SSA)

Case 3   Two sides and the included angle (SAS)

Case 4   Three sides (SSS)

The first two cases are solved using the Law of Sines; Cases 3 and 4 require the Law of Cosines.

The Law of Sines

The **Law of Sines** says that in any triangle the lengths of the sides are proportional to the sines of the corresponding opposite angles.

> **THE LAW OF SINES**
>
> In triangle ABC we have
>
> $$\frac{\sin A}{a} = \frac{\sin B}{b} = \frac{\sin C}{c}$$

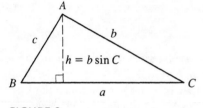

FIGURE 3

■ **Proof**   To see why the Law of Sines is true, refer to Figure 3. By the formula in Section 6.3 the area of triangle ABC is $\frac{1}{2} ab \sin C$. By the same formula the area of this triangle is also $\frac{1}{2} ac \sin B$ and $\frac{1}{2} bc \sin A$. Thus

$$\tfrac{1}{2} bc \sin A = \tfrac{1}{2} ac \sin B = \tfrac{1}{2} ab \sin C$$

Multiplying by $2/(abc)$ gives the Law of Sines.   □

EXAMPLE 1 ■ Tracking a Satellite (ASA)

A satellite orbiting the earth passes directly overhead at observation stations in Phoenix and Los Angeles, 340 mi apart. At an instant when the satellite is between these two stations, its angle of elevation is simultaneously observed to be 60° at Phoenix and 75° at Los Angeles. How far is the satellite from Los Angeles? In other words, find the distance AC in Figure 4.

SOLUTION

Whenever two angles in a triangle are known, the third angle can be determined immediately because the sum of the angles of a triangle is 180°. In this case, $\angle C = 180° - (75° + 60°) = 45°$ (see Figure 3), so we have

$$\frac{\sin B}{b} = \frac{\sin C}{c} \qquad \text{Law of Sines}$$

$$\frac{\sin 60°}{b} = \frac{\sin 45°}{340} \qquad \text{Substitute}$$

$$b = \frac{340 \sin 60°}{\sin 45°} \approx 416 \qquad \text{Solve for } b$$

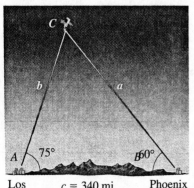

FIGURE 4

The distance of the satellite from Los Angeles is approximately 416 mi.   ■

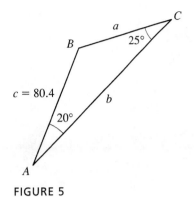

FIGURE 5

EXAMPLE 2 ■ Solving a Triangle (SAA)

Solve the triangle in Figure 5.

SOLUTION

First, $\angle B = 180° - (20° + 25°) = 135°$. Since side c is known, to find side a we use the relation

$$\frac{\sin A}{a} = \frac{\sin C}{c} \qquad \text{Law of Sines}$$

$$a = \frac{c \sin A}{\sin C} = \frac{80.4 \sin 20°}{\sin 25°} \approx 65.1 \qquad \text{Solve for } a$$

Similarly, to find b we use

$$\frac{\sin B}{b} = \frac{\sin C}{c} \qquad \text{Law of Sines}$$

$$b = \frac{c \sin B}{\sin C} = \frac{80.4 \sin 135°}{\sin 25°} \approx 134.5 \qquad \text{Solve for } b \qquad ■$$

The Ambiguous Case

In Examples 1 and 2 a unique triangle was determined by the information given. This is always true of Case 1 (ASA or SAA). But in Case 2 (SSA) there may be two triangles, one triangle, or no triangle with the given properties. For this reason, Case 2 is sometimes called the **ambiguous case**. To see why this is so, we show in Figure 6 the possibilities when angle A and sides a and b are given. In part (a) no solution is possible, since side a is too short to complete the triangle. In part (b) the solution is a right triangle. In part (c) two solutions are possible, and in part (d) there is a unique triangle with the given properties. We illustrate the possibilities of Case 2 in the following examples.

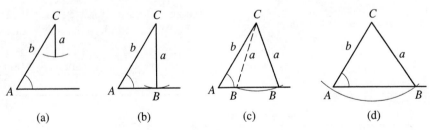

FIGURE 6

The ambiguous case

(a)   (b)   (c)   (d)

EXAMPLE 3 ■ SSA, the One-Solution Case

Solve triangle ABC, where $\angle A = 45°$, $a = 7\sqrt{2}$, and $b = 7$.

SOLUTION

We first sketch the triangle with the information we have (see Figure 7). Our sketch is necessarily tentative, since we don't yet know the other angles. Nevertheless, we can now see the possibilities.

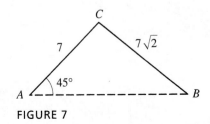

FIGURE 7

We first find $\angle B$.

$$\frac{\sin A}{a} = \frac{\sin B}{b} \qquad \text{Law of Sines}$$

$$\sin B = \frac{b \sin A}{a} = \frac{7}{7\sqrt{2}} \sin 45° = \left(\frac{1}{\sqrt{2}}\right)\left(\frac{\sqrt{2}}{2}\right) = \frac{1}{2} \qquad \text{Solve for } \sin B$$

We consider only angles smaller than 180°, since no triangle can contain an angle of 180° or larger.

Which angles B have $\sin B = \frac{1}{2}$? From the preceding section we know that there are two such angles smaller than 180° (they are 30° and 150°). Which of these angles is compatible with what we know about triangle ABC? Since $\angle A = 45°$, we cannot have $\angle B = 150°$, because 45° + 150° > 180°. So $\angle B = 30°$, and the remaining angle is $\angle C = 180° - (30° + 45°) = 105°$.

Now we can find side c.

$$\frac{\sin B}{b} = \frac{\sin C}{c} \qquad \text{Law of Sines}$$

$$c = \frac{b \sin C}{\sin B} = \frac{7 \sin 105°}{\sin 30°} = \frac{7 \sin 105°}{\frac{1}{2}} \approx 13.5 \qquad \text{Solve for } c \qquad ■$$

In Example 3 there were two possibilities for angle B, and one of these was not compatible with the rest of the information. In general, if $\sin A < 1$, we must check the angle and its supplement as possibilities, because any angle smaller that 180° can be in the triangle. To decide whether either possibility works, we check to see whether the resulting sum of the angles exceeds 180°. It can happen, as in Figure 6(c), that both possibilities are compatible with the given information. In that case, two different triangles are solutions to the problem.

EXAMPLE 4 ■ SSA, the Two-Solution Case

Solve triangle ABC if $\angle A = 43.1°$, $a = 186.2$, and $b = 248.6$.

SOLUTION

From the given information we sketch the triangle shown in Figure 8. Note that side a may be drawn in two possible positions to complete the triangle. From the Law of Sines

$$\sin B = \frac{b \sin A}{a} = \frac{248.6 \sin 43.1°}{186.2} \approx 0.91225$$

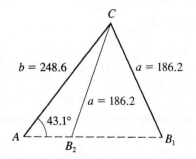

FIGURE 8

method, the only distance measured is the initial baseline; all other distances are calculated from the Law of Sines. This method is practical because it is much easier to measure angles than distances.

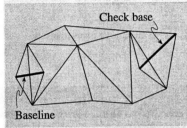

Check base

Baseline

One of the most ambitious map-making efforts of all time was the Great Trigonometric Survey of India, which required several expeditions and took over a century to complete. The famous expedition of 1823, led by **Sir George Everest**, lasted 20 years. Ranging over treacherous terrain and encountering the dreaded malaria-carrying mosquitoes, this expedition reached the foothills of the Himalayas. A later expedition, using triangulation, calculated the height of the highest peak of the Himalayas to be 29,002 ft. The peak was named in honor of Sir George Everest. Today, using satellites, the height of Mt. Everest is estimated to be 29,028 ft. The very close agreement of these two estimates shows the great accuracy of the trigonometric method.

There are two possible angles B between $0°$ and $180°$ such that $\sin B = 0.91225$. Using the $\boxed{\text{SIN}^{-1}}$ key on a calculator (or $\boxed{\text{INV}}$ $\boxed{\text{SIN}}$ or $\boxed{\text{ARCSIN}}$), we find that one of these angles is approximately $65.8°$. The other is approximately $180° - 65.8° = 114.2°$. We denote these two angles by B_1 and B_2 so that

$$\angle B_1 \approx 65.8° \quad \text{and} \quad \angle B_2 \approx 114.2°$$

Thus, two triangles satisfy the given conditions: triangle $A_1B_1C_1$ and triangle $A_2B_2C_2$.

Solve triangle $A_1B_1C_1$:

$$\angle C_1 \approx 180° - (43.1° + 65.8°) = 71.1° \quad \text{Find } \angle C_1$$

Thus

$$c_1 = \frac{a_1 \sin C_1}{\sin A_1} \approx \frac{186.2 \sin 71.1°}{\sin 43.1°} \approx 257.8 \quad \text{Law of Sines}$$

Solve triangle $A_2B_2C_2$:

$$\angle C_2 \approx 180° - (43.1° + 114.2°) = 22.7° \quad \text{Find } \angle C_2$$

Thus

$$c_2 = \frac{a_2 \sin C_2}{\sin A_2} \approx \frac{186.2 \sin 22.7°}{\sin 43.1°} \approx 105.2 \quad \text{Law of Sines}$$

Triangles $A_1B_1C_1$ and $A_2B_2C_2$ are shown in Figure 9.

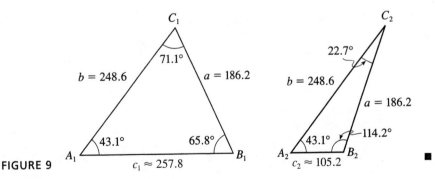

FIGURE 9

The next example presents a situation for which no triangle is compatible with the given data.

EXAMPLE 5 ■ SSA, the No-Solution Case

Solve triangle ABC, where $\angle A = 42°$, $a = 70$, and $b = 122$.

SOLUTION

First, let's try to find $\angle B$. We have

$$\frac{\sin A}{a} = \frac{\sin B}{b} \qquad \text{Law of Sines}$$

$$\sin B = \frac{b \sin A}{a} = \frac{122 \sin 42°}{70} \approx 1.17 \qquad \text{Solve for } \sin B$$

Since the sine of an angle is never greater than 1, we conclude that no triangle satisfies the conditions given in this problem.   ■

6.4 EXERCISES

1–6 ■ Use the Law of Sines to find the indicated side x or angle θ.

1.

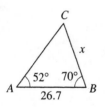

2.

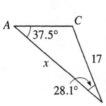

3.

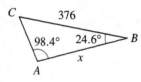

4.

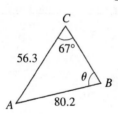

5.

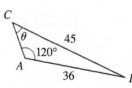

6.

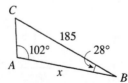

7–8 ■ Solve the triangle using the Law of Sines.

7.

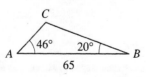

8.

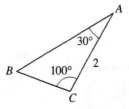

9–14 ■ Sketch each triangle and then solve the triangle using the Law of Sines.

9. $\angle A = 50°$, $\angle B = 68°$, $c = 230$

10. $\angle A = 23°$, $\angle B = 110°$, $c = 50$

11. $\angle A = 30°$, $\angle C = 65°$, $b = 10$

12. $\angle A = 22°$, $\angle B = 95°$, $a = 420$

13. $\angle B = 29°$, $\angle C = 51°$, $b = 44$

14. $\angle B = 10°$, $\angle C = 100°$, $c = 115$

15–22 ■ Use the Law of Sines to solve for all possible triangles that satisfy the given conditions.

15. $a = 28$, $b = 15$, $\angle A = 110°$

16. $a = 30$, $c = 40$, $\angle A = 37°$

17. $a = 20$, $c = 45$, $\angle A = 125°$

18. $b = 45$, $c = 42$, $\angle C = 38°$

19. $b = 25$, $c = 30$, $\angle B = 25°$

20. $a = 75$, $b = 100$, $\angle A = 30°$

21. $a = 50$, $b = 100$, $\angle A = 50°$

22. $a = 100$, $b = 80$, $\angle A = 135°$

23. To find the distance across a river, a surveyor chooses points A and B, which are 200 ft apart on one side of the river (see the figure). She then chooses a reference point C on the opposite side of the river and finds that

$\angle BAC \approx 82°$ and $\angle ABC \approx 52°$. Approximate the distance from A to C.

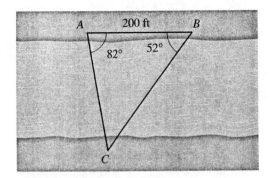

24. A pilot is flying over a straight highway. He determines the angles of depression to two mileposts, 5 mi apart, to be 32° and 48°, as shown in the figure.
    (a) Find the distance of the plane from point A.
    (b) Find the elevation of the plane.

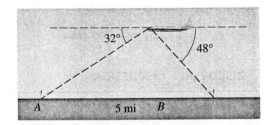

25. The path of a satellite orbiting the earth causes it to pass directly over two tracking stations A and B, which are 50 mi apart. When the satellite is on one side of the two stations, the angles of elevation at A and B are measured to be 87.0° and 84.2°, respectively.
    (a) How far is the satellite from station A?
    (b) How high is the satellite above the ground?

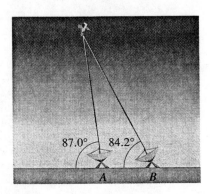

26. A tree on a hillside casts a shadow 215 ft down the hill. If the angle of inclination of the hillside is 22° to the horizontal and the angle of elevation of the sun is 52°, find the height of the tree.

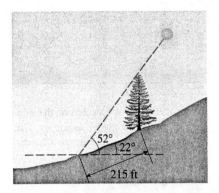

27. A communication tower is located at the top of a steep hill, as shown. The angle of inclination of the hill is 58°. A guy wire is to be attached to the top of the tower and to the ground, 100 m downhill from the base of the tower. The angle α in the figure is determined to be 12°. Find the length of cable required for the guy wire.

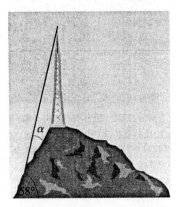

28. Points A and B are separated by a lake. To find the distance between them, a surveyor locates a point C on land such that $\angle CAB = 48.6°$. He also measures CA as 312 ft and CB as 527 ft. Find the distance between A and B.

29. To calculate the height of a mountain, angles α, β, and distance d are determined, as shown in the figure on page 512.
    (a) Find the length of BC in terms of α, β, and d.
    (b) Show that the height h of the mountain is given by the formula

    $$h = d \frac{\sin \alpha \sin \beta}{\sin(\beta - \alpha)}$$

(c) Use the formula in part (b) to find the height of a mountain if $\alpha \approx 25°$, $\beta \approx 29°$, and $d \approx 800$ ft.

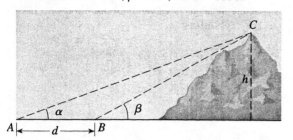

30. Observers at P and Q are located on the side of a hill that is inclined 32° to the horizontal, as shown. The observer at P determines the angle of elevation to a hot-air balloon to be 62°. At the same instant, the observer at Q measures the angle of elevation to the balloon to be 71°. If P is 60 m down the hill from Q, find the distance from Q to the balloon.

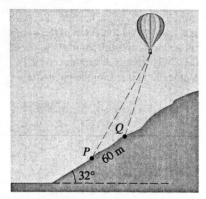

31. A water tower 30 m tall is located at the top of a hill. From a distance of 120 m down the hill, it is observed that the angle formed between the top and base of the tower is 8°. Find the angle of inclination of the hill.

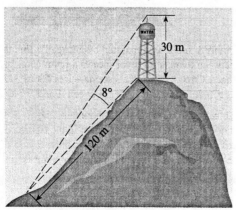

32. For the triangle shown, find (a) $\angle BCD$ and (b) $\angle DCA$.

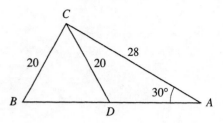

33. In triangle ABC, $\angle A = 40°$, $a = 15$, and $b = 20$.
   (a) Show that there are two triangles, ABC and $A'B'C'$, that satisfy these conditions.
   (b) Show that the areas of the triangles in part (a) are proportional to the sines of the angles C and C', that is,

$$\frac{\text{area of } \triangle ABC}{\text{area of } \triangle A'B'C'} = \frac{\sin C}{\sin C'}$$

34. Show that, given the three angles A, B, C of a triangle and one side, say a, the area of the triangle is

$$\text{area} = \frac{a^2 \sin B \sin C}{2 \sin A}$$

◈ DISCOVERY · DISCUSSION

35. Number of Solutions in the Ambiguous Case   We have seen that when using the Law of Sines to solve a triangle in the SSA case, there may be two, one, or no solution(s). Sketch triangles like those in Figure 6 to verify the criteria in the table for the number of solutions if you are given $\angle A$ and sides a and b.

Criterion	Number of solutions
$a \geqslant b$	1
$b > a > b \sin A$	2
$a = b \sin A$	1
$a < b \sin A$	0

If $\angle A = 30°$ and $b = 100$, use these crieteria to find the range of values of a for which the triangle ABC has two solutions, one solution, or no solution.

6.5 THE LAW OF COSINES

The Law of Sines cannot be used directly to solve triangles if we know two sides and the angle between them or if we know all three sides (these are Cases 3 and 4 of the preceding section). In these two cases, the **Law of Cosines** applies.

> ### THE LAW OF COSINES
>
> In any triangle ABC, we have
>
> $$a^2 = b^2 + c^2 - 2bc \cos A$$
>
> $$b^2 = a^2 + c^2 - 2ac \cos B$$
>
> $$c^2 = a^2 + b^2 - 2ab \cos C$$

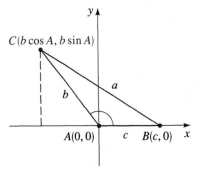

FIGURE 1

■ **Proof** To prove the Law of Cosines, place triangle ABC so that $\angle A$ is at the origin, as shown in Figure 1. The coordinates of the vertices B and C are $(c, 0)$ and $(b \cos A, b \sin A)$, respectively. (You should check that the coordinates of these points will be the same if we draw angle A as an acute angle.) Using the Distance Formula, we get

$$a^2 = (b \cos A - c)^2 + (b \sin A - 0)^2$$

$$= b^2 \cos^2 A - 2bc \cos A + c^2 + b^2 \sin^2 A$$

$$= b^2(\cos^2 A + \sin^2 A) - 2bc \cos A + c^2$$

$$= b^2 + c^2 - 2bc \cos A \qquad \text{Because } \sin^2 A + \cos^2 A = 1$$

This proves the first formula. The other two formulas are obtained in the same way by placing each of the other vertices of the triangle at the origin and repeating the preceding argument. □

In words, the Law of Cosines says that the square of any side of a triangle is equal to the sum of the squares of the other two sides, minus twice the product of those two sides times the cosine of the included angle.

If one of the angles of a triangle, say $\angle C$, is a right angle, then $\cos C = 0$ and the Law of Cosines reduces to the Pythagorean Theorem, $c^2 = a^2 + b^2$. Thus, the Pythagorean Theorem is a special case of the Law of Cosines.

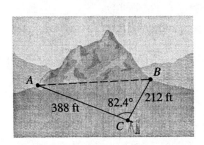

FIGURE 2

EXAMPLE 1 ■ Length of a Tunnel

A tunnel is to be built through a mountain. To estimate the length of the tunnel, a surveyor makes the measurements shown in Figure 2. Use the surveyor's data to approximate the length of the tunnel.

SOLUTION

To approximate the length c of the tunnel, we use the Law of Cosines:

$$c^2 = a^2 + b^2 - 2ab \cos C \qquad \text{Law of Cosines}$$

$$= 388^2 + 212^2 - 2(388)(212) \cos 82.4° \qquad \text{Substitute}$$

$$\approx 173730.2367 \qquad \text{Use a calculator}$$

$$c \approx \sqrt{173730.2367} \approx 416.8 \qquad \text{Take square roots}$$

Thus, the tunnel will be approximately 417 ft long.   ∎

EXAMPLE 2 ■ SSS, the Law of Cosines

The sides of a triangle are $a = 5$, $b = 8$, and $c = 12$ (see Figure 3). Find the angles of the triangle.

SOLUTION

We first find $\angle A$. From the Law of Cosines, we have $a^2 = b^2 + c^2 - 2bc \cos A$. Solving for $\cos A$, we get

$$\cos A = \frac{b^2 + c^2 - a^2}{2bc} = \frac{8^2 + 12^2 - 5^2}{2(8)(12)} = \frac{183}{192} = 0.953125$$

Using a calculator, we find that $\angle A \approx 18°$. In the same way the equations

$$\cos B = \frac{a^2 + c^2 - b^2}{2ac} = \frac{5^2 + 12^2 - 8^2}{2(5)(12)} = 0.875$$

$$\cos C = \frac{a^2 + b^2 - c^2}{2ab} = \frac{5^2 + 8^2 - 12^2}{2(5)(8)} = -0.6875$$

give $\angle B \approx 29°$ and $\angle C \approx 133°$. Of course, once two angles are calculated, the third can more easily be found from the fact that the sum of the angles of a triangle is 180°. However, it's a good idea to calculate all three angles using the Law of Cosines and add the three angles as a check on your computations.   ∎

EXAMPLE 3 ■ SAS, the Law of Cosines and the Law of Sines

Solve triangle ABC, where $\angle A = 46.5°$, $b = 10.5$, and $c = 18.0$.

SOLUTION

We can find a using the Law of Cosines.

$$a^2 = b^2 + c^2 - 2bc \cos A$$

$$= (10.5)^2 + (18.0)^2 - 2(10.5)(18.0)(\cos 46.5°) \approx 174.05$$

Thus, $a \approx \sqrt{174.05} \approx 13.2$. The two remaining angles can now be found using the

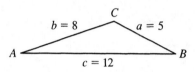

FIGURE 3

Law of Sines. We have

$$\sin B = \frac{b \sin A}{a} \approx \frac{10.5 \sin 46.5°}{13.2} \approx 0.577$$

So B is the angle whose sine is 0.577. For this, we use our calculator to get $\angle B \approx 35.2°$. Since angle B can have measure between 0° and 180°, another possibility for angle B is $\angle B = 180° - 35.2° = 144.8°$. It's a simple matter to choose between these two possibilities, since the largest angle in a triangle must be opposite the longest side. So the correct choice is $\angle B \approx 35.2°$. In this case, $\angle C \approx 180° - (46.5° + 35.2°) = 98.3°$, and indeed the largest angle, $\angle C$, is opposite the longest side, $c = 18.0$.

To summarize: $\angle B \approx 35.2°$, $\angle C \approx 98.3°$, and $a \approx 13.2$. (See Figure 4.) ∎

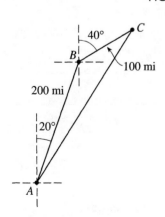

FIGURE 4

We see from Example 3 that, when using both the Law of Cosines and the Law of Sines to solve a triangle in the SAS case, we must be careful to choose the correct measure for the remaining angle. In any triangle, the longest side is opposite the largest angle, and the shortest side is opposite the smallest angle. Thus, when using the Law of Sines, we must choose the angle so that this condition is satisfied. That's why it's a good idea to sketch the triangle so you can check your final answer.

In navigation a direction is often given as a **bearing**, that is, as an acute angle measured from due north or due south. The bearing N 30° E, for example, indicates a direction that points 30° to the east of due north (see Figure 5).

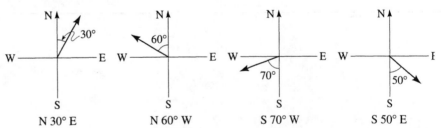

FIGURE 5

EXAMPLE 4 ■ Navigation

A pilot sets out from an airport and heads in the direction N 20° E, flying at 200 mi/h. After one hour, he makes a course correction and heads in the direction N 40° E. Half an hour after that, engine trouble forces him to make an emergency landing.

(a) Find the distance between the airport and his final landing point.
(b) Find the bearing from the airport to his final landing point.

SOLUTION

(a) In one hour the plane travels 200 mi, and in half an hour it travels 100 mi, so we can plot the pilot's course as in Figure 6. When he makes his course correction, he turns 20° to the right, so the angle between the two legs of his trip

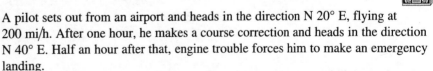

FIGURE 6

is $180° - 20° = 160°$. So by the Law of Cosines we have

$$b^2 = 200^2 + 100^2 - 2 \cdot 200 \cdot 100 \cos 160°$$

$$\approx 87{,}587.70$$

Thus, $b \approx 295.95$. The pilot lands about 296 mi from his starting point.

(b) We first use the Law of Sines to find $\angle A$.

$$\frac{\sin A}{100} = \frac{\sin 160°}{295.95}$$

$$\sin A = 100 \cdot \frac{\sin 160°}{295.95} \approx 0.11557$$

Another angle with sine 0.11557 is $180° - 6.636° = 173.364°$. But this is clearly too large to be $\angle A$ in $\angle ABC$.

Using the $\boxed{\text{SIN}^{-1}}$ key on a calculator, we find that $\angle A \approx 6.636°$. From Figure 6 we see that the line from the airport to the final landing site points in the direction $20° + 6.636° = 26.636°$ east of due north. Thus, the bearing is about N 26.6° E.   ■

The Area of a Triangle

An interesting application of the Law of Cosines involves a formula for finding the area of a triangle from the lengths of its three sides (see Figure 7).

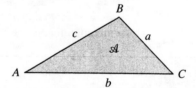

FIGURE 7

HERON'S FORMULA

The area $\mathcal{A}$ of triangle ABC is given by

$$\mathcal{A} = \sqrt{s(s - a)(s - b)(s - c)}$$

where $s = \frac{1}{2}(a + b + c)$ is the **semiperimeter** of the triangle; that is, s is half the perimeter.

■ **Proof**   We start with the formula $\mathcal{A} = \frac{1}{2}ab \sin C$ from Section 6.3. Thus

$$\mathcal{A}^2 = \tfrac{1}{4} a^2 b^2 \sin^2 C$$

$$= \tfrac{1}{4} a^2 b^2 (1 - \cos^2 C) \qquad \text{Pythagorean identity}$$

$$= \tfrac{1}{4} a^2 b^2 (1 - \cos C)(1 + \cos C) \qquad \text{Factor}$$

Next, we write the expressions $1 - \cos C$ and $1 + \cos C$ in terms of a, b and c.

By the Law of Cosines we have

$$\cos C = \frac{a^2 + b^2 - c^2}{2ab} \qquad \text{Law of Cosines}$$

$$1 + \cos C = 1 + \frac{a^2 + b^2 - c^2}{2ab} \qquad \text{Add 1}$$

$$= \frac{2ab + a^2 + b^2 - c^2}{2ab} \qquad \text{Common denominator}$$

$$= \frac{(a + b)^2 - c^2}{2ab} \qquad \text{Factor}$$

$$= \frac{(a + b + c)(a + b - c)}{2ab} \qquad \text{Difference of squares}$$

Similarly

$$1 - \cos C = \frac{(c + a - b)(c - a + b)}{2ab}$$

Substituting these expressions in the formula we obtained for $\mathcal{A}^2$ gives

$$\mathcal{A}^2 = \tfrac{1}{4} a^2 b^2 \frac{(a + b + c)(a + b - c)}{2ab} \frac{(c + a - b)(c - a + b)}{2ab}$$

$$= \frac{(a + b + c)}{2} \frac{(a + b - c)}{2} \frac{(c + a - b)}{2} \frac{(c - a + b)}{2}$$

$$= s(s - c)(s - b)(s - a)$$

Showing that each factor in the last expression equals the corresponding factor in the preceding expression is left as an exercise. Heron's Formula now follows by taking the square root of each side.   □

EXAMPLE 5 ■ Area of a Lot

A businessman wishes to buy a triangular lot in a busy downtown location (see Figure 8). The lot frontages on the three adjacent streets are 125, 280, and 315 ft. Find the area of the lot.

SOLUTION

The semiperimeter of the lot is

$$s = \frac{125 + 280 + 315}{2} = 360$$

By Heron's Formula the area is

$$\mathcal{A} = \sqrt{360(360 - 125)(360 - 280)(360 - 315)} \approx 17{,}451.6$$

Thus, the area is approximately 17,452 ft². ■

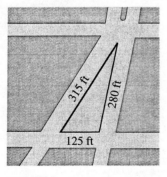

315 ft   280 ft

125 ft

FIGURE 8

6.5 EXERCISES

1–8 ■ Use the Law of Cosines to determine the indicated side x or angle θ.

1.

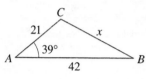

2.

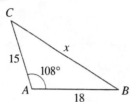

3.

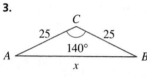

4.

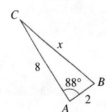

5.

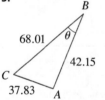

6.

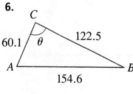

7.

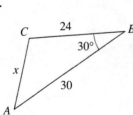

8.

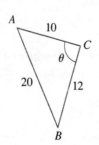

9–18 ■ Solve triangle ABC.

9.

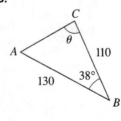

10.

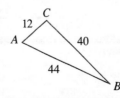

11. $a = 3.0,\quad b = 4.0,\quad \angle C = 53°$

12. $b = 60,\quad c = 30,\quad \angle A = 70°$

13. $a = 20,\quad b = 25,\quad c = 22$

14. $a = 10,\quad b = 12,\quad c = 16$

15. $b = 125,\quad c = 162,\quad \angle B = 40°$

16. $a = 65,\quad c = 50,\quad \angle C = 52°$

17. $a = 50,\quad b = 65,\quad \angle A = 55°$

18. $a = 73.5,\quad \angle B = 61°,\quad \angle C = 83°$

19–26 ■ Find the indicated side x or angle θ. (Use either the Law of Sines or the Law of Cosines, as appropriate.)

19.

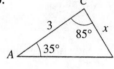

20.

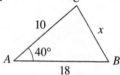

21.

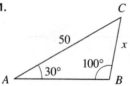

22.

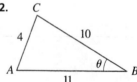

23.

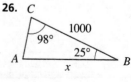

24.

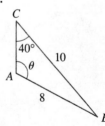

25.

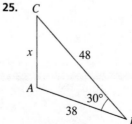

26.

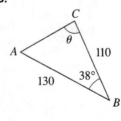

27. To find the distance across a small lake, a surveyor has taken the measurements shown. Find the distance across the lake using this information.

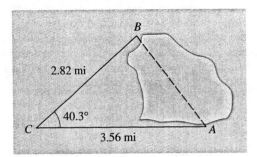

28. A parallelogram has sides of lengths 3 and 5, and one angle is 50°. Find the lengths of the diagonals.

29. Two straight roads diverge at an angle of 65°. Two cars leave the intersection at 2:00 P.M., one traveling at 50 mi/h and the other at 30 mi/h. How far apart are the cars at 2:30 P.M.?

30. A car travels along a straight road, heading east for 1 h, then traveling for 30 min on another road that leads northeast. If the car has maintained a constant speed of 40 mi/h, how far is it from its starting position?

31. A pilot flies in a straight path for 1 h 30 min. She then makes a course correction, heading 10° to the right of her original course, and flies 2 h in the new direction. If she maintains a constant speed of 625 mi/h, how far is she from her starting position?

32. Two boats leave the same port at the same time. One travels at a speed of 30 mi/h in the direction N 50° E and the other travels at a speed of 26 mi/h in a direction S 70° E (see the figure). How far apart are the two boats after one hour?

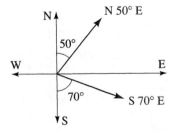

33. A fisherman leaves his home port and heads in the direction N 70° W. He travels 30 mi and reaches Egg Island. The next day he sails N 10° E for 50 mi, reaching Forrest Island.
(a) Find the distance between the fisherman's home part and Forrest Island.

(b) Find the bearing from Forrest Island back to his home port.

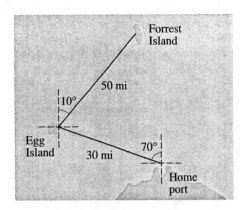

34. Airport B is 300 mi from airport A at a bearing N 50° E (see the figure). A pilot wishing to fly from A to B mistakenly flies due east at 200 mi/h for 30 minutes, when he notices his error.
(a) How far is the pilot from his destination at the time he notices the error?
(b) What bearing should he head his plane in order to arrive at airport B?

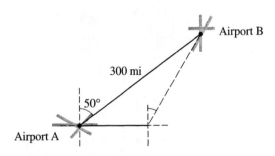

35. A triangular field has sides of lengths 22, 36, and 44 yd. Find the largest angle.

36. Two tugboats that are 120 ft apart pull a barge, as shown. If the length of one cable is 212 ft and the length of the other is 230 ft, find the angle formed by the two cables.

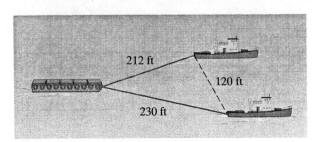

37. A boy is flying two kites at the same time. He has 380 ft of line out to one kite and 420 ft to the other. He estimates the angle between the two lines to be 30°. Approximate the distance between the kites.

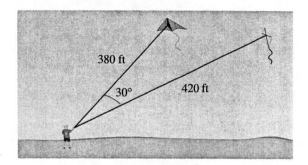

38. A 125-ft tower is located on the side of a mountain that is inclined 32° to the horizontal. A guy wire is to be attached to the top of the tower and anchored at a point 55 ft downhill from the base of the tower. Find the shortest length of wire needed.

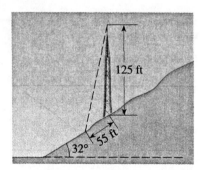

39. A steep mountain is inclined 74° to the horizontal and rises 3400 ft above the surrounding plain. A cable car is to be installed from a point 800 ft from the base to the top of the mountain, as shown. Find the shortest length of cable needed.

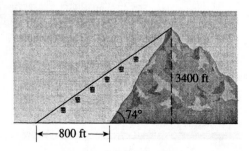

40. The CN Tower in Toronto, Canada, is the tallest free-standing structure in the world. A woman on the observation deck, 1150 ft above the ground, wants to determine the distance between two landmarks on the ground below. She observes that the angle formed by the lines of sight to these two landmarks is 43°. She also observes that the angle between the vertical and the line of sight to one of the landmarks is 62° and to the other landmark is 54°. Find the distance between the two landmarks.

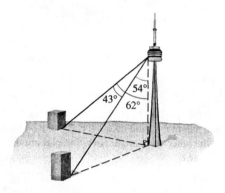

41. Three circles of radii 4, 5, and 6 cm are mutually tangent. Find the shaded area enclosed between the circles.

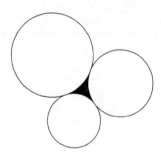

42. Prove that in triangle ABC

$$a = b \cos C + c \cos B$$

$$b = c \cos A + a \cos C$$

$$c = a \cos B + b \cos A$$

These are called the *Projection Laws*. [*Hint:* To get the first equation, add together the second and third equations in the Law of Cosines and solve for a.]

43. A surveyor wishes to find the distance betwen two points A and B on the opposite side of a river. On her side of the river, she chooses two points C and D that are 20 m apart

and measures the angles shown. Find the distance between
A and B.

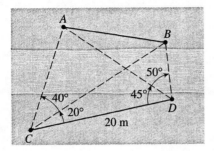

44. Find the area of a triangle with sides of lengths 12, 18, and
24 m.

45. Land in downtown Columbia is valued at $20 a square
foot. What is the value of a triangular lot with sides of
lengths 112, 148, and 190 ft?

46. Find the area of the quadrilateral
in the figure, correct to two
decimal places.

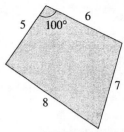

● DISCOVERY · DISCUSSION

47. Solving for the Angles in a Triangle When we solved
for ∠B in Example 3 using the Law of Sines, we had to be
careful because there were two possibilities, 35.2° and
144.8°. That is because these are the *two* angles between 0°
and 180° whose sine is 0.577. What if we use the Law of
Cosines to find ∠B? Would the problem of two possible
measures for ∠B still arise? Which method do you prefer
here: the Law of Sines or the Law of Cosines?

6 REVIEW

CONCEPT CHECK

1. (a) Explain the difference between a positive angle and a
negative angle.
  (b) How is an angle of measure 1 degree formed?
  (c) How is an angle of measure 1 radian formed?
  (d) How is the radian measure of an angle θ defined?
  (e) How do you convert from degrees to radians?
  (f) How do you convert from radians to degrees?

2. (a) When is an angle in standard position?
  (b) When are two angles coterminal?

3. (a) What is the length s of an arc of a circle with radius r
that subtends a central angle of θ radians?
  (b) What is the area A of a sector of a circle with radius r
and central angle θ radians?

4. If θ is an acute angle in a right triangle, define the six
trigonometric ratios in terms of the adjacent and opposite
sides and the hypotenuse.

5. What does it mean to solve a triangle?

6. If θ is an angle in standard position, $P(x, y)$ is a point on the
terminal side, and r is the distance from the origin to P,
write expressions for the six trigonometric functions of θ.

7. Which trigonometric functions are positive in quadrants I,
II, III, and IV?

8. If θ is an angle in standard position, what is its reference
angle $\bar{\theta}$?

9. (a) State the reciprocal identities.
  (b) State the Pythagorean identities.

10. (a) What is the area of a triangle with sides of length a and
b and with included angle θ?
  (b) What is the area of a triangle with sides of length a, b
and c?

11. (a) State the Law of Sines.
  (b) State the Law of Cosines.

12. Explain the ambiguous case in the Law of Sines.

EXERCISES

1–2 ■ Find the radian measure that corresponds to the given degree measure.

1. (a) 60°   (b) 330°   (c) −135°   (d) −90°

2. (a) 24°   (b) −330°   (c) 750°   (d) 5°

3–4 ■ Find the degree measure that corresponds to the given radian measure.

3. (a) $\dfrac{5\pi}{2}$ (b) $-\dfrac{\pi}{6}$ (c) $\dfrac{9\pi}{4}$ (d) 3.1

4. (a) 8   (b) $-\dfrac{5}{2}$ (c) $\dfrac{11\pi}{6}$ (d) $\dfrac{3\pi}{5}$

5. Find the length of an arc of a circle of radius 8 m if the arc subtends a central angle of 1 rad.

6. Find the measure of a central angle θ in a circle of radius 5 ft if the angle is subtended by an arc of length 7 ft.

7. A circular arc of length 100 ft subtends a central angle of 70°. Find the radius of the circle.

8. How many revolutions will a car wheel of diameter 28 in. make over a period of half an hour if the car is traveling at 60 mi/h?

9. New York and Los Angeles are 2450 mi apart. Find the angle that the arc between these two cities subtends at the center of the earth. (The radius of the earth is 3960 mi.)

10. Find the area of a sector with central angle 2 rad in a circle of radius 5 m.

11. Find the area of a sector with central angle 52° in a circle of radius 200 ft.

12. A sector in a circle of radius 25 ft has an area of 125 ft². Find the central angle of the sector.

13. A potter's wheel with radius 8 in. spins at 150 rpm. Find the angular and linear speeds of a point on the rim of the wheel.

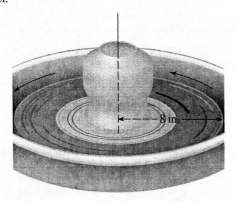

14. In an automobile transmission a *gear ratio g* is the ratio

$$g = \frac{\text{angular speed of engine}}{\text{angular speed of wheels}}$$

The angular speed of the engine is shown on the tachometer (in rpm).

A certain sports car has wheels with radius 11 in. Its gear ratios are shown in the table. Suppose the car is in fourth gear and the tachometer reads 3500 rpm.

(a) Find the angular speed of the engine.

(b) Find the angular speed of the wheels.

(c) How fast (in mi/h) is the car traveling?

Gear	Ratio
1st	4.1
2nd	3.0
3rd	1.6
4th	0.9
5th	0.7

15–16 ■ Find the values of the six trigonometric ratios of θ.

15.

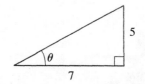

16.

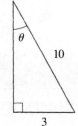

17–20 ■ Find the sides labeled x and y, correct to two decimal places.

17.

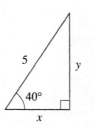

18.

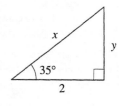

19.

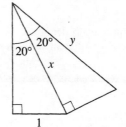

20.

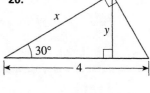

21–22 ■ Solve the triangle.

21.

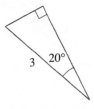

22.

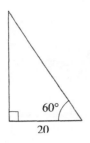

23. Express the lengths a and b in the figure in terms of the trigonometric ratios of θ.

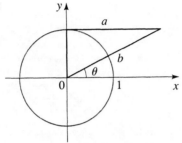

24. The highest tower in the world is the CN Tower in Toronto, Canada. From a distance of 1 km from its base, the angle of elevation to the top of the tower is 28.81°. Find the height of the tower.

25. Find the perimeter of a regular hexagon that is inscribed in a circle of radius 8 m.

26. The pistons in a car engine move up and down repeatedly to turn the crankshaft, as shown. Find the height of the point P above the center O of the crankshaft in terms of the angle θ.

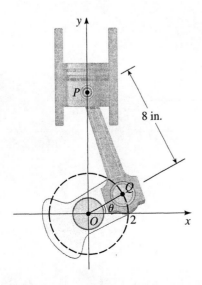

27. As viewed from the earth, the angle subtended by the full moon is 0.518°. Use this information and the fact that the distance AB from the earth to the moon is 236,900 mi to find the radius of the moon.

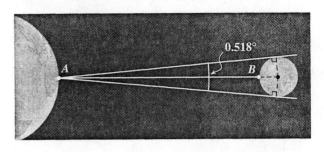

28. A pilot measures the angles of depression to two ships to be 40° and 52° (see the figure). If the pilot is flying at an elevation of 35,000 ft, find the distance between the two ships.

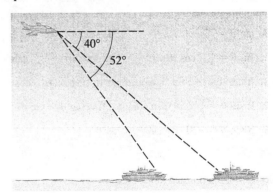

29–40 ■ Find the exact value.

29. $\sin 315°$

30. $\csc \dfrac{9\pi}{4}$

31. $\tan(-135°)$

32. $\cos \dfrac{5\pi}{6}$

33. $\cot\left(-\dfrac{22\pi}{3}\right)$

34. $\sin 405°$

35. $\cos 585°$

36. $\sec \dfrac{22\pi}{3}$

37. $\csc \dfrac{8\pi}{3}$

38. $\sec \dfrac{13\pi}{6}$

39. $\cot(-390°)$

40. $\tan \dfrac{23\pi}{4}$

41. Find the values of the six trigonometric ratios of the angle θ in standard position if the point $(-5, 12)$ is on the terminal side of θ.

42. Find $\sin \theta$ if θ is in standard position and its terminal side intersects the circle of radius 1 centered at the origin at the point $\left(-\sqrt{3}/2, \frac{1}{2}\right)$.

43. Find the acute angle that is formed by the line $y - \sqrt{3}\, x + 1 = 0$ and the x-axis.

44. Find the six trigonometric ratios of the angle θ in standard position if its terminal side is in quadrant III and is parallel to the line $4y - 2x - 1 = 0$.

45–48 ■ Write the first expression in terms of the second, for θ in the given quadrant.

45. $\tan \theta$, $\cos \theta$; θ in quadrant II

46. $\sec \theta$, $\sin \theta$; θ in quadrant III

47. $\tan^2\theta$, $\sin \theta$; θ in any quadrant

48. $\csc^2\theta \cos^2\theta$, $\sin \theta$; θ in any quadrant

49–52 ■ Find the values of the six trigonometric functions of θ from the information given.

49. $\tan \theta = \sqrt{7}/3$, $\sec \theta = \frac{4}{3}$ **50.** $\sec \theta = \frac{41}{40}$, $\csc \theta = -\frac{41}{9}$

51. $\sin \theta = \frac{3}{5}$, $\cos \theta < 0$ **52.** $\sec \theta = -\frac{13}{5}$, $\tan \theta > 0$

53. If $\tan \theta = -\frac{1}{2}$ for θ in quadrant II, find $\sin \theta + \cos \theta$.

54. If $\sin \theta = \frac{1}{2}$ for θ in quadrant I, find $\tan \theta + \sec \theta$.

55. If $\tan \theta = -1$, find $\sin^2\theta + \cos^2\theta$.

56. If $\cos \theta = -\sqrt{3}/2$ and $\pi/2 < \theta < \pi$, find $\sin 2\theta$.

57–62 ■ Find the side labeled x.

57.

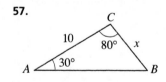

58.

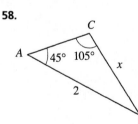

59.

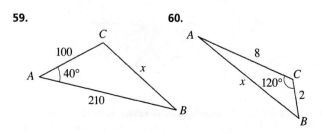

60.

61.

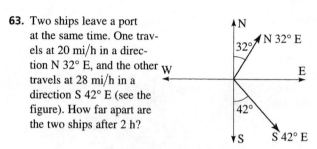

62.

63. Two ships leave a port at the same time. One travels at 20 mi/h in a direction N 32° E, and the other travels at 28 mi/h in a direction S 42° E (see the figure). How far apart are the two ships after 2 h?

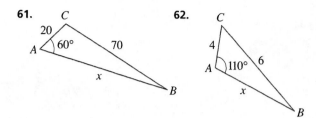

64. From a point A on the ground, the angle of elevation to the top of a tall building is 24.1°. From a point B, which is 600 ft closer to the building, the angle of elevation is measured to be 30.2°. Find the height of the building.

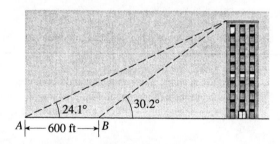

65. Find the distance between points A and B on opposite sides of a lake from the information shown.

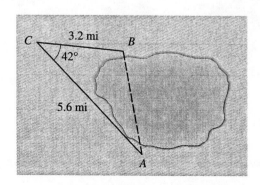

66. A boat is cruising the ocean off a straight shoreline. Points
A and *B* are 120 mi apart on the shore, as shown. It is
found that ∠*A* = 42.3° and ∠*B* = 68.9°. Find the shortest
distance from the boat to the shore.

Shoreline

A

42.3°

120 mi

C

68.9°

B

67. To measure the height of an inaccessible cliff on the opposite side of a river, a surveyor makes the measurements
shown. Find the height of the cliff.

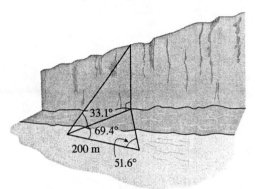

33.1°

69.4°

200 m

51.6°

68. Find the area of a triangle with sides of length 8 and 14 and
included angle 35°.

69. Find the area of a triangle with sides of length 5, 6, and 8.

6 | TEST

1. Find the radian measures that correspond to the degree measures $300°$ and $-18°$.

2. Find the degree measures that correspond to the radian measures $\dfrac{5\pi}{6}$ and 2.4.

3. The rotor blades of a helicopter are 25 ft long and are rotating at 200 rpm.
   (a) Find the angular speed of the rotor.
   (b) Find the linear speed of a point on the tip of a blade.

4. Find the exact value of each of the following.
   (a) $\sin 405°$ (b) $\tan(-150°)$
   (c) $\sec \dfrac{5\pi}{3}$ (d) $\csc \dfrac{5\pi}{2}$

5. Find $\tan\theta + \sin\theta$ for the angle θ shown.

   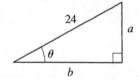

6. Find the lengths a and b shown in the figure in terms of θ.

   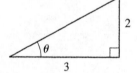

7. If $\cos\theta = -\frac{1}{3}$ and θ is in quadrant III, find $\tan\theta \cot\theta + \csc\theta$.

8. If $\sin\theta = \frac{5}{13}$ and $\tan\theta = -\frac{5}{12}$, find $\sec\theta$.

9. Express $\tan\theta$ in terms of $\sec\theta$ for θ in quadrant II.

10. The base of the ladder in the figure is 6 ft from the building, and the angle formed by the ladder and the ground is $73°$. How high up the building does the ladder touch?

    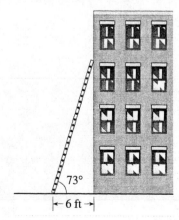

11–14 ■ Find the side labeled x.

11.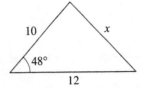

12.

13.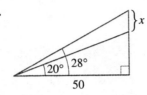

14.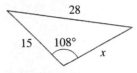

15. Refer to the figure at the left.
    (a) Find the area of the shaded region.
    (b) Find the perimeter of the shaded region.

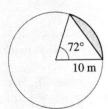

16. Refer to the figure at the right.
    (a) Find the angle opposite the longest side.
    (b) Find the area of the triangle.

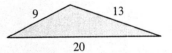

17. Two wires tether a balloon to the ground, as shown. How high is the balloon above the ground?

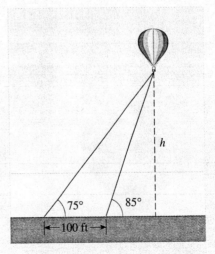

Focus on Problem Solving
Taking Cases

One important problem-solving technique is the strategy of **taking cases**. A classic use of this strategy is in the classification of the regular polyhedra. These are called *Platonic solids* because they were mentioned in the writings of Plato.

A *regular polygon* is one in which all sides and all angles are equal. There are infinitely many regular polygons, as indicated in Figure 1.

FIGURE 1
The regular polygons

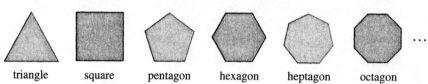

| triangle | square | pentagon | hexagon | heptagon | octagon |

For three-dimensional shapes, the analogous concept is that of regular polyhedra. A *regular polyhedron* is a solid in which all faces are congruent regular polygons, and the same number of polygons meet at each corner, or *vertex*. We would like to find all possible regular polyhedra. It might seem at first that there should be infinitely many, just as for regular polygons. But we will see that there are just finitely many polyhedra.

▧ Classifying the Regular Polyhedra

We now prove that there are exactly five regular polyhedra (see Figure 2). To show this, we consider all possible cases.

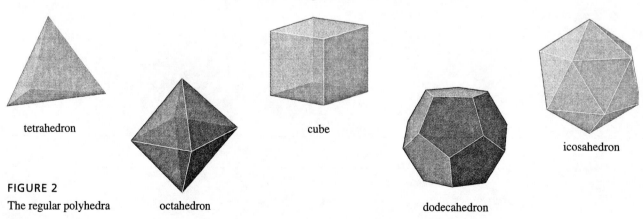

tetrahedron

octahedron

cube

dodecahedron

icosahedron

FIGURE 2
The regular polyhedra

■ **CASE 1** Suppose the faces of a regular polyhedron are equilateral triangles. How many such triangles can meet at a corner? To make a corner, there must be at least three triangles. We can also have four or five. But six equilateral triangles can-

Three, four, and five equilateral triangles can be folded up to make a corner, but six such triangles lie flat.

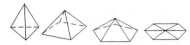

not meet at a point to make a corner. (Why?) If three triangles meet at each vertex, we can complete the polyhedron by adding one more triangle to make a *tetrahedron*. If four triangles meet at each vertex, we have an *octahedron*. If five triangles meet at each vertex, the resulting regular polyhedron is an *icosahedron*. Thus, we have found all the regular polyhedra with triangular faces.

■ **CASE 2** Suppose the faces of a regular polygon are squares. If three squares meet at each point, then the polyhedron is a *cube*. It's impossible for four or more squares to meet at a point to make a corner. (Why?) Thus, the only regular polyhedron with square faces is the cube.

■ **CASE 3** Suppose the faces of a regular polygon are pentagons. If three pentagons meet at each vertex, the resulting polyhedron is a *dodecahedron*. Since the angles of a regular pentagon are 108°, it's impossible for more than three regular pentagons to meet at a vertex. Thus, the only regular polyhedron with pentagonal faces is the dodecahedron.

■ **CASE 4** Is it possible for the faces of a regular polygon to be regular hexagons? Since the angle of a regular hexagon is 120°, when three such hexagons meet at a point they do not form a corner, so it's impossible for a regular polyhedron to have hexagonal faces. The same reasoning shows that no other regular polygon can be the face of a regular polyhedron.

Since these four cases account for all the possibilities, we have shown that there are exactly five regular polyhedra.

Euler's Formula

How many faces, edges, and vertices does a regular polyhedron have? In the 18th century, Euler observed that

$$F - E + V = 2 \qquad \text{Euler's Formula}$$

where F is the number of faces, E is the number of edges, and V is the number of vertices. We can use Euler's Formula to answer the question. For example, the icosahedron is assembled from F equilateral triangles:

It's interesting to note that there are infinitely many 2-dimensional regular polygons but only five 3-dimensional regular polyhedra. Although it's impossible to draw the 4-dimensional regular polyhedra, mathematicians have shown that there are six of them. Surprisingly, in all higher dimensions there are exactly three regular polyhedra—the *n*-dimensional cube, tetrahedron, and octahedron.

$$\triangle, \triangle, \triangle, \ldots$$

In these triangles the total number of sides is $3F$, and the total number of angles is also $3F$. In an icosahedron, five angles of these triangles meet to form a vertex, so the total number of vertices must be

$$V = \frac{3F}{5}$$

Since two sides of adjacent triangles meet to form one edge of the polyhedron, the number of edges must be

$$E = \frac{3F}{2}$$

Substituting into Euler's Formula gives

$$F - \frac{3F}{2} + \frac{3F}{5} = 2$$

Solving gives $F = 20$. Substituting this value of F into the formulas for edges and faces gives $E = 30$ and $V = 12$. Thus, for the icosahedron, $F = 20$, $E = 30$, and $V = 12$. Using similar reasoning we can find the number of faces, edges, and vertices for the other regular polyhedra.

Problems

1. Find the number of faces, edges, and vertices for each of the regular polyhedra, not by counting them, but by using Euler's Formula.

2. Describe the polyhedron whose edges are the line segments joining the centers of the faces of an octahedron, as shown in the figure. Do the same for the other Platonic solids.

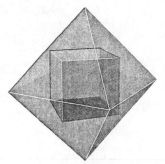

3. As the following figures indicate, it's possible to *tile* the plane (that is, completely cover it) with equilateral triangles and with squares. Find all other regular polygons that tile the plane. Prove your answer.

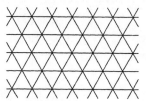 

4. (a) Find a formula for the area A_n of the regular polygon with n sides inscribed in a circle of radius 1 (see the figure). Express your answer as a trigonometric function of n.

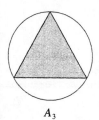 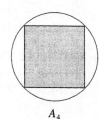 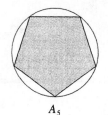 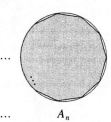

A_3 A_4 A_5 ... A_n

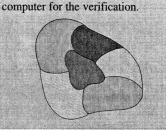

(b) Find A_3, A_4, A_{100}, and A_{1000}, correct to six decimal places. Notice that the values get closer and closer to π. Why?

5. A group of n pulleys, all of radius 1, is fixed so that their centers form a convex n-gon of perimeter P. (The figure shows the case $n = 4$.) Find the length of the belt that fits around the pulleys. [*Hint:* Try fitting together the sectors of the pulleys that touch the belt.]

6. A pair of pulleys is connected by a belt, as shown in each figure. Find the length of the belt.

(a)   (b)

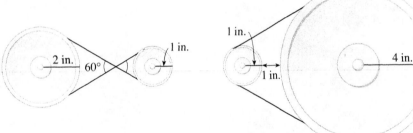

7. Two circles of radius 1 are placed so that their centers are one unit apart. Find the area of the region common to both circles.

8. Suppose that the lengths of the sides of a triangle are rational numbers. Prove that the cosine of each angle is a rational number.

9. Find the exact value of

$$\sin \frac{\pi}{100} + \sin \frac{2\pi}{100} + \sin \frac{3\pi}{100} + \sin \frac{4\pi}{100} + \cdots + \sin \frac{199\pi}{100}$$

where the sum contains the sines of all numbers of the form $k\pi/100$, with k varying from 1 to 199.

10. In order to draw a map of the spherical earth on a flat sheet of paper, several ingenious methods have been developed. One of these is the *cylindrical projection.** In this

---

*This type of map is often erroneously referred to as the Mercator "projection." The Mercator map actually involves procedures much more complicated than simple projection—in fact, constructing an accurate Mercator map requires knowledge of calculus.

Pierre de Fermat (1601–1665) was a French lawyer who became interested in mathematics at the age of 30. Because of his job as a magistrate, Fermat had little time to write complete proofs of his discoveries and often wrote them in the margin of whatever book he was reading at the time. After his death, his copy of Diophantus' *Arithmetica* (see page 37) was found to contain a particularly tantalizing comment. Where Diophantus discusses the solutions of $x^2 + y^2 = z^2$ (for example, $x = 3$, $y = 4$, $z = 5$), Fermat states in the margin that for $n \geq 3$ there are no natural number solutions to the equation $x^n + y^n = z^n$. In other words, it's impossible for a cube to equal the sum of two cubes, a fourth power to equal the sum of two fourth powers, and so on. Fermat writes "I have discovered a truly wonderful proof for this but the margin is too small to contain it." All the other margin comments in Fermat's copy of *Arithmetica* have been proved. This one, however, remained unproved, and it came to be known as "Fermat's Last Theorem."

In 1994, Andrew Wiles of Princeton University announced a proof of Fermat's Last Theorem, an astounding 350 years after it was conjectured. His proof is one of the most widely reported mathematical results in the popular press.

method, illustrated in the figure, each point on the spherical earth is projected onto a circumscribed cylinder (tangent to the sphere on the equator) by a line through the center of the earth. By what factor are the following distances distorted using this method of projection? That is, what is the ratio of the projected distance on the cylinder to the actual distance on the sphere?

(a) The distance between 20° and 21° N latitude along a meridian
(b) The distance between 40° and 41° N latitude along a meridian
(c) The distance between 80° and 81° N latitude along a meridian
(d) The distance between two points that are 1° apart on the 20th parallel
(e) The distance between two points that are 1° apart on the 40th parallel
(f) The distance between two points that are 1° apart on the 80th parallel

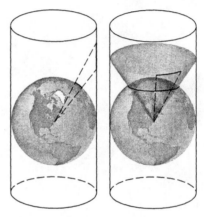

11. A bug is sitting at point A in one corner of a room and wants to crawl to point B in the corner diagonally opposite (see the figure). Find the shortest path for the bug.

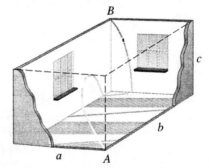

12. Prove that every prime number is the leg of exactly one right triangle with integer sides. (This problem was first stated by Fermat.)

13. Show that the equation $x^2 + y^2 = 4z + 3$ has no solution in integers. [*Hint:* Recall that an even number is of the form $2n$ and an odd number is of the form $2n + 1$. Consider all possible cases for x and y even or odd.]

14. (a) Find all prime numbers p such that $2p + 1$ is a perfect square.
    [*Hint:* Write the equation $2p + 1 = n^2$ as $2p = n^2 - 1$ and factor. Then consider cases.]
    (b) Find all prime numbers p such that $2p + 1$ is a perfect cube.

15. (a) Write 13 as the sum of two squares. Then do the same for 41.
    (b) Verify that $(a^2 + b^2)(c^2 + d^2) = (ac + bd)^2 + (ad - bc)^2$.
    (c) Express 533 as the sum of two squares in two different ways.
    [*Hint:* Factor 533 and use parts (a) and (b).]

16. Find the area of the region between the two concentric circles shown in the figure.

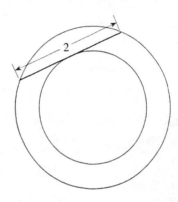

Bhaskara (born 1114) was an Indian mathematician, astronomer, and astrologer. Among his many accomplishments was an ingenious proof of the Pythagorean Theorem (see Problem 17). His important mathematical book *Lilavati* [*The Beautiful*] consists of algebra problems posed in the form of stories to his daughter Lilavati. Many of the problems begin "Oh beautiful maiden, suppose . . ." The story is told that using astrology, Bhaskara had determined that great misfortune would befall his daughter if she married at any time other than at a certain hour of a certain day. On her wedding day, as she was anxiously watching the water clock, a pearl fell unnoticed from her headdress. It stopped the flow of water in the clock, causing her to miss the opportune moment for marriage. Bhaskara's *Lilavati* was written to console her.

17. The Indian mathematician Bhaskara sketched the two figures shown here and wrote below them, "Behold!" Explain how his sketches prove the Pythagorean Theorem.

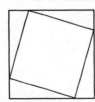

18. If the lengths of the sides of a right triangle, in increasing order, are a, b, and c, show that $a^3 + b^3 < c^3$.

7 Analytic Trigonometry

Trigonometry is used to analyze directed quantities, or vectors. The path of a jet aircraft is determined by resolving the vector forces of thrust, wind, and shear that act on the plane; the heading of a sailboat is determined by resolving the forces of the wind on the sails and the water currents on the hull of the boat.

In Chapters 5 and 6 we studied the graphical and geometric properties of trigonometric functions. In this chapter we study the algebraic aspects of trigonometry, that is, simplifying and factoring expressions and solving equations that involve trigonometric functions. The basic tools in the algebra of trigonometry are trigonometric identities. We will find identities for trigonometric functions of sums and differences of real numbers, multiple-angle formulas, and other related identities. These identities are used in the study of complex numbers, vectors, and analytic geometry.

7.1 TRIGONOMETRIC IDENTITIES

We begin this section by reviewing some of the basic trigonometric identities that we studied in Chapters 5 and 6.

FUNDAMENTAL TRIGONOMETRIC IDENTITIES

Reciprocal Identities

$$\csc x = \frac{1}{\sin x} \qquad \sec x = \frac{1}{\cos x} \qquad \cot x = \frac{1}{\tan x}$$

$$\tan x = \frac{\sin x}{\cos x} \qquad \cot x = \frac{\cos x}{\sin x}$$

Pythagorean Identities

$$\sin^2 x + \cos^2 x = 1 \qquad \tan^2 x + 1 = \sec^2 x \qquad 1 + \cot^2 x = \csc^2 x$$

Even-Odd Identities

$$\sin(-x) = -\sin x \qquad \cos(-x) = \cos x \qquad \tan(-x) = -\tan x$$

Cofunction Identities

$$\sin\left(\frac{\pi}{2} - u\right) = \cos u \qquad \tan\left(\frac{\pi}{2} - u\right) = \cot u \qquad \sec\left(\frac{\pi}{2} - u\right) = \csc u$$

$$\cos\left(\frac{\pi}{2} - u\right) = \sin u \qquad \cot\left(\frac{\pi}{2} - u\right) = \tan u \qquad \csc\left(\frac{\pi}{2} - u\right) = \sec u$$

Simplifying Trigonometric Expressions

Identities enable us to write the same expression in different ways. It is often possible to rewrite a complicated looking expression as a much simpler one. To simplify algebraic expressions, we used factoring, common denominators, and the Special Product Formulas. To simplify trigonometric expressions, we use these same techniques together with the fundamental trigonometric identities.

EXAMPLE 1 ■ Simplifying a Trigonometric Expression

Simplify the expression $\cos t + \tan t \sin t$.

SOLUTION

We start by rewriting the expression in terms of sine and cosine.

$$\cos t + \tan t \sin t = \cos t + \left(\frac{\sin t}{\cos t}\right) \sin t \qquad \text{Reciprocal identity}$$

$$= \frac{\cos^2 t + \sin^2 t}{\cos t} \qquad \text{Common denominator}$$

$$= \frac{1}{\cos t} \qquad \text{Pythagorean identity}$$

$$= \sec t \qquad \text{Reciprocal identity} \qquad ■$$

EXAMPLE 2 ■ Simplifying by Combining Fractions

Simplify the expression $\dfrac{\sin \theta}{\cos \theta} + \dfrac{\cos \theta}{1 + \sin \theta}$.

SOLUTION

We combine the fractions by using a common denominator.

$$\frac{\sin \theta}{\cos \theta} + \frac{\cos \theta}{1 + \sin \theta} = \frac{\sin \theta (1 + \sin \theta) + \cos^2 \theta}{\cos \theta (1 + \sin \theta)} \qquad \text{Common denominator}$$

$$= \frac{\sin \theta + \sin^2 \theta + \cos^2 \theta}{\cos \theta (1 + \sin \theta)} \qquad \text{Expand}$$

$$= \frac{\sin \theta + 1}{\cos \theta (1 + \sin \theta)} \qquad \text{Pythagorean identity}$$

$$= \frac{1}{\cos \theta} = \sec \theta \qquad \text{Cancel and use reciprocal identity} \qquad ■$$

Proving Trigonometric Identities

Many identities follow from the fundamental identities. In the examples that follow, we learn how to prove that a given trigonometric equation is an identity, and in the process we will see how to discover new identities.

First, it's easy to decide when a given equation is *not* an identity. All we need to do is show that the equation does not hold for some value of the variable (or variables). Thus, the equation

$$\sin x + \cos x = 1$$

is not an identity, because when $x = \pi/4$, we have

$$\sin \frac{\pi}{4} + \cos \frac{\pi}{4} = \frac{\sqrt{2}}{2} + \frac{\sqrt{2}}{2} = \sqrt{2} \neq 1$$

To verify that a trigonometric equation is an identity, we transform one side of the equation into the other side by a series of steps, each of which is itself an identity.

GUIDELINES FOR PROVING TRIGONOMETRIC IDENTITIES

1. START WITH ONE SIDE.   Pick one side of the equation and write it down. Your goal is to transform it into the other side. It's usually easier to start with the more complicated side.

2. USE KNOWN IDENTITIES.   Use algebra and the identities you know to change the side you started with. Bring fractional expressions to a common denominator, factor, and use the fundamental identities to simplify expressions.

3. CONVERT TO SINES AND COSINES.   If you are stuck, you may find it helpful to rewrite all functions in terms of sines and cosines.

EXAMPLE 3 ■ Proving an Identity by Rewriting in Terms of Sine and Cosine

Verify the identity $\cos \theta \, (\sec \theta - \cos \theta) = \sin^2\theta$.

SOLUTION

The left-hand side looks more complicated, so we start with it and try to transform it into the right-hand side.

$$\text{LHS} = \cos \theta \, (\sec \theta - \cos \theta)$$

$$= \cos \theta \left(\frac{1}{\cos \theta} - \cos \theta \right) \qquad \text{Reciprocal identity}$$

$$= 1 - \cos^2\theta \qquad \text{Expand}$$

$$= \sin^2\theta = \text{RHS} \qquad \text{Pythagorean identity} \qquad ■$$

In Example 3 it isn't easy to see how to change the right-hand side into the left-hand side, but it's definitely possible. Simply notice that each step is reversible. In other words, if we start with the last expression in the proof and work backward through the steps, the right side is transformed into the left side. You will probably agree, however, that it's more difficult to prove the identity this way. That's why it's often better to change the more complicated side of the identity into the simpler side.

EXAMPLE 4 ■ Proving an Identity by Combining Fractions

Verify the identity

$$2 \tan x \sec x = \frac{1}{1 - \sin x} - \frac{1}{1 + \sin x}$$

SOLUTION

Finding a common denominator and combining the fractions on the right-hand side of this equation, we get

$$\text{RHS} = \frac{1}{1 - \sin x} - \frac{1}{1 + \sin x}$$

$$= \frac{(1 + \sin x) - (1 - \sin x)}{(1 - \sin x)(1 + \sin x)} \qquad \text{Common denominator}$$

$$= \frac{2 \sin x}{1 - \sin^2 x} \qquad \text{Simplify}$$

$$= \frac{2 \sin x}{\cos^2 x} \qquad \text{Pythagorean identity}$$

$$= 2 \frac{\sin x}{\cos x} \left(\frac{1}{\cos x} \right) \qquad \text{Factor}$$

$$= 2 \tan x \sec x = \text{LHS} \qquad \text{Reciprocal identities} \qquad ■$$

See Focus on Problem Solving, pages 134–137.

In Example 5 we introduce "something extra" to the problem by multiplying the numerator and the denominator by a trigonometric expression, chosen so that we can simplify the result.

EXAMPLE 5 ■ Proving an Identity by Introducing Something Extra

Verify the identity $\dfrac{\cos u}{1 - \sin u} = \sec u + \tan u$.

SOLUTION

We start with the left-hand side and multiply numerator and denominator by $1 + \sin u$.

$$\text{LHS} = \frac{\cos u}{1 - \sin u}$$

We multiply by $1 + \sin u$ because we know by the difference of squares formula that $(1 - \sin u)(1 + \sin u) = 1 - \sin^2 u$, and this is just $\cos^2 u$, a simpler expression.

$$= \frac{\cos u}{1 - \sin u} \cdot \frac{1 + \sin u}{1 + \sin u} \qquad \text{Multiply numerator and denominator by } 1 + \sin u$$

$$= \frac{\cos u(1 + \sin u)}{1 - \sin^2 u} \qquad \text{Expand denominator}$$

$$= \frac{\cos u(1 + \sin u)}{\cos^2 u} \qquad \text{Pythagorean identity}$$

$$= \frac{1 + \sin u}{\cos u} \qquad \text{Cancel common factor}$$

$$= \frac{1}{\cos u} + \frac{\sin u}{\cos u} \qquad \text{Separate into two fractions}$$

$$= \sec u + \tan u \qquad \text{Reciprocal identities} \qquad \blacksquare$$

Here is another method for proving that an equation is an identity. If we can transform each side of the equation separately, by way of identities, to arrive at the same result, then the equation is an identity. Example 6 illustrates this procedure.

EXAMPLE 6 ■ Proving an Identity by Working with Both Sides

Verify the identity $\dfrac{1 + \cos \theta}{\cos \theta} = \dfrac{\tan^2 \theta}{\sec \theta - 1}$.

SOLUTION

We prove the identity by changing each side separately into the same expression. Supply the reasons for each step.

$$\text{LHS} = \frac{1 + \cos \theta}{\cos \theta} = \frac{1}{\cos \theta} + \frac{\cos \theta}{\cos \theta} = \sec \theta + 1$$

$$\text{RHS} = \frac{\tan^2 \theta}{\sec \theta - 1} = \frac{\sec^2 \theta - 1}{\sec \theta - 1} = \frac{(\sec \theta - 1)(\sec \theta + 1)}{\sec \theta - 1} = \sec \theta + 1$$

It follows that LHS = RHS, so the equation is an identity. $\qquad \blacksquare$

     Warning: To prove an identity, we do *not* just perform the same operations on both sides of the equation. For example, if we start with an equation that is not an identity, such as

(1) $$\sin x = -\sin x$$

and square both sides, we get the equation

(2) $$\sin^2 x = \sin^2 x$$

which is clearly an identity. Does this mean that the original equation is an identity? Of course not. The problem here is that the operation of squaring is not **reversible** in the sense that we cannot arrive back at (1) from (2) by taking square roots (reversing the procedure). Only operations that are reversible will necessarily transform an identity into an identity.

We end this section by describing the technique of *trigonometric substitution*, which we use to convert algebraic expressions to trigonometric ones. This is often useful in calculus, for instance, in finding the area of a circle or an ellipse.

EXAMPLE 7 ■ Trigonometric Substitution

Substitute $\sin \theta$ for x in the expression $\sqrt{1 - x^2}$ and simplify. Assume that $0 \leqslant \theta \leqslant \pi/2$.

SOLUTION

Setting $x = \sin \theta$, we have

$$\sqrt{1 - x^2} = \sqrt{1 - \sin^2\theta} \qquad \text{Substitute } x = \sin \theta$$

$$= \sqrt{\cos^2\theta} \qquad \text{Pythagorean identity}$$

$$= \cos \theta \qquad \text{Take square root}$$

The last equality is true because $\cos \theta \geqslant 0$ for the values of θ in question. ■

7.1 EXERCISES

1–8 ■ Write the trigonometric expression in terms of sine and cosine, and then simplify.

1. $\sin t \cot t$

2. $\sin t \sec t$

3. $\tan x \csc x$

4. $\sin x \cos x \sec x$

5. $\tan^2 x - \sec^2 x$

6. $\dfrac{\sec x}{\csc x}$

7. $\sin u + \cot u \cos u$

8. $\cos^2\theta(1 + \tan^2\theta)$

9–22 ■ Simplify the trigonometric expression.

9. $\dfrac{\sin x \sec x}{\tan x}$

10. $\cos^3 x + \sin^2 x \cos x$

11. $\dfrac{1 + \cos y}{1 + \sec y}$

12. $\dfrac{\tan x}{\sec(-x)}$

13. $\dfrac{\sec^2 x - 1}{\sec^2 x}$

14. $\dfrac{\sec x - \cos x}{\tan x}$

15. $\dfrac{1 + \csc x}{\cos x + \cot x}$

16. $\dfrac{\sin x}{\csc x} + \dfrac{\cos x}{\sec x}$

17. $\dfrac{1 + \sin u}{\cos u} + \dfrac{\cos u}{1 + \sin u}$

18. $\tan x \cos x \csc x$

19. $\dfrac{2 + \tan^2 x}{\sec^2 x} - 1$

20. $\dfrac{1 + \cot A}{\csc A}$

21. $\tan \theta + \cos(-\theta) + \tan(-\theta)$

22. $\dfrac{\cos x}{\sec x + \tan x}$

23–84 ■ Verify the identity.

23. $\dfrac{\sin \theta}{\tan \theta} = \cos \theta$

24. $\dfrac{\tan x}{\sec x} = \sin x$

25. $\dfrac{\cos u \sec u}{\tan u} = \cot u$

26. $\dfrac{\cot x \sec x}{\csc x} = 1$

27. $\dfrac{\tan y}{\csc y} = \sec y - \cos y$

28. $\dfrac{\cos v}{\sec v \sin v} = \csc v - \sin v$

29. $\sin B + \cos B \cot B = \csc B$

30. $\cos(-x) - \sin(-x) = \cos x + \sin x$

31. $\cot(-\alpha) \cos(-\alpha) + \sin(-\alpha) = -\csc \alpha$

32. $\csc x \left[\csc x + \sin(-x)\right] = \cot^2 x$

33. $\tan \theta + \cot \theta = \sec \theta \csc \theta$

34. $(\sin x + \cos x)^2 = 1 + 2 \sin x \cos x$

35. $(1 - \cos \beta)(1 + \cos \beta) = \dfrac{1}{\csc^2\beta}$

36. $\dfrac{\cos x}{\sec x} + \dfrac{\sin x}{\csc x} = 1$

37. $\dfrac{(\sin x + \cos x)^2}{\sin^2 x - \cos^2 x} = \dfrac{\sin^2 x - \cos^2 x}{(\sin x - \cos x)^2}$

38. $(\sin x + \cos x)^4 = (1 + 2 \sin x \cos x)^2$

39. $\dfrac{\sec t - \cos t}{\sec t} = \sin^2 t$

40. $\dfrac{1 - \sin x}{1 + \sin x} = (\sec x - \tan x)^2$

41. $\dfrac{1}{1 - \sin^2 y} = 1 + \tan^2 y$

42. $\csc x - \sin x = \cos x \cot x$

43. $(\cot x - \csc x)(\cos x + 1) = -\sin x$

44. $\sin^4 \theta - \cos^4 \theta = \sin^2 \theta - \cos^2 \theta$

45. $(1 - \cos^2 x)(1 + \cot^2 x) = 1$

46. $\cos^2 x - \sin^2 x = 2 \cos^2 x - 1$

47. $2 \cos^2 x - 1 = 1 - 2 \sin^2 x$

48. $(\tan y + \cot y)\sin y \cos y = 1$

49. $\dfrac{1 - \cos \alpha}{\sin \alpha} = \dfrac{\sin \alpha}{1 + \cos \alpha}$

50. $\sin^2 \alpha + \cos^2 \alpha + \tan^2 \alpha = \sec^2 \alpha$

51. $\dfrac{\sin x - 1}{\sin x + 1} = \dfrac{-\cos^2 x}{(\sin x + 1)^2}$

52. $\dfrac{\sin w}{\sin w + \cos w} = \dfrac{\tan w}{1 + \tan w}$

53. $\dfrac{(\sin t + \cos t)^2}{\sin t \cos t} = 2 + \sec t \csc t$

54. $\sec t \csc t (\tan t + \cot t) = \sec^2 t + \csc^2 t$

55. $\dfrac{1 + \tan^2 u}{1 - \tan^2 u} = \dfrac{1}{\cos^2 u - \sin^2 u}$

56. $\dfrac{1 + \sec^2 x}{1 + \tan^2 x} = 1 + \cos^2 x$

57. $\dfrac{\sec x}{\sec x - \tan x} = \sec x (\sec x + \tan x)$

58. $\dfrac{\sec x + \csc x}{\tan x + \cot x} = \sin x + \cos x$

59. $\sec v - \tan v = \dfrac{1}{\sec v + \tan v}$

60. $\dfrac{\sin A}{1 - \cos A} - \cot A = \csc A$

61. $\dfrac{\sin x + \cos x}{\sec x + \csc x} = \sin x \cos x$

62. $\dfrac{1 - \cos x}{\sin x} + \dfrac{\sin x}{1 - \cos x} = 2 \csc x$

63. $\dfrac{\csc x - \cot x}{\sec x - 1} = \cot x$

64. $\dfrac{\csc^2 x - \cot^2 x}{\sec^2 x} = \cos^2 x$

65. $\tan^2 u - \sin^2 u = \tan^2 u \sin^2 u$

66. $\dfrac{\tan v \sin v}{\tan v + \sin v} = \dfrac{\tan v - \sin v}{\tan v \sin v}$

67. $\sec^4 x - \tan^4 x = \sec^2 x + \tan^2 x$

68. $\dfrac{\cos \theta}{1 - \sin \theta} = \sec \theta + \tan \theta$

69. $\dfrac{\cos \theta}{1 - \sin \theta} = \dfrac{\sin \theta - \csc \theta}{\cos \theta - \cot \theta}$

70. $\dfrac{1 + \tan x}{1 - \tan x} = \dfrac{\cos x + \sin x}{\cos x - \sin x}$

71. $\dfrac{\cos^2 t + \tan^2 t - 1}{\sin^2 t} = \tan^2 t$

72. $\dfrac{1}{1 - \sin x} - \dfrac{1}{1 + \sin x} = 2 \sec x \tan x$

73. $\dfrac{1}{\sec x + \tan x} + \dfrac{1}{\sec x - \tan x} = 2 \sec x$

74. $\dfrac{1 + \sin x}{1 - \sin x} - \dfrac{1 - \sin x}{1 + \sin x} = 4 \tan x \sec x$

75. $(\tan x + \cot x)^2 = \sec^2 x + \csc^2 x$

76. $\tan^2 x - \cot^2 x = \sec^2 x - \csc^2 x$

77. $\dfrac{\sec u - 1}{\sec u + 1} = \dfrac{1 - \cos u}{1 + \cos u}$ **78.** $\dfrac{\cot x + 1}{\cot x - 1} = \dfrac{1 + \tan x}{1 - \tan x}$

79. $\dfrac{\sin^3 x + \cos^3 x}{\sin x + \cos x} = 1 - \sin x \cos x$

80. $\dfrac{\tan v - \cot v}{\tan^2 v - \cot^2 v} = \sin v \cos v$

81. $\dfrac{1 + \sin x}{1 - \sin x} = (\tan x + \sec x)^2$

82. $\dfrac{\tan x + \tan y}{\cot x + \cot y} = \tan x \tan y$

83. $(\tan x + \cot x)^4 = \csc^4 x \sec^4 x$

84. $(\sin \alpha - \tan \alpha)(\cos \alpha - \cot \alpha) = (\cos \alpha - 1)(\sin \alpha - 1)$

85–90 ■ Make the indicated trigonometric substitution in the given algebraic expression and simplify (see Example 7). Assume $0 \le \theta < \pi/2$.

85. $\dfrac{x}{\sqrt{1 - x^2}}, \quad x = \sin \theta$

86. $\sqrt{1 + x^2}, \quad x = \tan \theta$

87. $\sqrt{x^2 - 1}, \quad x = \sec \theta$

88. $\dfrac{1}{x^2 \sqrt{4 + x^2}}, \quad x = 2 \tan \theta$

89. $\sqrt{9 - x^2}, \quad x = 3 \sin \theta$

90. $\dfrac{\sqrt{x^2 - 25}}{x}, \quad x = 5 \sec \theta$

91–94 ■ Graph f and g in the same viewing rectangle. Do the graphs suggest that the equation $f(x) = g(x)$ is an identity? Prove your answer.

91. $f(x) = \cos^2 x - \sin^2 x, \quad g(x) = 1 - 2 \sin^2 x$

92. $f(x) = \tan x \,(1 + \sin x), \quad g(x) = \dfrac{\sin x \cos x}{1 + \sin x}$

93. $f(x) = (\sin x + \cos x)^2, \quad g(x) = 1$

94. $f(x) = \cos^4 x - \sin^4 x, \quad g(x) = 2 \cos^2 x - 1$

95. Show that the equation is not an identity.

(a) $\sin 2x = 2 \sin x$

(b) $\sin(x + y) = \sin x + \sin y$

(c) $\sec^2 x + \csc^2 x = 1$

(d) $\dfrac{1}{\sin x + \cos x} = \csc x + \sec x$

DISCOVERY · DISCUSSION

96. Cofunction Identities   In the right triangle shown, explain why

$$v = \frac{\pi}{2} - u$$

Explain how you can obtain all six cofunction identities from this triangle, for $0 < u < \pi/2$.

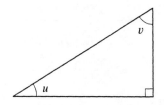

97. Graphs and Identities   Suppose you graph two functions, f and g, on a graphing device, and their graphs appear identical in the viewing rectangle. Does this prove that the equation $f(x) = g(x)$ is an identity? Explain.

98. Making Up Your Own Identity   If you start with a trigonometric expression and rewrite it or simplify it, then setting the original expression equal to the rewritten expression yields a trigonometric identity. For instance, from Example 1, we get the identity

$$\cos t + \tan t \sin t = \sec t$$

Use this technique to make up your own identity, then give it to a classmate to verify.

7.2 ADDITION AND SUBTRACTION FORMULAS

We now derive identities for trigonometric functions of sums and differences.

ADDITION AND SUBTRACTION FORMULAS

Formulas for sine

$$\sin(s + t) = \sin s \cos t + \cos s \sin t$$

$$\sin(s - t) = \sin s \cos t - \cos s \sin t$$

Formulas for cosine

$$\cos(s + t) = \cos s \cos t - \sin s \sin t$$

$$\cos(s - t) = \cos s \cos t + \sin s \sin t$$

Formulas for tangent

$$\tan(s + t) = \frac{\tan s + \tan t}{1 - \tan s \tan t}$$

$$\tan(s - t) = \frac{\tan s - \tan t}{1 + \tan s \tan t}$$

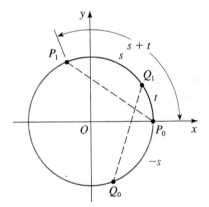

FIGURE 1

■ **Proof of Addition Formula for Cosine** To prove the formula $\cos(s + t) = \cos s \cos t - \sin s \sin t$, we use Figure 1. In the figure, the distances t, $s + t$, and $-s$ have been marked on the unit circle, starting at $P_0(1, 0)$ and terminating at Q_1, P_1, and Q_0, respectively. The coordinates of these points are

$$P_0(1, 0) \qquad\qquad Q_0(\cos(-s), \sin(-s))$$

$$P_1(\cos(s + t), \sin(s + t)) \qquad Q_1(\cos t, \sin t)$$

Since $\cos(-s) = \cos s$ and $\sin(-s) = -\sin s$, it follows that the point Q_0 has the coordinates $Q_0(\cos s, -\sin s)$. Notice that the distances between P_0 and P_1 and between Q_0 and Q_1 measured along the arc of the circle are equal. Since equal arcs are subtended by equal chords, it follows that $d(P_0, P_1) = d(Q_0, Q_1)$. Using the Distance Formula, we get

$$\sqrt{[\cos(s + t) - 1]^2 + [\sin(s + t) - 0]^2} = \sqrt{(\cos t - \cos s)^2 + (\sin t + \sin s)^2}$$

Squaring both sides and expanding, we have

these add to 1

$$\cos^2(s + t) - 2\cos(s + t) + 1 + \sin^2(s + t)$$

$$= \cos^2 t - 2\cos s \cos t + \cos^2 s + \sin^2 t + 2\sin s \sin t + \sin^2 s$$

these add to 1

these add to 1

Using the Pythagorean identity $\sin^2 z + \cos^2 z = 1$ three times gives

$$2 - 2\cos(s + t) = 2 - 2\cos s \cos t + 2 \sin s \sin t$$

Finally, subtracting 2 from each side and dividing both sides by -2, we get

$$\cos(s + t) = \cos s \cos t - \sin s \sin t$$

which proves the addition formula for cosine.

■ **Proof of Subtraction Formula for Cosine** Replacing t with $-t$ in the addition formula for cosine, we get

$$\cos(s - t) = \cos(s + (-t))$$

$$= \cos s \cos(-t) - \sin s \sin(-t) \qquad \text{Addition formula for cosine}$$

$$= \cos s \cos t + \sin s \sin t \qquad \text{Even-odd identities}$$

This proves the subtraction formula for cosine. □

See Exercises 52 and 53 for proofs of the other addition formulas.

EXAMPLE 1 ■ Using the Addition and Subtraction Formulas

Find the exact value of each expression: (a) $\cos 75°$ (b) $\cos \dfrac{\pi}{12}$

SOLUTION

(a) Notice that $75° = 45° + 30°$. Since we know the exact values of sine and cosine at $45°$ and $30°$, we use the addition formula for cosine to get

$$\cos 75° = \cos(45° + 30°)$$

$$= \cos 45° \cos 30° - \sin 45° \sin 30°$$

$$= \frac{\sqrt{2}}{2}\frac{\sqrt{3}}{2} - \frac{\sqrt{2}}{2}\frac{1}{2} = \frac{\sqrt{2}\sqrt{3} - \sqrt{2}}{4} = \frac{\sqrt{6} - \sqrt{2}}{4}$$

(b) Since $\dfrac{\pi}{12} = \dfrac{\pi}{4} - \dfrac{\pi}{6}$, the subtraction formula for cosine gives

$$\cos \frac{\pi}{12} = \cos\left(\frac{\pi}{4} - \frac{\pi}{6}\right)$$

$$= \cos \frac{\pi}{4} \cos \frac{\pi}{6} + \sin \frac{\pi}{4} \sin \frac{\pi}{6}$$

$$= \frac{\sqrt{2}}{2}\frac{\sqrt{3}}{2} + \frac{\sqrt{2}}{2}\frac{1}{2} = \frac{\sqrt{6} + \sqrt{2}}{4}$$

■

EXAMPLE 2 ■ Using the Addition Formula for Sine

Find the exact value of the expression: $\sin 20° \cos 40° + \cos 20° \sin 40°$

SOLUTION

We recognize the expression as the right-hand side of the addition formula for sine with $s = 20°$ and $t = 40°$. So we have

$$\sin 20° \cos 40° + \cos 20° \sin 40° = \sin(20° + 40°) = \sin 60° = \frac{\sqrt{3}}{2} \qquad ■$$

EXAMPLE 3 ■ Proving an Identity

Prove the cofunction identity: $\cos\left(\dfrac{\pi}{2} - u\right) = \sin u$

SOLUTION

By the subtraction formula for cosine,

$$\cos\left(\frac{\pi}{2} - u\right) = \cos\frac{\pi}{2}\cos u + \sin\frac{\pi}{2}\sin u$$

$$= 0 \cdot \cos u + 1 \cdot \sin u = \sin u \qquad ■$$

EXAMPLE 4 ■ Proving an Identity

Verify the identity: $\dfrac{1 + \tan x}{1 - \tan x} = \tan\left(\dfrac{\pi}{4} + x\right)$

SOLUTION

Starting with the right-hand side and using the addition formula for tangent, we get

$$\text{RHS} = \tan\left(\frac{\pi}{4} + x\right) = \frac{\tan\dfrac{\pi}{4} + \tan x}{1 - \tan\dfrac{\pi}{4}\tan x}$$

$$= \frac{1 + \tan x}{1 - \tan x} = \text{LHS} \qquad ■$$

The next example is a typical use of the addition and subtraction formulas in calculus.

EXAMPLE 5 ■ An Identity from Calculus

If $f(x) = \sin x$, show that

$$\frac{f(x + h) - f(x)}{h} = \sin x\left(\frac{\cos h - 1}{h}\right) + \cos x\left(\frac{\sin h}{h}\right)$$

SOLUTION

$$\frac{f(x + h) - f(x)}{h} = \frac{\sin(x + h) - \sin x}{h} \qquad \text{Definition of } f$$

$$= \frac{\sin x \cos h + \cos x \sin h - \sin x}{h} \qquad \text{Addition formula for sine}$$

$$= \frac{\sin x \, (\cos h - 1) + \cos x \sin h}{h} \qquad \text{Factor}$$

$$= \sin x \left(\frac{\cos h - 1}{h}\right) + \cos x \left(\frac{\sin h}{h}\right) \qquad \text{Separate the fraction} \qquad \blacksquare$$

Expressions of the Form $A \sin x + B \cos x$

We can write expressions of the form $A \sin x + B \cos x$ in terms of a single trigonometric function using the addition formula for sine. For example, consider the expression

$$\frac{1}{2} \sin x + \frac{\sqrt{3}}{2} \cos x$$

If we set $\phi = \pi/3$, then $\cos \phi = \frac{1}{2}$ and $\sin \phi = \sqrt{3}/2$, and we can write

$$\frac{1}{2} \sin x + \frac{\sqrt{3}}{2} \cos x = \cos \phi \sin x + \sin \phi \cos x$$

$$= \sin(x + \phi) = \sin\left(x + \frac{\pi}{3}\right)$$

We are able to do this because the coefficients $\frac{1}{2}$ and $\sqrt{3}/2$ are precisely the cosine and sine of a particular number, in this case, $\pi/3$. We can use this same idea in general to write $A \sin x + B \cos x$ in the form $k \sin(x + \phi)$. We start by multiplying the numerator and denominator by $\sqrt{A^2 + B^2}$ to get

$$A \sin x + B \cos x = \sqrt{A^2 + B^2} \left(\frac{A}{\sqrt{A^2 + B^2}} \sin x + \frac{B}{\sqrt{A^2 + B^2}} \cos x\right)$$

We need a number ϕ with the property that

$$\cos \phi = \frac{A}{\sqrt{A^2 + B^2}} \qquad \text{and} \qquad \sin \phi = \frac{B}{\sqrt{A^2 + B^2}}$$

Figure 2 shows that the point (A, B) in the plane determines a number ϕ with precisely this property. With this ϕ, we have

$$A \sin x + B \cos x = \sqrt{A^2 + B^2} \, (\cos \phi \sin x + \sin \phi \cos x)$$

$$= \sqrt{A^2 + B^2} \, \sin(x + \phi)$$

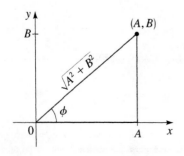

FIGURE 2

We have proved the following theorem.

SUMS OF SINES AND COSINES

If A and B are real numbers, then

$$A \sin x + B \cos x = k \sin(x + \phi)$$

where $k = \sqrt{A^2 + B^2}$ and ϕ satisfies

$$\cos \phi = \frac{A}{\sqrt{A^2 + B^2}} \qquad \text{and} \qquad \sin \phi = \frac{B}{\sqrt{A^2 + B^2}}$$

EXAMPLE 6 ■ A Sum of Sine and Cosine Terms

Express $3 \sin x + 4 \cos x$ in the form $k \sin(x + \phi)$.

SOLUTION

By the preceding theorem, $k = \sqrt{A^2 + B^2} = \sqrt{3^2 + 4^2} = 5$. The angle ϕ has the property that $\sin \phi = \frac{4}{5}$ and $\cos \phi = \frac{3}{5}$. Using a calculator, we find $\phi \approx 53.1°$. Thus

$$3 \sin x + 4 \cos x \approx 5 \sin(x + 53.1°)$$ ■

EXAMPLE 7 ■ Graphing a Trigonometric Function

Write the function $f(x) = -\sin 2x + \sqrt{3} \cos 2x$ in the form $k \sin(2x + \phi)$ and use the new form to graph the function.

SOLUTION

Since $A = -1$ and $B = \sqrt{3}$, we have $k = \sqrt{A^2 + B^2} = \sqrt{1 + 3} = 2$. The angle ϕ satisfies $\cos \phi = -\frac{1}{2}$ and $\sin \phi = \sqrt{3}/2$. From the signs of these quantities we conclude that ϕ is in quadrant II. Thus, $\phi = 2\pi/3$. By the preceding theorem we can write

$$f(x) = -\sin 2x + \sqrt{3} \cos 2x = 2 \sin\left(2x + \frac{2\pi}{3}\right)$$

Using the form

$$f(x) = 2 \sin 2\left(x + \frac{\pi}{3}\right)$$

we see that the graph is a sine curve with amplitude 2, period $2\pi/2 = \pi$, and phase shift $-\pi/3$. The graph is shown in Figure 3. ■

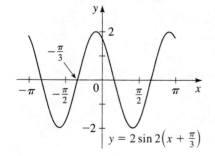

$$y = 2 \sin 2\left(x + \frac{\pi}{3}\right)$$

FIGURE 3

7.2 EXERCISES

1–10 ■ Use an addition or subtraction formula to find the exact value of the expression, as demonstrated in Example 1.

1. $\cos 15°$

2. $\sin 105°$

3. $\sin 165°$

4. $\tan 195°$

5. $\tan 75°$

6. $\cos \dfrac{11\pi}{12}$

7. $\sin \dfrac{19\pi}{12}$

8. $\tan \dfrac{17\pi}{12}$

9. $\cos\left(-\dfrac{\pi}{12}\right)$

10. $\sin\left(-\dfrac{5\pi}{12}\right)$

11–16 ■ Use an addition or subtraction formula to write the expression as a trigonometric function of one number, and find its exact value.

11. $\sin 18° \cos 27° + \cos 18° \sin 27°$

12. $\cos 10° \cos 80° - \sin 10° \sin 80°$

13. $\cos \dfrac{3\pi}{7} \cos \dfrac{2\pi}{21} + \sin \dfrac{3\pi}{7} \sin \dfrac{2\pi}{21}$

14. $\dfrac{\tan \dfrac{\pi}{18} + \tan \dfrac{\pi}{9}}{1 - \tan \dfrac{\pi}{18} \tan \dfrac{\pi}{9}}$

15. $\dfrac{\tan 73° - \tan 13°}{1 + \tan 73° \tan 13°}$

16. $\cos \dfrac{13\pi}{15} \cos\left(-\dfrac{\pi}{5}\right) - \sin \dfrac{13\pi}{15} \sin\left(-\dfrac{\pi}{5}\right)$

17–20 ■ Prove the cofunction identity using the addition and subtraction formulas.

17. $\tan\left(\dfrac{\pi}{2} - u\right) = \cot u$

18. $\cot\left(\dfrac{\pi}{2} - u\right) = \tan u$

19. $\sec\left(\dfrac{\pi}{2} - u\right) = \csc u$

20. $\csc\left(\dfrac{\pi}{2} - u\right) = \sec u$

21–38 ■ Prove the identity.

21. $\sin\left(x - \dfrac{\pi}{2}\right) = -\cos x$

22. $\cos\left(x - \dfrac{\pi}{2}\right) = \sin x$

23. $\sin(x - \pi) = -\sin x$

24. $\cos(x - \pi) = -\cos x$

25. $\tan(x - \pi) = \tan x$

26. $\sin\left(\dfrac{\pi}{2} - x\right) = \sin\left(\dfrac{\pi}{2} + x\right)$

27. $\cos\left(x + \dfrac{\pi}{6}\right) + \sin\left(x - \dfrac{\pi}{3}\right) = 0$

28. $\tan\left(x - \dfrac{\pi}{4}\right) = \dfrac{\tan x - 1}{\tan x + 1}$

29. $\sin(x + y) - \sin(x - y) = 2 \cos x \sin y$

30. $\cos(x + y) + \cos(x - y) = 2 \cos x \cos y$

31. $\cot(x - y) = \dfrac{\cot x \cot y + 1}{\cot y - \cot x}$

32. $\cot(x + y) = \dfrac{\cot x \cot y - 1}{\cot x + \cot y}$

33. $\tan x - \tan y = \dfrac{\sin(x - y)}{\cos x \cos y}$

34. $1 - \tan x \tan y = \dfrac{\cos(x + y)}{\cos x \cos y}$

35. $\dfrac{\sin(x + y) - \sin(x - y)}{\cos(x + y) + \cos(x - y)} = \tan y$

36. $\cos(x + y) \cos(x - y) = \cos^2 x - \sin^2 y$

37. $\sin(x + y + z) = \sin x \cos y \cos z + \cos x \sin y \cos z$
$+ \cos x \cos y \sin z - \sin x \sin y \sin z$

38. $\tan(x - y) + \tan(y - z) + \tan(z - x)$
$= \tan(x - y) \tan(y - z) \tan(z - x)$

39–42 ■ Write the expression in terms of sine only.

39. $-\sqrt{3} \sin x + \cos x$

40. $\sin x + \cos x$

41. $5(\sin 2x - \cos 2x)$

42. $3 \sin \pi x + 3\sqrt{3} \cos \pi x$

43–44 ■ (a) Express the function in terms of sine only.
(b) Graph the function.

43. $f(x) = \sin x + \cos x$

44. $g(x) = \cos 2x + \sqrt{3} \sin 2x$

45. Show that if $\beta - \alpha = \pi/2$, then
$$\sin(x + \alpha) + \cos(x + \beta) = 0$$

46. Let $g(x) = \cos x$. Show that

$$\frac{g(x + h) - g(x)}{h} = -\cos x\left(\frac{1 - \cos h}{h}\right) - \sin x\left(\frac{\sin h}{h}\right)$$

47. Refer to the figure. Show that $\alpha + \beta = \gamma$, and find $\tan \gamma$.

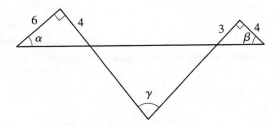

48. (a) If L is a line in the plane and θ is the angle formed by the line and the x-axis as shown in the figure, show that the slope m of the line is given by

$$m = \tan \theta$$

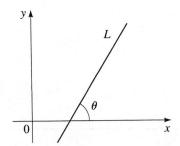

(b) Let L_1 and L_2 be two nonparallel lines in the plane with slopes m_1 and m_2, respectively. Let ψ be the acute angle formed by the two lines (see the figure). Show that

$$\tan \psi = \frac{m_2 - m_1}{1 + m_1 m_2}$$

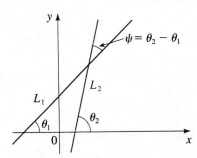

(c) Find the acute angle formed by the two lines

$$y = \tfrac{1}{3}x + 1 \quad \text{and} \quad y = -\tfrac{1}{2}x - 3$$

(d) Show that if two lines are perpendicular, then the slope of one is the negative reciprocal of the slope of the other. [*Hint:* First find an expression for $\cot \psi$.]

49–50 ■ (a) Graph the function and make a conjecture, then (b) prove that your conjecture is true.

49. $y = \sin^2\left(x + \dfrac{\pi}{4}\right) + \sin^2\left(x - \dfrac{\pi}{4}\right)$

50. $y = -\tfrac{1}{2}[\cos(x + \pi) + \cos(x - \pi)]$

51. A digital delay-device echoes an input signal by repeating it a fixed length of time after it is received. If such a device receives the pure note $f_1(t) = 5 \sin t$ and echoes the pure note $f_2(t) = 5 \cos t$, then the combined sound is $f(t) = f_1(t) + f_2(t)$.

(a) Graph $y = f(t)$ and observe that the graph has the form of a sine curve $y = k \sin(t + \phi)$.

(b) Find k and ϕ.

DISCOVERY · DISCUSSION

52. Addition Formula for Sine   In the text we proved only the addition and subtraction formulas for cosine. Use these formulas and the cofunction identities

$$\sin x = \cos\left(\frac{\pi}{2} - x\right)$$

$$\cos x = \sin\left(\frac{\pi}{2} - x\right)$$

to prove the addition formula for sine. [*Hint:* To get started, use the first cofunction identity to write

$$\sin(s + t) = \cos\left(\frac{\pi}{2} - (s + t)\right)$$

$$= \cos\left(\left(\frac{\pi}{2} - s\right) - t\right)$$

and use the subtraction formula for cosine.]

53. Addition Formula for Tangent   Use the addition formulas for cosine and sine to prove the addition formula for tangent. [*Hint:* Use

$$\tan(s + t) = \frac{\sin(s + t)}{\cos(s + t)}$$

and divide the numerator and denominator by $\cos s \cos t$.]

7.3 DOUBLE-ANGLE, HALF-ANGLE, AND PRODUCT-SUM FORMULAS

The identities we consider in this section are consequences of the addition formulas. The **double-angle formulas** allow us to find the values of the trigonometric functions at $2x$ from their values at x. The **half-angle formulas** relate the values of the trigonometric functions at $\frac{1}{2}x$ to their values at x. The **product-sum formulas** relate products of sines and cosines to sums of sines and cosines.

Double-Angle Formulas

The formulas in the following box are consequences of the addition formulas, which we proved in the preceding section.

DOUBLE-ANGLE FORMULAS

Formula for sine

$$\sin 2x = 2 \sin x \cos x$$

Formulas for cosine

$$\cos 2x = \cos^2 x - \sin^2 x$$

$$= 1 - 2 \sin^2 x$$

$$= 2 \cos^2 x - 1$$

Formula for tangent

$$\tan 2x = \frac{2 \tan x}{1 - \tan^2 x}$$

■ **Proof of Double-Angle Formula for Sine**   We use the addition formula for sine.

$$\sin 2x = \sin(x + x)$$

$$= \sin x \cos x + \sin x \cos x$$

$$= 2 \sin x \cos x$$

■ **Proof of Double-Angle Formulas for Cosine**

$$\cos 2x = \cos(x + x)$$

$$= \cos x \cos x - \sin x \sin x$$

$$= \cos^2 x - \sin^2 x$$

The second and third formulas for $\cos 2x$ are obtained from the formula we just proved and the Pythagorean identity. Substituting $\cos^2 x = 1 - \sin^2 x$ gives

$$\cos 2x = \cos^2 x - \sin^2 x$$

$$= (1 - \sin^2 x) - \sin^2 x$$

$$= 1 - 2 \sin^2 x$$

The third formula is obtained in the same way, by substituting $\sin^2 x = 1 - \cos^2 x$.

■ **Proof of Double-Angle Formula for Tangent** We use the addition formula for tangent.

$$\tan 2x = \tan(x + x)$$

$$= \frac{\tan x + \tan x}{1 - \tan x \tan x}$$

$$= \frac{2 \tan x}{1 - \tan^2 x}$$

EXAMPLE 1 ■ **Using the Double-Angle Formulas**

If $\cos x = -\frac{2}{3}$ and x is in quadrant II, find $\cos 2x$ and $\sin 2x$.

SOLUTION

Using one of the double-angle formulas for cosine, we get

$$\cos 2x = 2 \cos^2 x - 1$$

$$= 2\left(-\frac{2}{3}\right)^2 - 1 = \frac{8}{9} - 1 = -\frac{1}{9}$$

To use the formula $\sin 2x = 2 \sin x \cos x$, we need to find $\sin x$ first. We have

$$\sin x = \sqrt{1 - \cos^2 x} = \sqrt{1 - \left(-\frac{2}{3}\right)^2} = \frac{\sqrt{5}}{3}$$

where we have used the positive square root because $\sin x$ is positive in quadrant II. Thus

$$\sin 2x = 2 \sin x \cos x$$

$$= 2\left(\frac{\sqrt{5}}{3}\right)\left(-\frac{2}{3}\right) = -\frac{4\sqrt{5}}{9}$$

EXAMPLE 2 ■ **A Triple-Angle Formula**

Write $\cos 3x$ in terms of $\cos x$.

SOLUTION

$$\cos 3x = \cos(2x + x)$$

$$= \cos 2x \cos x - \sin 2x \sin x \qquad \text{Addition formula}$$

$$= (2\cos^2 x - 1)\cos x - (2\sin x \cos x)\sin x \qquad \text{Double-angle formulas}$$

$$= 2\cos^3 x - \cos x - 2\sin^2 x \cos x \qquad \text{Expand}$$

$$= 2\cos^3 x - \cos x - 2\cos x\,(1 - \cos^2 x) \qquad \text{Pythagorean identity}$$

$$= 2\cos^3 x - \cos x - 2\cos x + 2\cos^3 x \qquad \text{Expand}$$

$$= 4\cos^3 x - 3\cos x \qquad \text{Simplify} \qquad \blacksquare$$

Example 2 shows that $\cos 3x$ can be written as a polynomial of degree 3 in $\cos x$. The identity $\cos 2x = 2\cos^2 x - 1$ shows that $\cos 2x$ is a polynomial of degree 2 in $\cos x$. In fact, for any natural number n, we can write $\cos nx$ as a polynomial in $\cos x$ of degree n (see Exercise 83). The analogous result for $\sin nx$ is not true in general.

EXAMPLE 3 ■ **Proving an Identity**

Prove the identity: $\dfrac{\sin 3x}{\sin x \cos x} = 4\cos x - \sec x$

SOLUTION

We start with the left-hand side.

$$\frac{\sin 3x}{\sin x \cos x} = \frac{\sin(x + 2x)}{\sin x \cos x}$$

$$= \frac{\sin x \cos 2x + \cos x \sin 2x}{\sin x \cos x} \qquad \text{Addition formula}$$

$$= \frac{\sin x\,(2\cos^2 x - 1) + \cos x\,(2\sin x \cos x)}{\sin x \cos x} \qquad \text{Double-angle formulas}$$

$$= \frac{\sin x\,(2\cos^2 x - 1)}{\sin x \cos x} + \frac{\cos x\,(2\sin x \cos x)}{\sin x \cos x} \qquad \text{Separate fraction}$$

$$= \frac{2\cos^2 x - 1}{\cos x} + 2\cos x \qquad \text{Cancel}$$

$$= 2\cos x - \frac{1}{\cos x} + 2\cos x \qquad \text{Separate fraction}$$

$$= 4\cos x - \sec x \qquad \text{Reciprocal identity} \qquad \blacksquare$$

Half-Angle Formulas

The following formulas allow us to write any trigonometric expression involving even powers of sine and cosine in terms of the first power of cosine only. This technique is important in calculus. The half-angle formulas are immediate consequences of these formulas.

FORMULAS FOR LOWERING POWERS

$$\sin^2 x = \frac{1 - \cos 2x}{2} \qquad \cos^2 x = \frac{1 + \cos 2x}{2}$$

$$\tan^2 x = \frac{1 - \cos 2x}{1 + \cos 2x}$$

■ **Proof**   The first formula is obtained by solving for $\sin^2 x$ in the double-angle formula $\cos 2x = 1 - 2\sin^2 x$. Similarly, the second formula is obtained by solving for $\cos^2 x$ in the double-angle formula $\cos 2x = 2\cos^2 x - 1$.

The last formula follows from the first two and the reciprocal identities as follows:

$$\tan^2 x = \frac{\sin^2 x}{\cos^2 x} = \frac{\dfrac{1 - \cos 2x}{2}}{\dfrac{1 + \cos 2x}{2}} = \frac{1 - \cos 2x}{1 + \cos 2x}$$

$\square$

EXAMPLE 4 ■ Lowering Powers in a Trigonometric Expression

Express $\sin^2 x \cos^2 x$ in terms of the first power of cosine.

SOLUTION

We use the formulas for lowering powers repeatedly.

$$\sin^2 x \cos^2 x = \left(\frac{1 - \cos 2x}{2}\right)\left(\frac{1 + \cos 2x}{2}\right)$$

$$= \frac{1 - \cos^2 2x}{4} = \frac{1}{4} - \frac{1}{4}\cos^2 2x$$

$$= \frac{1}{4} - \frac{1}{4}\left(\frac{1 + \cos 4x}{2}\right) = \frac{1}{4} - \frac{1}{8} - \frac{\cos 4x}{8}$$

$$= \tfrac{1}{8} - \tfrac{1}{8}\cos 4x = \tfrac{1}{8}(1 - \cos 4x)$$

Another way to obtain this identity is to use the double-angle formula for sine in the form $\sin x \cos x = \frac{1}{2}\sin 2x$. Thus

$$\sin^2 x \cos^2 x = \frac{1}{4}\sin^2 2x = \frac{1}{4}\left(\frac{1 - \cos 4x}{2}\right) = \frac{1}{8}(1 - \cos 4x)$$

■

HALF-ANGLE FORMULAS

$$\sin\frac{u}{2} = \pm\sqrt{\frac{1-\cos u}{2}} \qquad \cos\frac{u}{2} = \pm\sqrt{\frac{1+\cos u}{2}}$$

$$\tan\frac{u}{2} = \frac{1-\cos u}{\sin u} = \frac{\sin u}{1+\cos u}$$

The choice of the $+$ or $-$ sign depends on the quadrant in which $u/2$ lies.

■ **Proof** We substitute $x = u/2$ in the formulas for lowering powers and take the square root of each side. This yields the first two half-angle formulas. In the case of the half-angle formula for tangent, we get

$$\tan\frac{u}{2} = \pm\sqrt{\frac{1-\cos u}{1+\cos u}}$$

$$= \pm\sqrt{\left(\frac{1-\cos u}{1+\cos u}\right)\left(\frac{1-\cos u}{1-\cos u}\right)} \qquad \text{Multiply numerator and denominator by } 1-\cos u$$

$$= \pm\sqrt{\frac{(1-\cos u)^2}{1-\cos^2 u}} \qquad \text{Simplify}$$

$$= \pm\frac{|1-\cos u|}{|\sin u|} \qquad \sqrt{A^2} = |A|$$

Now, $1 - \cos u$ is nonnegative for all values of u. It is also true that $\sin u$ and $\tan(u/2)$ always have the same sign. (Verify this.) It follows that

$$\tan\frac{u}{2} = \frac{1-\cos u}{\sin u}$$

The other half-angle formula for tangent is derived from this by multiplying the numerator and denominator by $1 + \cos u$. ☐

EXAMPLE 5 ■ Using a Half-Angle Formula

Find the exact value of $\sin 22.5°$.

SOLUTION

Since $22.5°$ is half of $45°$, we use the half-angle formula for sine with $u = 45°$. We choose the $+$ sign because $22.5°$ is in the first quadrant.

$$\sin\frac{45°}{2} = \sqrt{\frac{1-\cos 45°}{2}} \qquad \text{Half-angle formula}$$

$$= \sqrt{\frac{1-\sqrt{2}/2}{2}} \qquad \cos 45° = \sqrt{2}/2$$

$$= \sqrt{\frac{2-\sqrt{2}}{4}} \qquad \text{Common denominator}$$

$$= \tfrac{1}{2}\sqrt{2-\sqrt{2}} \qquad \text{Simplify}$$

■

EXAMPLE 6 ■ Using a Half-Angle Formula

Find $\tan(u/2)$ if $\sin u = \frac{2}{5}$ and u is in quadrant II.

SOLUTION

To use the half-angle formulas for tangent, we first need to find $\cos u$. Since cosine is negative in quadrant II, we have

$$\cos u = -\sqrt{1 - \sin^2 u}$$

$$= -\sqrt{1 - \left(\tfrac{2}{5}\right)^2} = -\frac{\sqrt{21}}{5}$$

Thus

$$\tan\frac{u}{2} = \frac{1 - \cos u}{\sin u}$$

$$= \frac{1 + \sqrt{21}/5}{\tfrac{2}{5}} = \frac{5 + \sqrt{21}}{2}$$ ■

Product-Sum Formulas

It is possible to write the product $\sin u \cos v$ as a sum of trigonometric functions. To see this, consider the addition and subtraction formulas for the sine function:

$$\sin(u + v) = \sin u \cos v + \cos u \sin v$$

$$\sin(u - v) = \sin u \cos v - \cos u \sin v$$

Adding the left- and right-hand sides of these formulas gives

$$\sin(u + v) + \sin(u - v) = 2 \sin u \cos v$$

Dividing by 2 yields the formula

$$\sin u \cos v = \tfrac{1}{2}[\sin(u + v) + \sin(u - v)]$$

The other three **product-to-sum formulas** follow from the addition formulas in a similar way.

PRODUCT-TO-SUM FORMULAS
$\sin u \cos v = \tfrac{1}{2}[\sin(u + v) + \sin(u - v)]$
$\cos u \sin v = \tfrac{1}{2}[\sin(u + v) - \sin(u - v)]$
$\cos u \cos v = \tfrac{1}{2}[\cos(u + v) + \cos(u - v)]$
$\sin u \sin v = \tfrac{1}{2}[\cos(u - v) - \cos(u + v)]$

EXAMPLE 7 ■ **Expressing a Trigonometric Product as a Sum**

Express $\sin 3x \sin 5x$ as a sum of trigonometric functions.

SOLUTION

Using the fourth product-to-sum formula with $u = 3x$ and $v = 5x$ and the fact that cosine is an even function, we get

$$\sin 3x \sin 5x = \tfrac{1}{2}\left[\cos(3x - 5x) - \cos(3x + 5x)\right]$$

$$= \tfrac{1}{2}\cos(-2x) - \tfrac{1}{2}\cos 8x$$

$$= \tfrac{1}{2}\cos 2x - \tfrac{1}{2}\cos 8x \qquad ■$$

The product-to-sum formulas can also be used as sum-to-product formulas. This is possible because the right-hand side of each product-to-sum formula is a sum and the left side is a product. For example, if we let

$$u = \frac{x + y}{2} \qquad \text{and} \qquad v = \frac{x - y}{2}$$

in the first product-to-sum formula, we get

$$\sin\frac{x + y}{2}\cos\frac{x - y}{2} = \tfrac{1}{2}\left[\sin x + \sin y\right]$$

so

$$\sin x + \sin y = 2\sin\frac{x + y}{2}\cos\frac{x - y}{2}$$

The remaining three of the following **sum-to-product formulas** are obtained in a similar manner.

SUM-TO-PRODUCT FORMULAS

$$\sin x + \sin y = 2\sin\frac{x + y}{2}\cos\frac{x - y}{2}$$

$$\sin x - \sin y = 2\cos\frac{x + y}{2}\sin\frac{x - y}{2}$$

$$\cos x + \cos y = 2\cos\frac{x + y}{2}\cos\frac{x - y}{2}$$

$$\cos x - \cos y = -2\sin\frac{x + y}{2}\sin\frac{x - y}{2}$$

EXAMPLE 8 ■ Expressing a Trigonometric Sum as a Product

Write $\sin 7x + \sin 3x$ as a product.

SOLUTION

The first sum-to-product formula gives

$$\sin 7x + \sin 3x = 2 \sin \frac{7x + 3x}{2} \cos \frac{7x - 3x}{2}$$

$$= 2 \sin 5x \cos 2x \quad ■$$

EXAMPLE 9 ■ Proving an Identity

Verify the identity: $\dfrac{\sin 3x - \sin x}{\cos 3x + \cos x} = \tan x$

SOLUTION

We apply the second sum-to-product formula to the numerator and the third formula to the denominator.

$$\text{LHS} = \frac{\sin 3x - \sin x}{\cos 3x + \cos x} = \frac{2 \cos \dfrac{3x + x}{2} \sin \dfrac{3x - x}{2}}{2 \cos \dfrac{3x + x}{2} \cos \dfrac{3x - x}{2}} \qquad \text{Sum-to-product formulas}$$

$$= \frac{2 \cos 2x \sin x}{2 \cos 2x \cos x} \qquad \text{Simplify}$$

$$= \frac{\sin x}{\cos x} = \tan x = \text{RHS} \qquad \text{Cancel} \quad ■$$

7.3 EXERCISES

1–8 ■ Find $\sin 2x$, $\cos 2x$, and $\tan 2x$ from the given information.

1. $\sin x = \frac{5}{13}$, x in quadrant I

2. $\tan x = -\frac{4}{3}$, x in quadrant II

3. $\cos x = \frac{4}{5}$, $\csc x < 0$ **4.** $\csc x = 4$, $\tan x < 0$

5. $\sin x = -\frac{3}{5}$, x in quadrant III

6. $\sec x = 2$, x in quadrant IV

7. $\tan x = -\frac{1}{3}$, $\cos x > 0$

8. $\cot x = \frac{2}{3}$, $\sin x > 0$

9–14 ■ Use the formulas for lowering powers to rewrite the expression in terms of the first power of cosine, as in Example 4.

9. $\sin^4 x$ **10.** $\cos^4 x$

11. $\cos^4 x \sin^4 x$ **12.** $\cos^4 x \sin^2 x$

13. $\cos^2 x \sin^4 x$ **14.** $\cos^6 x$

15–22 ■ Use an appropriate half-angle formula to find the exact value of the expression.

15. $\sin 15°$ **16.** $\tan 15°$

17. $\cos 22.5°$ **18.** $\sin 75°$

19. $\tan \dfrac{\pi}{8}$

20. $\cos \dfrac{3\pi}{8}$

21. $\sin \dfrac{\pi}{12}$

22. $\cos \dfrac{5\pi}{12}$

23–28 ■ Simplify the expression by using a double-angle formula or a half-angle formula.

23. (a) $2 \sin 18° \cos 18°$ **(b)** $2 \sin 3\theta \cos 3\theta$

24. (a) $\dfrac{2 \tan 7°}{1 - \tan^2 7°}$ **(b)** $\dfrac{2 \tan 7\theta}{1 - \tan^2 7\theta}$

25. (a) $\cos^2 34° - \sin^2 34°$ **(b)** $\cos^2 5\theta - \sin^2 5\theta$

26. (a) $\cos^2 \dfrac{\theta}{2} - \sin^2 \dfrac{\theta}{2}$ **(b)** $2 \sin \dfrac{\theta}{2} \cos \dfrac{\theta}{2}$

27. (a) $\dfrac{\sin 8°}{1 + \cos 8°}$ **(b)** $\dfrac{1 - \cos 4\theta}{\sin 4\theta}$

28. (a) $\sqrt{\dfrac{1 - \cos 30°}{2}}$ **(b)** $\sqrt{\dfrac{1 - \cos 8\theta}{2}}$

29–34 ■ Find $\sin \dfrac{x}{2}$, $\cos \dfrac{x}{2}$, and $\tan \dfrac{x}{2}$ from the given information.

29. $\sin x = \frac{3}{5}$, $0° < x < 90°$

30. $\cos x = -\frac{4}{5}$, $180° < x < 270°$

31. $\csc x = 3$, $90° < x < 180°$

32. $\tan x = 1$, $0° < x < 90°$

33. $\sec x = \frac{3}{2}$, $270° < x < 360°$

34. $\cot x = 5$, $180° < x < 270°$

35–40 ■ Write the product as a sum.

35. $\sin 2x \cos 3x$

36. $\sin x \sin 5x$

37. $\cos x \sin 4x$

38. $\cos 5x \cos 3x$

39. $3 \cos 4x \cos 7x$

40. $11 \sin \dfrac{x}{2} \cos \dfrac{x}{4}$

41–46 ■ Write the sum as a product.

41. $\sin 5x + \sin 3x$

42. $\sin x - \sin 4x$

43. $\cos 4x - \cos 6x$

44. $\cos 9x + \cos 2x$

45. $\sin 2x - \sin 7x$

46. $\sin 3x + \sin 4x$

47–52 ■ Find the value of the product or sum.

47. $2 \sin 52.5° \sin 97.5°$

48. $3 \cos 37.5° \cos 7.5°$

49. $\cos 37.5° \sin 7.5°$

50. $\sin 75° + \sin 15°$

51. $\cos 255° - \cos 195°$

52. $\cos \dfrac{\pi}{12} + \cos \dfrac{5\pi}{12}$

53–70 ■ Prove the identity.

53. $\cos^2 5x - \sin^2 5x = \cos 10x$

54. $\sin 8x = 2 \sin 4x \cos 4x$

55. $(\sin x + \cos x)^2 = 1 + \sin 2x$

56. $\dfrac{2 \tan x}{1 + \tan^2 x} = \sin 2x$ **57.** $\dfrac{\sin 4x}{\sin x} = 4 \cos x \cos 2x$

58. $\dfrac{1 + \sin 2x}{\sin 2x} = 1 + \frac{1}{2} \sec x \csc x$

59. $\dfrac{2(\tan x - \cot x)}{\tan^2 x - \cot^2 x} = \sin 2x$ **60.** $\cot 2x = \dfrac{1 - \tan^2 x}{2 \tan x}$

61. $\tan 3x = \dfrac{3 \tan x - \tan^3 x}{1 - 3 \tan^2 x}$

62. $4(\sin^6 x + \cos^6 x) = 4 - 3 \sin^2 2x$

63. $\cos^4 x - \sin^4 x = \cos 2x$ **64.** $\tan^2\left(\dfrac{x}{2} + \dfrac{\pi}{4}\right) = \dfrac{1 + \sin x}{1 - \sin x}$

65. $\dfrac{\sin x + \sin 5x}{\cos x + \cos 5x} = \tan 3x$ **66.** $\dfrac{\sin 3x + \sin 7x}{\cos 3x - \cos 7x} = \cot 2x$

67. $\dfrac{\sin 10x}{\sin 9x + \sin x} = \dfrac{\cos 5x}{\cos 4x}$

68. $\dfrac{\sin x + \sin 3x + \sin 5x}{\cos x + \cos 3x + \cos 5x} = \tan 3x$

69. $\dfrac{\sin x + \sin y}{\cos x + \cos y} = \tan\left(\dfrac{x + y}{2}\right)$

70. $\tan y = \dfrac{\sin(x + y) - \sin(x - y)}{\cos(x + y) + \cos(x - y)}$

71. Show that $\sin 45° + \sin 15° = \sin 75°$.

72. Show that $\cos 87° + \cos 33° = \sin 63°$.

73. Prove the identity

$$\dfrac{\sin x + \sin 2x + \sin 3x + \sin 4x + \sin 5x}{\cos x + \cos 2x + \cos 3x + \cos 4x + \cos 5x} = \tan 3x$$

74. Use the identity

$$\sin 2x = 2 \sin x \cos x$$

n times to show that

$$\sin(2^n x) = 2^n \sin x \cos x \cos 2x \cos 4x \cdots \cos 2^{n-1} x$$

75. (a) Graph $f(x) = \dfrac{\sin 3x}{\sin x} - \dfrac{\cos 3x}{\cos x}$ and make a conjecture.

(b) Prove the conjecture you made in part (a).

76. (a) Graph $f(x) = \cos 2x + 2 \sin^2 x$ and make a conjecture.

(b) Prove the conjecture you made in part (a).

77. Let $f(x) = \sin 6x + \sin 7x$.

(a) Graph $y = f(x)$.

(b) Verify that $f(x) = 2 \cos \frac{1}{2} x \sin \frac{13}{2} x$.

(c) Graph $y = 2 \cos \frac{1}{2} x$ and $y = -2 \cos \frac{1}{2} x$, together with the graph in part (a), in the same viewing rectangle. How are these graphs related to the graph of f?

78. When two pure notes that are close in frequency are played together, their sounds interfere to produce *beats*; that is, the loudness (or amplitude) of the sound alternately increases and decreases. If the two notes are given by

$$f_1(t) = \cos 11t \qquad \text{and} \qquad f_2(t) = \cos 13t$$

the resulting sound is $f(t) = f_1(t) + f_2(t)$.

(a) Graph the function $y = f(t)$.

(b) Verify that $f(t) = 2 \cos t \cos 12t$.

(c) Graph $y = 2 \cos t$ and $y = -2 \cos t$, together with the graph in part (a), in the same viewing rectangle. How do these graphs describe the variation in the loudness of the sound?

79–81 ■ In these exercises you are asked to use the trigonometric functions to model real-life situations. See the guidelines on modeling with functions in Section 2.7.

79. A rectangular beam is to be cut from a cylindrical log of diameter 20 in.

(a) Show that the cross-sectional area of the beam is modeled by the function

$$A(\theta) = 200 \sin 2\theta$$

where θ is as shown in the figure.

(b) Show that the maximum cross-sectional area of such a beam is 200 in². [*Hint:* Use the fact that $\sin u$ achieves its maximum value at $u = \pi/2$.]

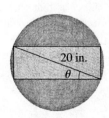

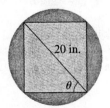

80. A rectangle is to be inscribed in a semicircle of radius 5 cm as shown in the figure.

(a) Show that the area of the rectangle is modeled by the function

$$A(\theta) = 25 \sin 2\theta$$

(b) Find the largest possible area for such an inscribed rectangle.

(c) Find the dimensions of the inscribed rectangle with the largest possible area.

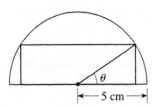

81. The lower right-hand corner of a long piece of paper 6 in. wide is folded over to the left-hand edge as shown. The length L of the fold depends on the angle θ. Show that

$$L = \frac{3}{\sin \theta \cos^2 \theta}$$

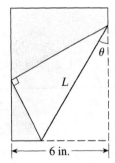

82. Let $3x = \pi/3$ and let $y = \cos x$. Use the result of Example 2 to show that y satisfies the equation

$$8y^3 - 6y - 1 = 0$$

NOTE This equation has roots of a certain kind that are used to show that the angle $\pi/3$ cannot be trisected using a ruler and compass only.

83. (a) Show that there is a polynomial $P(t)$ of degree 4 such that $\cos 4x = P(\cos x)$ (see Example 2).

(b) Show that there is a polynomial $Q(t)$ of degree 5 such that $\cos 5x = Q(\cos x)$.

NOTE In general, there is a polynomial $P_n(t)$ of degree n such that $\cos nx = P_n(\cos x)$. These polynomials are called Tchebycheff polynomials, after the Russian mathematician P. L. Tchebycheff (1821–1894).

84. In triangle ABC (see the figure) the line segment s bisects angle C. Show that the length of s is given by

$$s = \frac{2ab \cos x}{a + b}$$

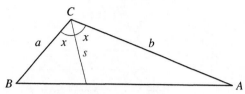

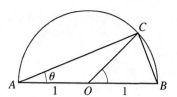

Hint: Find the area of triangle ABC in two different ways. You will need the following facts from geometry:

An angle inscribed in a semicircle is a right angle, so $\angle ACB$ is a right angle.

 DISCOVERY · DISCUSSION

85. Geometric Proof of a Double-Angle Formula Use the figure to prove that $\sin 2\theta = 2 \sin \theta \cos \theta$.

The central angle subtended by the chord of a circle is twice the angle subtended by the chord on the circle, so $\angle BOC$ is 2θ.

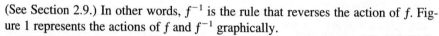

If f is a one-to-one function with domain A and range B, then its inverse f^{-1} is the function with domain B and range A defined by

$$f^{-1}(x) = y \iff f(y) = x$$

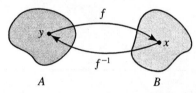

FIGURE 1
$f^{-1}(x) = y \Leftrightarrow f(y) = x$

(See Section 2.9.) In other words, f^{-1} is the rule that reverses the action of f. Figure 1 represents the actions of f and f^{-1} graphically.

For a function to have an inverse, it must be one-to-one. Since the trigonometric functions are not one-to-one, they do not have inverses. It is possible, however, to restrict the domains of the trigonometric functions in such a way that the resulting functions are one-to-one.

The Inverse Sine Function

Let's first consider the sine function. There are many ways to restrict the domain of sine so that the new function is one-to-one. A natural way to do this is to restrict the domain to the interval $[-\pi/2, \pi/2]$. The reason for this choice is that sine attains each of its values exactly once on this interval. We write Sin x (with a capital S) for the new function, which has the domain $[-\pi/2, \pi/2]$ and the same values as sin x on this interval. The graphs of sin x and Sin x are shown in Figure 2. The function Sin x is one-to-one (by the Horizontal Line Test), and so has an inverse.

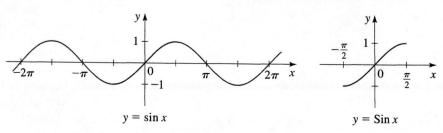

FIGURE 2

$y = \sin x$

$y = \text{Sin } x$

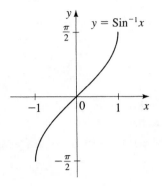

FIGURE 3

The inverse of the function Sin is the function Sin^{-1} defined by

$$\text{Sin}^{-1}x = y \iff \text{Sin } y = x$$

for $-1 \leq x \leq 1$ and $-\pi/2 \leq y \leq \pi/2$. The graph of $y = \text{Sin}^{-1}x$ is shown in Figure 3; it is obtained by reflecting the graph of $y = \text{Sin } x$ in the line $y = x$. It is customary to write $\text{Sin}^{-1}x$ simply as $\sin^{-1}x$.

DEFINITION OF THE INVERSE SINE FUNCTION

The **inverse sine function** is the function $\sin^{-1}$ with domain $[-1, 1]$ and range $[-\pi/2, \pi/2]$ defined by

$$\sin^{-1}x = y \iff \sin y = x$$

The inverse sine function is also called **arcsine** and is denoted by **arcsin**.

Thus, $\sin^{-1}x$ *is the number in the interval* $[-\pi/2, \pi/2]$ *whose sine is* x. In other words, $\sin(\sin^{-1}x) = x$. In fact, from the general properties of inverse functions studied in Section 2.9, we have the following relations.

$$\sin(\sin^{-1}x) = x \qquad \text{for } -1 \leq x \leq 1$$

$$\sin^{-1}(\sin x) = x \qquad \text{for } -\frac{\pi}{2} \leq x \leq \frac{\pi}{2}$$

EXAMPLE 1 ■ Evaluating the Inverse Sine Function

Find (a) $\sin^{-1}\frac{1}{2}$, (b) $\sin^{-1}\left(-\frac{1}{2}\right)$, and (c) $\sin^{-1}\frac{3}{2}$.

SOLUTION

(a) The number in the interval $[-\pi/2, \pi/2]$ whose sine is $\frac{1}{2}$ is $\pi/6$. Thus, $\sin^{-1}\frac{1}{2} = \pi/6$.

(b) The number in the interval $[-\pi/2, \pi/2]$ whose sine is $-\frac{1}{2}$ is $-\pi/6$. Thus, $\sin^{-1}\left(-\frac{1}{2}\right) = -\pi/6$.

(c) Since $\frac{3}{2} > 1$, it is not in the domain of $\sin^{-1}x$, so $\sin^{-1}\frac{3}{2}$ is not defined. ∎

EXAMPLE 2 ■ Using a Calculator to Evaluate Inverse Sine

Find approximate values for (a) $\sin^{-1}(0.82)$ and (b) $\sin^{-1}\frac{1}{3}$.

SOLUTION

Since no rational multiple of π has a sine of 0.82 or $\frac{1}{3}$, we use a calculator to approximate these values. Using the $\boxed{\text{INV}}\,\boxed{\text{SIN}}$, or $\boxed{\text{SIN}^{-1}}$, or $\boxed{\text{ARCSIN}}$ key(s) on the calculator (with the calculator in radian mode), we get

(a) $\sin^{-1}(0.82) \approx 0.96141$ 　　　　　 (b) $\sin^{-1}\frac{1}{3} \approx 0.33984$ ∎

EXAMPLE 3 ■ Composing Trigonometric Functions and Their Inverses

Find $\cos\left(\sin^{-1}\frac{3}{5}\right)$.

SOLUTION 1

It's easy to find $\sin\left(\sin^{-1}\frac{3}{5}\right)$. In fact, by the properties of inverse functions, this value is exactly $\frac{3}{5}$. To find $\cos\left(\sin^{-1}\frac{3}{5}\right)$, we reduce this to the easier problem by writing the cosine function in terms of the sine function. Let $u = \sin^{-1}\frac{3}{5}$. Since $-\pi/2 \leq u \leq \pi/2$, $\cos u$ is positive and we can write

$$\cos u = +\sqrt{1 - \sin^2 u}$$

Thus
$$\cos\left(\sin^{-1}\tfrac{3}{5}\right) = \sqrt{1 - \sin^2\left(\sin^{-1}\tfrac{3}{5}\right)}$$
$$= \sqrt{1 - \left(\tfrac{3}{5}\right)^2} = \sqrt{1 - \tfrac{9}{25}} = \sqrt{\tfrac{16}{25}} = \tfrac{4}{5}$$

SOLUTION 2

Let $\theta = \sin^{-1}\frac{3}{5}$. Then θ is the number in the interval $\left[-\pi/2, \pi/2\right]$ whose sine is $\frac{3}{5}$. Let's interpret θ as an angle and draw a right triangle with θ as one of its acute angles, with opposite side 3 and hypotenuse 5 (see Figure 4). The remaining leg of the triangle is found by the Pythagorean Theorem to be 4. From the figure we get

$$\cos\left(\sin^{-1}\tfrac{3}{5}\right) = \cos \theta = \tfrac{4}{5}$$ ■

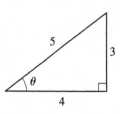

FIGURE 4

From Solution 2 of Example 3 we can immediately find the values of the other trigonometric functions of $\theta = \sin^{-1}\frac{3}{5}$ from the triangle. Thus

$$\tan\left(\sin^{-1}\tfrac{3}{5}\right) = \tfrac{3}{4} \qquad \sec\left(\sin^{-1}\tfrac{3}{5}\right) = \tfrac{5}{4} \qquad \csc\left(\sin^{-1}\tfrac{3}{5}\right) = \tfrac{5}{3}$$

The Inverse Cosine Function

If the domain of the cosine function is restricted to the interval $[0, \pi]$, the resulting function is one-to-one and so has an inverse. We choose this interval because on it, cosine attains each of its values exactly once (see Figure 5).

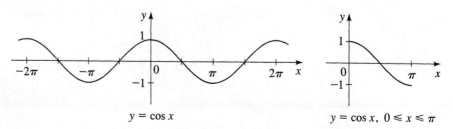

FIGURE 5

$y = \cos x$ $y = \cos x, \ 0 \leq x \leq \pi$

> ### DEFINITION OF THE INVERSE COSINE FUNCTION
>
> The **inverse cosine function** is the function $\cos^{-1}$ with domain $[-1, 1]$ and range $[0, \pi]$ defined by
>
> $$\cos^{-1}x = y \iff \cos y = x$$
>
> The inverse cosine function is also called **arccosine** and is denoted by **arccos**.

Thus, $y = \cos^{-1}x$ *is the number in the interval* $[0, \pi]$ *whose cosine is* x. The following relations follow from the inverse function properties.

$$\cos(\cos^{-1}x) = x \qquad \text{for } -1 \le x \le 1$$

$$\cos^{-1}(\cos x) = x \qquad \text{for } 0 \le x \le \pi$$

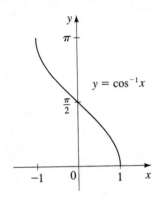

FIGURE 6

The graph of $y = \cos^{-1}x$ is shown in Figure 6; it is obtained by reflecting the graph of $y = \cos x$, $0 \le x \le \pi$, in the line $y = x$.

EXAMPLE 4 ■ Evaluating the Inverse Cosine Function

Find (a) $\cos^{-1}(\sqrt{3}/2)$, (b) $\cos^{-1}0$, and (c) $\cos^{-1}\frac{5}{7}$.

SOLUTION

(a) The number in the interval $[0, \pi]$ whose cosine is $\sqrt{3}/2$ is $\pi/6$. Thus, $\cos^{-1}(\sqrt{3}/2) = \pi/6$.

(b) The number in the interval $[0, \pi]$ whose cosine is 0 is $\pi/2$. Thus, $\cos^{-1}0 = \pi/2$.

(c) Since no rational multiple of π has cosine $\frac{5}{7}$, we use a calculator to find this value approximately: $\cos^{-1}\frac{5}{7} \approx 0.77519$. ■

EXAMPLE 5 ■ Composing Trigonometric Functions and Their Inverses

Write $\sin(\cos^{-1}x)$ and $\tan(\cos^{-1}x)$ as algebraic expressions in x for $-1 \le x \le 1$.

SOLUTION 1

Let $u = \cos^{-1}x$. We need to find $\sin u$ and $\tan u$ in terms of x. As in Example 3 the idea here is to write sine and tangent in terms of cosine. We have

$$\sin u = \pm\sqrt{1 - \cos^2u} \qquad \text{and} \qquad \tan u = \frac{\sin u}{\cos u} = \frac{\pm\sqrt{1 - \cos^2u}}{\cos u}$$

To choose the proper signs, note that u lies in the interval $[0, \pi]$ because $u = \cos^{-1}x$. Since $\sin u$ is positive on this interval, the $+$ sign is the correct choice. Substituting $u = \cos^{-1}x$ in the displayed equations and using the relation $\cos(\cos^{-1}x) = x$ gives

$$\sin(\cos^{-1}x) = \sqrt{1 - x^2} \qquad \text{and} \qquad \tan(\cos^{-1}x) = \frac{\sqrt{1 - x^2}}{x}$$

SOLUTION 2

Let $\theta = \cos^{-1}x$, so $\cos \theta = x$. In Figure 7 we draw a right triangle with an acute angle θ, adjacent side x, and hypotenuse 1. By the Pythagorean Theorem, the remaining leg is $\sqrt{1 - x^2}$. From the figure,

$$\sin(\cos^{-1}x) = \sin \theta = \sqrt{1 - x^2} \qquad \text{and} \qquad \tan(\cos^{-1}x) = \tan \theta = \frac{\sqrt{1 - x^2}}{x} \qquad \blacksquare$$

NOTE In Solution 2 of Example 5 it may seem that because we are sketching a triangle, the angle $\theta = \cos^{-1}x$ must be acute. But it turns out that the triangle method works for any θ and for any x. The domains and ranges of all six inverse trigonometric functions have been chosen in such a way that we can always use a triangle to find $S(T^{-1}(x))$, where S and T are any trigonometric functions.

EXAMPLE 6 ■ Composing a Trigonometric Function and an Inverse

Write $\sin(2 \cos^{-1}x)$ as an algebraic expression in x for $-1 \le x \le 1$.

SOLUTION

Let $\theta = \cos^{-1}x$ and sketch a triangle as shown in Figure 8. We need to find $\sin 2\theta$, but from the triangle we can find trigonometric functions only of θ, not of 2θ. The double-angle identity for sine is useful here. We have

$$\sin(2 \cos^{-1}x) = \sin 2\theta$$

$$= 2 \sin \theta \cos \theta \qquad \text{Double-angle formula}$$

$$= 2 \sqrt{1 - x^2}\, x \qquad \text{From triangle}$$

$$= 2x \sqrt{1 - x^2} \qquad \blacksquare$$

▌ The Inverse Tangent Function

We restrict the domain of the tangent function to the interval $(-\pi/2, \pi/2)$ in order to obtain a one-to-one function.

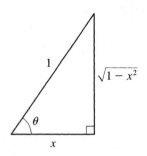

FIGURE 7

$\cos \theta = \dfrac{x}{1} = x$

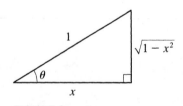

FIGURE 8

$\cos \theta = \dfrac{x}{1} = x$

DEFINITION OF THE INVERSE TANGENT FUNCTION

The **inverse tangent function** is the function **tan⁻¹** with domain $\mathbb{R}$ and range $(-\pi/2, \pi/2)$ defined by

$$\tan^{-1}x = y \quad \Longleftrightarrow \quad \tan y = x$$

The inverse tangent function is also called **arctangent** and is denoted by **arctan**.

Thus, $\tan^{-1}x$ *is the number in the interval* $(-\pi/2, \pi/2)$ *whose tangent is* x. The following relations follow from the inverse function properties.

$$\tan(\tan^{-1}x) = x \qquad \text{for } x \in \mathbb{R}$$

$$\tan^{-1}(\tan x) = x \qquad \text{for } -\frac{\pi}{2} < x < \frac{\pi}{2}$$

Figure 9 shows the graph of $y = \tan x$ on the interval $(-\pi/2, \pi/2)$ and the graph of its inverse function, $y = \tan^{-1}x$.

FIGURE 9

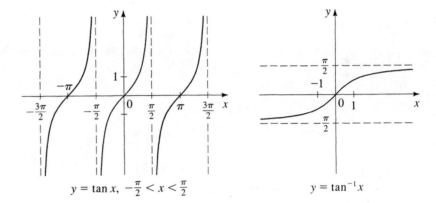

$y = \tan x, \ -\frac{\pi}{2} < x < \frac{\pi}{2}$ $y = \tan^{-1}x$

EXAMPLE 7 ■ Evaluating the Inverse Tangent Function

Find (a) $\tan^{-1}1$, (b) $\tan^{-1}\sqrt{3}$, and (c) $\tan^{-1}(-20)$.

SOLUTION

(a) The number in the interval $(-\pi/2, \pi/2)$ with tangent 1 is $\pi/4$. Thus, $\tan^{-1}1 = \pi/4$.

(b) The number in the interval $(-\pi/2, \pi/2)$ with tangent $\sqrt{3}$ is $\pi/3$. Thus, $\tan^{-1}\sqrt{3} = \pi/3$.

(c) We use a calculator to find that $\tan^{-1}(-20) \approx -1.52084$.   ■

EXAMPLE 8 ■ The Angle of a Beam of Light

A lighthouse is located on an island that is 2 mi off a straight shoreline (see Figure 10). Express the angle formed by the beam of light and the shoreline in terms of the distance d in the figure.

SOLUTION

From the figure we see that $\tan \theta = 2/d$. Taking the inverse tangent of both sides, we get

$$\tan^{-1}(\tan \theta) = \tan^{-1}\left(\frac{2}{d}\right)$$

$$\theta = \tan^{-1}\left(\frac{2}{d}\right) \qquad \text{Cancellation property}$$

■

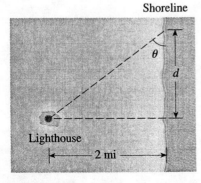

FIGURE 10

The Inverse Secant, Cosecant, and Cotangent Functions

To define the inverse functions of the secant, cosecant, and cotangent functions, we restrict the domain of each function to a set on which it is one-to-one and on which it attains all its values. Although any interval satisfying these criteria is appropriate, we choose to restrict the domains in a way that simplifies the choice of sign in computations involving inverse trigonometric functions. The choices we make are also appropriate for calculus. This explains the seemingly strange restriction for the domains of the secant and cosecant functions. We end this section by displaying the graphs of the secant, cosecant, and cotangent functions with their restricted domains and the graphs of their inverse functions (Figures 11–13).

See Exercise 58 for a way of finding the values of these inverse trigonometric functions on a calculator.

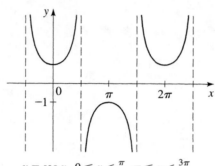

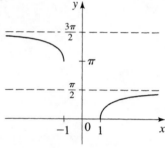

FIGURE 11

The inverse secant function

$$y = \sec x, \ 0 \le x < \frac{\pi}{2}, \ \pi \le x < \frac{3\pi}{2}$$

$$y = \sec^{-1} x$$

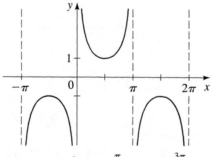

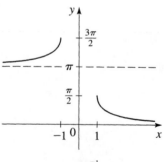

FIGURE 12

The inverse cosecant function

$$y = \csc x, \ 0 < x \le \frac{\pi}{2}, \ \pi < x \le \frac{3\pi}{2}$$

$$y = \csc^{-1} x$$

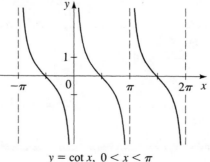

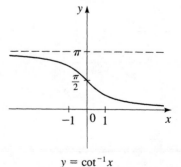

FIGURE 13

The inverse cotangent function

$$y = \cot x, \ 0 < x < \pi$$

$$y = \cot^{-1} x$$

7.4 EXERCISES

1–8 ■ Find the exact value of each expression, if it is defined.

1. (a) $\sin^{-1}\frac{1}{2}$ (b) $\cos^{-1}\frac{1}{2}$ (c) $\cos^{-1}2$

2. (a) $\sin^{-1}\frac{\sqrt{3}}{2}$ (b) $\cos^{-1}\frac{\sqrt{3}}{2}$ (c) $\cos^{-1}\left(-\frac{\sqrt{3}}{2}\right)$

3. (a) $\sin^{-1}\frac{\sqrt{2}}{2}$ (b) $\cos^{-1}\frac{\sqrt{2}}{2}$ (c) $\sin^{-1}\left(-\frac{\sqrt{2}}{2}\right)$

4. (a) $\tan^{-1}\sqrt{3}$ (b) $\tan^{-1}\left(-\sqrt{3}\right)$ (c) $\sin^{-1}\sqrt{3}$

5. (a) $\sin^{-1}1$ (b) $\cos^{-1}1$ (c) $\cos^{-1}(-1)$

6. (a) $\tan^{-1}1$ (b) $\tan^{-1}(-1)$ (c) $\tan^{-1}0$

7. (a) $\tan^{-1}\frac{\sqrt{3}}{3}$ (b) $\tan^{-1}\left(-\frac{\sqrt{3}}{3}\right)$ (c) $\sin^{-1}(-2)$

8. (a) $\sin^{-1}0$ (b) $\cos^{-1}0$ (c) $\cos^{-1}\left(-\frac{1}{2}\right)$

9–12 ■ Use a calculator to find an approximate value of each expression correct to five decimal places, if it is defined.

9. (a) $\sin^{-1}(0.13844)$ (b) $\cos^{-1}(-0.92761)$

10. (a) $\cos^{-1}(0.31187)$ (b) $\tan^{-1}(26.23110)$

11. (a) $\tan^{-1}(1.23456)$ (b) $\sin^{-1}(1.23456)$

12. (a) $\cos^{-1}(-0.25713)$ (b) $\tan^{-1}(-0.25713)$

13–28 ■ Find the exact value of the expression, if it is defined.

13. $\sin\left(\sin^{-1}\frac{1}{4}\right)$ **14.** $\cos\left(\cos^{-1}\frac{2}{3}\right)$

15. $\tan(\tan^{-1}5)$ **16.** $\sin(\sin^{-1}5)$

17. $\cos^{-1}\left(\cos\frac{\pi}{3}\right)$ **18.** $\tan^{-1}\left(\tan\frac{\pi}{6}\right)$

19. $\sin^{-1}\left[\sin\left(-\frac{\pi}{6}\right)\right]$ **20.** $\sin^{-1}\left(\sin\frac{5\pi}{6}\right)$

21. $\tan^{-1}\left(\tan\frac{2\pi}{3}\right)$ **22.** $\cos^{-1}\left[\cos\left(-\frac{\pi}{4}\right)\right]$

23. $\tan\left(\sin^{-1}\frac{1}{2}\right)$ **24.** $\sin(\sin^{-1}0)$

25. $\cos\left(\sin^{-1}\frac{\sqrt{3}}{2}\right)$ **26.** $\tan\left(\sin^{-1}\frac{\sqrt{2}}{2}\right)$

27. $\tan^{-1}\left(2\sin\frac{\pi}{3}\right)$ **28.** $\cos^{-1}\left(\sqrt{3}\sin\frac{\pi}{6}\right)$

29–40 ■ Evaluate the expression by sketching a triangle, as in Solution 2 of Example 3.

29. $\sin\left(\cos^{-1}\frac{3}{5}\right)$ **30.** $\tan\left(\sin^{-1}\frac{4}{5}\right)$

31. $\sin\left(\tan^{-1}\frac{12}{5}\right)$ **32.** $\cos(\tan^{-1}5)$

33. $\sec\left(\sin^{-1}\frac{12}{13}\right)$ **34.** $\csc\left(\cos^{-1}\frac{7}{25}\right)$

35. $\cos(\tan^{-1}2)$ **36.** $\cot\left(\sin^{-1}\frac{2}{3}\right)$

37. $\sin\left(2\cos^{-1}\frac{3}{5}\right)$ **38.** $\tan\left(2\tan^{-1}\frac{5}{13}\right)$

39. $\sin\left(\sin^{-1}\frac{1}{2}+\cos^{-1}\frac{1}{2}\right)$ **40.** $\cos\left(\sin^{-1}\frac{3}{5}-\cos^{-1}\frac{3}{5}\right)$

41–48 ■ Rewrite the expression as an algebraic expression in x.

41. $\cos(\sin^{-1}x)$ **42.** $\sin(\tan^{-1}x)$

43. $\tan(\sin^{-1}x)$ **44.** $\cos(\tan^{-1}x)$

45. $\cos(2\tan^{-1}x)$ **46.** $\sin(2\sin^{-1}x)$

47. $\cos(\cos^{-1}x+\sin^{-1}x)$ **48.** $\sin(\tan^{-1}x-\sin^{-1}x)$

49–52 ■ In these exercises you are asked to use the inverse trigonometric functions to model real-life situations. See the guidelines on modeling with functions in Section 2.7.

49. An observer views the space shuttle from a distance of 2 miles from the launch pad.
(a) Express the height of the space shuttle as a function of the angle of elevation θ.
(b) Express the angle of elevation θ as a function of the height h of the space shuttle.

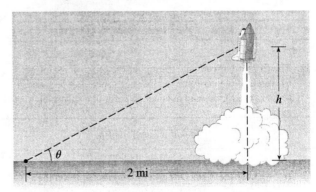

50. A 50-ft pole casts a shadow as shown in the figure.
(a) Express the angle of elevation θ of the sun as a function of the length s of the shadow.

(b) Find the angle θ of elevation of the sun when the shadow is 20 ft long.

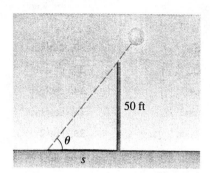

50 ft

θ

s

51. A 680-ft rope anchors a hot-air balloon as shown in the figure.

(a) Express the angle θ as a function of the height h of the balloon.

(b) Find the angle θ if the balloon is 500 ft high.

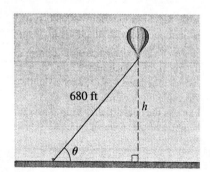

680 ft

h

θ

52. The figures indicate that the higher the orbit of a satellite, the more of the earth the satellite can "see." Let θ, s, and h be as in the figure, and assume the earth is a sphere of radius 3960 mi.

(a) Express the angle θ as a function of h.

(b) Express the distance s as a function of θ.

(c) Express the distance s as a function of h. [Find the composition of the functions in parts (a) and (b).]

(d) If the satellite is 100 mi above the earth, what is the distance s that it can see?

(e) How high does the satellite have to be in order to see both Los Angeles and New York, 2450 mi apart?

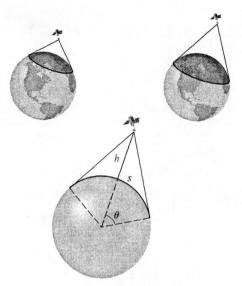

h

s

θ

53–54 ■ (a) Graph the function and make a conjecture, and (b) prove that your conjecture is true.

53. $y = \sin^{-1}x + \cos^{-1}x$ **54.** $y = \tan^{-1}x + \tan^{-1}\dfrac{1}{x}$

55–56 ■ (a) Use a graphing device to find all solutions of the equation, correct to two decimal places, and (b) find the exact solution.

55. $\tan^{-1}x + \tan^{-1}2x = \dfrac{\pi}{4}$ **56.** $\sin^{-1}x - \cos^{-1}x = 0$

● DISCOVERY · DISCUSSION

57. Two Different Compositions   The functions

$$f(x) = \sin(\sin^{-1}x) \quad \text{and} \quad g(x) = \sin^{-1}(\sin x)$$

both simplify to just x for suitable values of x. But these functions are not the same for all x. Graph both f and g to show how the functions differ. (Think carefully about the domain and range of $\sin^{-1}$.)

58. Inverse Trigonometric Functions on a Calculator Most calculators do not have keys for $\sec^{-1}$, $\csc^{-1}$, or $\cot^{-1}$. Prove the following identities, then use these identities and a calculator to find $\sec^{-1}2$, $\csc^{-1}3$, and $\cot^{-1}4$.

$$\sec^{-1}x = \cos^{-1}\left(\frac{1}{x}\right), \quad x \geq 1$$

$$\csc^{-1}x = \sin^{-1}\left(\frac{1}{x}\right), \quad x \geq 1$$

$$\cot^{-1}x = \tan^{-1}\left(\frac{1}{x}\right), \quad x > 0$$

Discovery Project

Where to Sit at the Movies

Everyone knows that the apparent size of an object depends on its distance from the viewer. The farther away an object, the smaller its apparent size. The apparent size is determined by the angle the object subtends at the eye of the viewer.

If you are looking at a painting hanging on a wall, how far away should you stand to get the maximum view? If the painting is hung above eye level, then the following figures show that the angle subtended at the eye is small if you are too close or too far away. The same situation occurs when choosing where to sit in a movie theatre.

Small θ

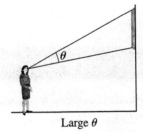

Large θ

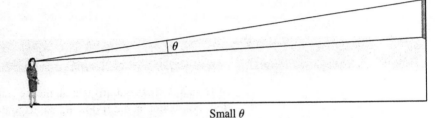

Small θ

1. The screen in a theatre is 22 ft high and is positioned 10 ft above the floor, which is flat. The first row of seats is 7 ft from the screen and the rows are 3 ft apart. You decide to sit in the row where you get the maximum view, that is, where the angle θ subtended by the screen at your eyes is a maximum. Suppose your eyes are 4 ft above the floor, as in the figure, and you sit at a distance x from the screen.

   (a) Show that $\theta = \tan^{-1}\left(\dfrac{28}{x}\right) - \tan^{-1}\left(\dfrac{6}{x}\right)$.

   (b) Use the subtraction formula for tangent to show that

   $$\theta = \tan^{-1}\left(\frac{22x}{x^2 + 168}\right)$$

   (c) Use a graphing device to graph θ as a function of x. What value of x maximizes θ? In which row should you sit? What is the viewing angle in this row?

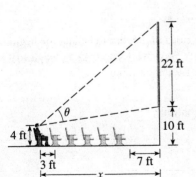

2. Now suppose that, starting with the first row of seats, the floor of the seating area is inclined at an angle of $\alpha = 25°$ above the horizontal, and the distance that you sit up the incline is x, as shown in the figure.

   (a) Use the Law of Cosines to show that

   $$\theta = \cos^{-1}\left(\frac{a^2 + b^2 - 484}{2ab}\right)$$

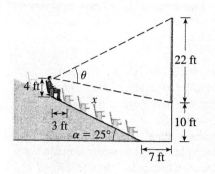

where

$$a^2 = (7 + x \cos \alpha)^2 + (28 - x \sin \alpha)^2$$

and

$$b^2 = (7 + x \cos \alpha)^2 + (x \sin \alpha - 6)^2$$

(b) Use a graphing device to graph θ as a function of x, and estimate the value of x that maximizes θ. In which row should you sit? What is the viewing angle θ in this row?

7.5 TRIGONOMETRIC EQUATIONS

An equation that contains trigonometric functions is called a **trigonometric equation**. For example, the following are trigonometric equations:

$$\sin^2 x + \cos^2 x = 1 \qquad 2 \sin x - 1 = 0 \qquad \tan^2 2x - 1 = 0$$

The first equation is an *identity*—that is, it is true for every value of the variable x. The other two equations are true only for certain values of x. To solve a trigonometric equation, we find all the values of the variable that make the equation true.

■ Solving Trigonometric Equations

To solve a trigonometric equation, we use the rules of algebra to isolate the trigonometric function on one side of the equal sign. Then we use our knowledge of the values of the trigonometric functions to solve for the variable.

EXAMPLE 1 ■ Solving a Trigonometric Equation

Solve the equation $2 \sin x - 1 = 0$.

SOLUTION

We start by isolating $\sin x$.

$$2 \sin x - 1 = 0 \qquad \text{Given equation}$$

$$2 \sin x = 1 \qquad \text{Add 1}$$

$$\sin x = \frac{1}{2} \qquad \text{Divide by 2}$$

Because sine has period 2π, we first find the solutions in the interval $[0, 2\pi)$. These are $x = \pi/6$ and $x = 5\pi/6$. To get all other solutions, we add any integer multiple of 2π to these solutions. Thus, the solutions are

$$x = \frac{\pi}{6} + 2k\pi, \qquad x = \frac{5\pi}{6} + 2k\pi$$

where k is any integer. Figure 1 gives a graphical representation of the solutions.

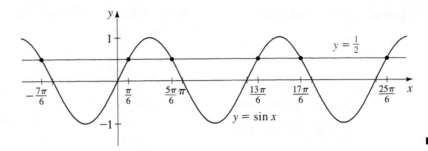

FIGURE 1

EXAMPLE 2 ■ Solving a Trigonometric Equation

Solve the equation $\tan^2 x - 3 = 0$.

SOLUTION

We start by isolating $\tan x$.

$$\tan^2 x - 3 = 0 \qquad \text{Given equation}$$

$$\tan^2 x = 3 \qquad \text{Add 3}$$

$$\tan x = \pm\sqrt{3} \qquad \text{Take square roots}$$

Because tangent has period π, we first find the solutions in the interval $(-\pi/2, \pi/2)$. These are $x = -\pi/3$ and $x = \pi/3$. To get all other solutions, we add any integer multiple of π to these solutions. Thus, the solutions are

$$x = -\frac{\pi}{3} + k\pi, \qquad x = \frac{\pi}{3} + k\pi$$

where k is any integer.   ■

EXAMPLE 3 ■ Finding Intersection Points

Find the values of x for which the graphs of $f(x) = \sin x$ and $g(x) = \cos x$ intersect.

SOLUTION 1: GRAPHICAL

The graphs intersect where $f(x) = g(x)$. In Figure 2 we graph $y_1 = \sin x$ and $y_2 = \cos x$ on the same screen, for x between 0 and 2π. Using TRACE or the

`Intersect` command on the graphing calculator, we see that the two points of intersection in this interval occur where $x \approx 0.785$ and $x \approx 3.927$. Since sin and cos are periodic with period 2π, the intersection points occur where

$$x \approx 0.785 + 2k\pi \qquad \text{and} \qquad x \approx 3.927 + 2k\pi$$

where k is any integer.

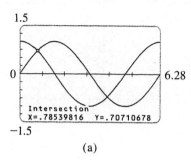

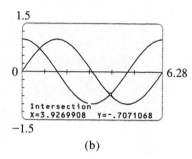

FIGURE 2   (a)   (b)

SOLUTION 2: ALGEBRAIC

To find the exact solution, we set $f(x) = g(x)$ and solve the resulting equation algebraically.

$$\sin x = \cos x \qquad \text{Equate functions}$$

Since the numbers x for which $\cos x = 0$ are not solutions of the equation, we can divide both sides by $\cos x$.

$$\frac{\sin x}{\cos x} = 1 \qquad \text{Divide by } \cos x$$

$$\tan x = 1 \qquad \text{Reciprocal identity}$$

Because tangent has period π, we first find the solutions in the interval $(-\pi/2, \pi/2)$. The only solution in this interval is $x = \pi/4$. To get all solutions, we add any integer multiple of π to this solution. Thus, the solutions are

$$x = \frac{\pi}{4} + k\pi$$

where k is any integer. The graphs intersect for these values of x. You should use your calculator to check that, correct to three decimals, these are the same values as we obtained in Solution 1.   ■

Solving Trigonometric Equations by Factoring

Zero-Product Property

If $AB = 0$, then $A = 0$ or $B = 0$.

Factoring is one of the most useful techniques for solving equations, including trigonometric equations. The idea is to move all terms to one side of the equation, factor, then use the Zero-Product Property (Section 1.5).

EXAMPLE 4 ■ An Equation of Quadratic Type

Solve the equation $2 \cos^2 x - 7 \cos x + 3 = 0$.

SOLUTION

We factor the left-hand side of the equation.

Equation of Quadratic Type

$2C^2 - 7C + 3 = 0$

$(2C - 1)(C - 3) = 0$

$2 \cos^2 x - 7 \cos x + 3 = 0$	Given equation
$(2 \cos x - 1)(\cos x - 3) = 0$	Factor
$2 \cos x - 1 = 0 \quad$ or $\quad \cos x - 3 = 0$	Set each factor equal to 0
$\cos x = \frac{1}{2} \quad$ or $\quad \cos x = 3$	Solve for cos x

Because cosine has period 2π, we first find the solutions in the interval $[0, 2\pi)$. For the first equation these are $x = \pi/3$ and $x = 5\pi/3$. The second equation has no solutions because $\cos x$ is never greater than 1. Thus, the solutions are

$$x = \frac{\pi}{3} + 2k\pi, \qquad x = \frac{5\pi}{3} + 2k\pi$$

where k is any integer.   ■

EXAMPLE 5 ■ Using a Trigonometric Identity

Solve the equation $1 + \sin x = 2 \cos^2 x$.

SOLUTION

We use a trigonometric identity to rewrite the equation in terms of a single trigonometric function.

Equation of Quadratic Type

$2S^2 + S - 1 = 0$

$(2S - 1)(S + 1) = 0$

$1 + \sin x = 2 \cos^2 x$	Given equation
$1 + \sin x = 2(1 - \sin^2 x)$	Pythagorean identity
$2 \sin^2 x + \sin x - 1 = 0$	Put all terms on one side of the equation
$(2 \sin x - 1)(\sin x + 1) = 0$	Factor
$2 \sin x - 1 = 0 \quad$ or $\quad \sin x + 1 = 0$	Set each factor equal to 0
$\sin x = \dfrac{1}{2} \quad$ or $\quad \sin x = -1$	Solve for sin x
$x = \dfrac{\pi}{6}, \dfrac{5\pi}{6} \quad$ or $\quad x = \dfrac{3\pi}{2}$	Solve for x in the interval $[0, 2\pi)$

Because sine has period 2π, we get all the solutions of the equation by adding any integer multiple of 2π to these solutions. Thus, the solutions are

$$x = \frac{\pi}{6} + 2k\pi, \qquad x = \frac{5\pi}{6} + 2k\pi, \qquad x = \frac{3\pi}{2} + 2k\pi$$

where k is any integer.   ∎

EXAMPLE 6 ■ Using a Trigonometric Identity

Solve the equation $\sin 2x - \cos x = 0$.

SOLUTION

The first term is a function of $2x$ and the second is a function of x, so we begin by using a trigonometric identity to rewrite the first term as a function of x only.

$\sin 2x - \cos x = 0$		Given equation
$2 \sin x \cos x - \cos x = 0$		Double-angle formula
$\cos x\,(2 \sin x - 1) = 0$		Factor
$\cos x = 0 \qquad$ or $\qquad 2 \sin x - 1 = 0$		Set each factor equal to 0
$\sin x = \dfrac{1}{2}$		Solve for $\sin x$
$x = \dfrac{\pi}{2}, \dfrac{3\pi}{2} \qquad$ or $\qquad x = \dfrac{\pi}{6}, \dfrac{5\pi}{6}$		Solve for x in the interval $[0, 2\pi)$

Both sine and cosine have period 2π, so we get all the solutions of the equation by adding any integer multiple of 2π to these solutions. Thus, the solutions are

$$x = \frac{\pi}{2} + 2k\pi, \qquad x = \frac{3\pi}{2} + 2k\pi, \qquad x = \frac{\pi}{6} + 2k\pi, \qquad x = \frac{5\pi}{6} + 2k\pi$$

where k is any integer.   ∎

EXAMPLE 7 ■ Squaring and Using an Identify

Solve the equation $\cos x + 1 = \sin x$ in the interval $[0, 2\pi)$.

SOLUTION

To get an equation that involves either sine only or cosine only, we square both sides and use a Pythagorean identity.

$$\cos x + 1 = \sin x \qquad \text{Given equation}$$

$$\cos^2 x + 2 \cos x + 1 = \sin^2 x \qquad \text{Square both sides}$$

$$\cos^2 x + 2 \cos x + 1 = 1 - \cos^2 x \qquad \text{Pythagorean identity}$$

$$2 \cos^2 x + 2 \cos x = 0 \qquad \text{Simplify}$$

$$2 \cos x \, (\cos x + 1) = 0 \qquad \text{Factor}$$

$2 \cos x = 0$	or	$\cos x + 1 = 0$	Set each factor equal to 0
$\cos x = 0$	or	$\cos x = -1$	Solve for $\cos x$
$x = \dfrac{\pi}{2}, \dfrac{3\pi}{2}$	or	$x = \pi$	Solve for x in the interval $[0, 2\pi)$

Because we squared both sides, we need to check for extraneous solutions. From *Check Your Answers*, we see that the solutions of the given equation are $\pi/2$ and π.

CHECK YOUR ANSWERS

$$x = \frac{\pi}{2}: \qquad\qquad\qquad x = \frac{3\pi}{2}: \qquad\qquad\qquad x = \pi:$$

$$\cos \frac{\pi}{2} + 1 \stackrel{?}{=} \sin \frac{\pi}{2} \qquad \cos \frac{3\pi}{2} + 1 \stackrel{?}{=} \sin \frac{3\pi}{2} \qquad \cos \pi + 1 \stackrel{?}{=} \sin \pi$$

$$0 + 1 = 1 \quad \checkmark \qquad\qquad 0 + 1 \stackrel{?}{=} -1 \quad \times \qquad\qquad -1 + 1 = 0 \quad \checkmark$$

 If we perform an operation on an equation that may introduce new roots, such as squaring both sides, then we must check that the solutions obtained are not extraneous; that is, we must verify that they satisfy the original equation, as in Example 7.

■ Equations with Trigonometric Functions of Multiple Angles

When solving trigonometric equations that involve functions of multiples of angles, we first solve for the multiple of the angle, then divide to solve for the angle.

EXAMPLE 8 ■ Trigonometric Functions of Multiple Angles

Consider the equation $2 \sin 3x - 1 = 0$.

(a) Find all solutions of the equation.
(b) Find the solutions in the interval $[0, 2\pi)$.

SOLUTION

(a) We start by isolating $\sin 3x$, and then solve for the multiple angle $3x$.

$$2 \sin 3x - 1 = 0 \qquad \text{Given equation}$$

$$2 \sin 3x = 1 \qquad \text{Add 1}$$

$$\sin 3x = \frac{1}{2} \qquad \text{Divide by 2}$$

$$3x = \frac{\pi}{6}, \frac{5\pi}{6} \qquad \text{Solve for } 3x \text{ in the interval } [0, 2\pi)$$

To get all solutions, we add any integer multiple of 2π to these solutions. Thus, the solutions are of the form

$$3x = \frac{\pi}{6} + 2k\pi, \qquad 3x = \frac{5\pi}{6} + 2k\pi$$

To solve for x, we divide by 3 to get the solutions

$$x = \frac{\pi}{18} + \frac{2k\pi}{3}, \qquad x = \frac{5\pi}{18} + \frac{2k\pi}{3}$$

where k is any integer.

(b) The solutions from part (a) that are in the interval $[0, 2\pi)$ correspond to $k = 0$, 1, and 2. For all other values of k, the corresponding values of x lie outside this interval. Thus, the solutions in the interval $[0, 2\pi)$ are

$$x = \frac{\pi}{18}, \frac{5\pi}{18}, \frac{13\pi}{18}, \frac{17\pi}{18}, \frac{25\pi}{18}, \frac{29\pi}{18} \qquad \blacksquare$$

EXAMPLE 9 ■ Trigonometric Functions of Multiple Angles

Consider the equation $\sqrt{3} \tan \frac{x}{2} - 1 = 0$.

(a) Find all solutions of the equation.

(b) Find the solutions in the interval $[0, 4\pi)$.

SOLUTION

(a) We start by isolating $\tan(x/2)$.

$$\sqrt{3} \tan \frac{x}{2} - 1 = 0 \qquad \text{Given equation}$$

$$\sqrt{3} \tan \frac{x}{2} = 1 \qquad \text{Add 1}$$

$$\tan \frac{x}{2} = \frac{1}{\sqrt{3}} \qquad \text{Divide by } \sqrt{3}$$

$$\frac{x}{2} = \frac{\pi}{3} \qquad \text{Solve for } \frac{x}{2} \text{ in the interval } \left(-\frac{\pi}{2}, \frac{\pi}{2}\right)$$

Since tan has period π, to get all solutions we add any integer multiple of π to these solutions. Thus, the solutions are of the form

$$\frac{x}{2} = \frac{\pi}{3} + k\pi$$

Multiplying by 2, we get the solutions

$$x = \frac{2\pi}{3} + 2k\pi$$

where k is any integer.

(b) The solutions from part (a) that are in the interval $[0, 4\pi)$ correspond to $k = 0$ and $k = 1$. For all other values of k, the corresponding values of x lie outside this interval. Thus, the solutions in the interval $[0, 4\pi)$ are

$$x = \frac{2\pi}{3}, \frac{8\pi}{3} \qquad \blacksquare$$

Using Inverse Trigonometric Functions to Solve Trigonometric Equations

So far, all the equations we've solved have had solutions like $\pi/4$, $\pi/3$, $5\pi/6$, and so on. We were able to find these solutions from the special values of the trigonometric functions that we've memorized. We now consider equations whose solution requires us to use the inverse trigonometric functions.

EXAMPLE 10 ■ Using Inverse Trigonometric Functions

Solve the equation $\tan^2 x - \tan x - 2 = 0$.

SOLUTION

We start by factoring the left-hand side.

Equation of Quadratic Type

$$T^2 - T - 2 = 0$$
$$(T - 2)(T + 1) = 0$$

$\tan^2 x - \tan x - 2 = 0$	Given equation
$(\tan x - 2)(\tan x + 1) = 0$	Factor
$\tan x - 2 = 0 \quad$ or $\quad \tan x + 1 = 0$	Set each factor equal to 0
$\tan x = 2 \qquad$ or $\qquad \tan x = -1$	Solve for $\tan x$
$x = \tan^{-1} 2 \text{ or } \qquad x = -\dfrac{\pi}{4}$	Solve for x in the interval $(-\pi/2, \pi/2)$

Because tangent has period π, we get all solutions by adding integer multiples of π to these solutions. Thus, all the solutions are

$$x = \tan^{-1}2 + k\pi, \qquad x = -\frac{\pi}{4} + k\pi$$

where k is any integer.   ∎

If we are using inverse trigonometric functions to solve an equation, we must keep in mind that $\sin^{-1}$ and $\tan^{-1}$ give values in quadrants I and IV, and $\cos^{-1}$ gives values in quadrants I and II. To find other solutions, we must look at the quadrant where the trigonometric function in the equation can take on the value we need.

EXAMPLE 11 ■ Using Inverse Trigonometric Functions

(a) Solve the equation $3 \sin \theta - 2 = 0$.

(b) Use a calculator to approximate the solutions in the interval $[0, 2\pi)$, correct to 5 decimals.

SOLUTION

(a) We start by isolating $\sin \theta$.

$$
\begin{array}{ll}
3 \sin \theta - 2 = 0 & \text{Given equation} \\[2mm]
3 \sin \theta = 2 & \text{Add 2} \\[2mm]
\sin \theta = \dfrac{2}{3} & \text{Divide by 3}
\end{array}
$$

From Figure 3 we see that $\sin \theta$ equals $\frac{2}{3}$ in quadrants I and II. The solution in quadrant I is $\theta = \sin^{-1}\frac{2}{3}$. The solution in quadrant II is $\theta = \pi - \sin^{-1}\frac{2}{3}$. Since these are the solutions in the interval $[0, 2\pi)$, we get all other solutions by adding integer multiples of 2π to these. Thus, all the solutions of the equation are

$$\theta = \left(\sin^{-1}\tfrac{2}{3}\right) + 2k\pi, \qquad \theta = \left(\pi - \sin^{-1}\tfrac{2}{3}\right) + 2k\pi$$

where k is any integer.

(b) Using a calculator set in radian mode, we see that $\sin^{-1}\frac{2}{3} \approx 0.72973$ and $\pi - \sin^{-1}\frac{2}{3} \approx 2.41186$, so the solutions in the interval $[0, 2\pi)$ are

$$\theta \approx 0.72973, \qquad \theta \approx 2.41186$$

∎

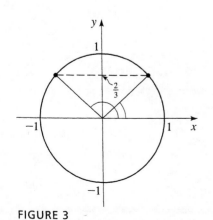

FIGURE 3

7.5 EXERCISES

1–38 ■ Find all solutions of the equation.

1. $\sin x - 1 = 0$

2. $\cos x + 1 = 0$

3. $2 \cos x - 1 = 0$

4. $\sqrt{2} \sin x - 1 = 0$

5. $2 \sin x + \sqrt{3} = 0$

6. $\tan x + 1 = 0$

7. $4 \cos^2 x - 1 = 0$

8. $2 \cos^2 x - 1 = 0$

9. $\sec^2 x - 2 = 0$

10. $\csc^2 x - 4 = 0$

11. $\cos x (2 \sin x + 1) = 0$

12. $\sec x (2 \cos x - \sqrt{2}) = 0$

13. $(\tan x + \sqrt{3})(\cos x + 2) = 0$

14. $(2 \cos x + \sqrt{3})(2 \sin x - 1) = 0$

15. $\cos x \sin x - 2 \cos x = 0$

16. $\tan x \sin x + \sin x = 0$

17. $4 \cos^2 x - 4 \cos x + 1 = 0$

18. $2 \sin^2 x - \sin x - 1 = 0$

19. $\sin^2 x = 2 \sin x + 3$

20. $3 \tan^3 x = \tan x$

21. $\sin^2 x = 4 - 2 \cos^2 x$

22. $2 \cos^2 x + \sin x = 1$

23. $2 \sin 3x + 1 = 0$

24. $2 \cos 2x + 1 = 0$

25. $\sec 4x - 2 = 0$

26. $\sqrt{3} \tan 3x + 1 = 0$

27. $\sqrt{3} \sin 2x = \cos 2x$

28. $\cos 3x = \sin 3x$

29. $\cos \dfrac{x}{2} - 1 = 0$

30. $2 \sin \dfrac{x}{3} + \sqrt{3} = 0$

31. $\tan \dfrac{x}{4} + \sqrt{3} = 0$

32. $\sec \dfrac{x}{2} = \cos \dfrac{x}{2}$

33. $\tan^5 x - 9 \tan x = 0$

34. $3 \tan^3 x - 3 \tan^2 x - \tan x + 1 = 0$

35. $4 \sin x \cos x + 2 \sin x - 2 \cos x - 1 = 0$

36. $\sin 2x = 2 \tan 2x$

37. $\cos^2 2x - \sin^2 2x = 0$

38. $\sec x - \tan x = \cos x$

39–46 ■ Find all solutions of the equation in the interval $[0, 2\pi)$.

39. $2 \cos 3x = 1$

40. $3 \csc^2 x = 4$

41. $2 \sin x \tan x - \tan x = 1 - 2 \sin x$

42. $\sec x \tan x - \cos x \cot x = \sin x$

43. $\tan x - 3 \cot x = 0$

44. $2 \sin^2 x - \cos x = 1$

45. $\tan 3x + 1 = \sec 3x$

46. $3 \sec^2 x + 4 \cos^2 x = 7$

47–54 ■ (a) Find all solutions of the equation. (b) Use a calculator to solve the equation in the interval $[0, 2\pi)$, correct to five decimal places.

47. $\cos x = 0.4$

48. $2 \tan x = 13$

49. $\sec x - 5 = 0$

50. $3 \sin x = 7 \cos x$

51. $5 \sin^2 x - 1 = 0$

52. $2 \sin 2x - \cos x = 0$

53. $3 \sin^2 x - 7 \sin x + 2 = 0$

54. $\tan^4 x - 13 \tan^2 x + 36 = 0$

55–58 ■ Graph f and g on the same axes, and find their points of intersection.

55. $f(x) = 3 \cos x + 1, \quad g(x) = \cos x - 1$

56. $f(x) = \sin 2x, \quad g(x) = 2 \sin 2x + 1$

57. $f(x) = \tan x, \quad g(x) = \sqrt{3}$

58. $f(x) = \sin x - 1, \quad g(x) = \cos x$

59. If a projectile is fired with velocity v_0 at an angle θ, then its *range*, the horizontal distance it travels (in feet), is modeled by the function

$$R(\theta) = \frac{v_0^2 \sin 2\theta}{32}$$

(See page 804.) If $v_0 = 2200$ ft/s, what angle should be chosen in order for the projectile to hit a target on the ground 5000 ft away?

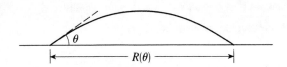

60. In Philadelphia the number of hours of daylight on day t (where t is the number of days after January 1) is modeled by the function

$$L(t) = 12 + 2.83 \sin\left(\frac{2\pi}{365}(t - 80)\right)$$

(a) Which days of the year have about 10 hours of daylight?

(b) How many days of the year have more than 10 hours of daylight?

61. It has been observed since ancient times that light refracts or "bends" as it travels from one medium to another (from air to water, for example). If v_1 is the speed of light in one medium and v_2 its speed in another medium, then according to **Snell's Law**,

$$\frac{\sin \theta_1}{\sin \theta_2} = \frac{v_1}{v_2}$$

where θ_1 is the *angle of incidence* and θ_2 is the *angle of refraction* (see the figure). The number v_1/v_2 is called the *index of refraction*. The index of refraction from air to water is 1.33. If a ray of light passes through the surface of a lake at an angle of incidence of 70°, find the angle of refraction.

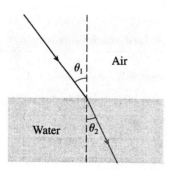

62. The displacement of a spring vibrating in damped harmonic motion is given by

$$y = 4e^{3t} \sin 2\pi t$$

Find the times when the spring is at its equilibrium position $(y = 0)$.

63–66 ■ Use an addition or subtraction formula to simplify the equation. Then find all solutions in the interval $[0, 2\pi)$.

63. $\cos x \cos 3x - \sin x \sin 3x = 0$

64. $\cos x \cos 2x + \sin x \sin 2x = \frac{1}{2}$

65. $\sin 2x \cos x + \cos 2x \sin x = \sqrt{3}/2$

66. $\sin 3x \cos x - \cos 3x \sin x = 0$

67–70 ■ Use a double- or half-angle formula to solve the equation in the interval $[0, 2\pi)$.

67. $\sin 2x + \cos x = 0$

68. $\tan \dfrac{x}{2} - \sin x = 0$

69. $\cos 2x + \cos x = 2$

70. $\tan x + \cot x = 4 \sin 2x$

71–74 ■ Solve the equation by first using a sum-to-product formula.

71. $\sin x + \sin 3x = 0$

72. $\cos 5x - \cos 7x = 0$

73. $\cos 4x + \cos 2x = \cos x$

74. $\sin 5x - \sin 3x = \cos 4x$

 75–80 ■ Use a graphing device to find the solutions of the equation, correct to two decimal places.

75. $\sin 2x = x$

76. $\cos x = \dfrac{x}{3}$

77. $2^{\sin x} = x$

78. $\sin x = x^3$

79. $\dfrac{\cos x}{1 + x^2} = x^2$

80. $\cos x = \frac{1}{2}(e^x + e^{-x})$

DISCOVERY · DISCUSSION

81. Equations and Identities   Which of the following statements is true?

A. Every identity is an equation.

B. Every equation is an identity.

Give examples to illustrate your answer. Write a short paragraph to explain the difference between an equation and an identity.

82. A Special Trigonometric Equation   What makes the equation $\sin(\cos x) = 0$ different from all the other equations we've looked at in this section? Find all solutions of this equation.

7.6 TRIGONOMETRIC FORM OF COMPLEX NUMBERS; DeMOIVRE'S THEOREM

Complex numbers were introduced in Chapter 3 in order to solve certain algebraic equations. The applications of complex numbers go far beyond this initial use, however. Complex numbers are now used routinely in physics, electrical engineering, aerospace engineering, and many other fields. In this section we represent complex numbers in trigonometric form, using the functions sine and cosine. This will enable us to find the nth roots of complex numbers. To describe the trigonometric form of complex numbers, we must first learn to work with complex numbers graphically.

Graphing Complex Numbers

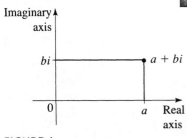

FIGURE 1

To graph real numbers or sets of real numbers, we have been using the number line, which has just one dimension. Complex numbers, however have two components: the real part and the imaginary part. This suggests that we need two axes to graph complex numbers: one for the real part and one for the imaginary part. We call these the **real axis** and the **imaginary axis**, respectively. The plane determined by these two axes is called the **complex plane**. To graph the complex number $a + bi$, we plot the ordered pair of numbers (a, b) in this plane, as indicated in Figure 1.

EXAMPLE 1 ■ Graphing Complex Numbers

Graph the complex numbers $z_1 = 2 + 3i$, $z_2 = 3 - 2i$, and $z_1 + z_2$.

SOLUTION

We have $z_1 + z_2 = (2 + 3i) + (3 - 2i) = 5 + i$. The graph is shown in Figure 2.

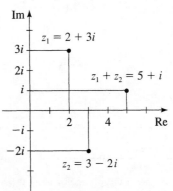

FIGURE 2

EXAMPLE 2 ■ Graphing Sets of Complex Numbers

Graph each of the following sets of complex numbers.
(a) $S = \{a + bi \mid a \geq 0\}$ (b) $T = \{a + bi \mid a < 1, b \geq 0\}$

SOLUTION

(a) S is the set of complex numbers whose real part is nonnegative. The graph is shown in Figure 3(a).

(b) T is the set of complex numbers for which the real part is less than 1 and the imaginary part is nonnegative. The graph is shown in Figure 3(b).

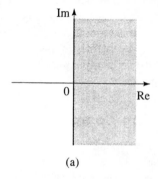

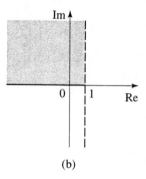

FIGURE 3   (a)   (b)   ∎

Recall from Section 1.1 that the absolute value of a real number can be thought of as its distance from the origin on the real number line. We define absolute value for complex numbers in a similar fashion. From Figure 4 we can see, using the Pythagorean Theorem, that the distance between $a + bi$ and the origin in the complex plane is $\sqrt{a^2 + b^2}$. This leads to the following definition.

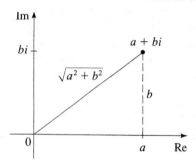

FIGURE 4

The plural of *modulus* is *moduli*.

> The **modulus** (or **absolute value**) of the complex number $z = a + bi$ is
> $$|z| = \sqrt{a^2 + b^2}$$

EXAMPLE 3 ∎ Calculating the Modulus

Find the moduli of the complex numbers $3 + 4i$ and $8 - 5i$.

SOLUTION

$$|3 + 4i| = \sqrt{3^2 + 4^2} = \sqrt{25} = 5$$
$$|8 - 5i| = \sqrt{8^2 + (-5)^2} = \sqrt{89}$$

∎

EXAMPLE 4 ∎ Absolute Value of Complex Numbers

Graph each of the following sets of complex numbers.

(a) $C = \{z \mid |z| = 1\}$ (b) $D = \{z \mid |z| \leq 1\}$

SOLUTION

(a) C is the set of complex numbers whose distance from the origin is 1. Thus, C is a circle of radius 1 with center at the origin.

(b) D is the set of complex numbers whose distance from the origin is less than or equal to 1. Thus, D is the disk that consists of all complex numbers on and inside the circle C of part (a).

The graphs of C and D are shown in Figure 5.

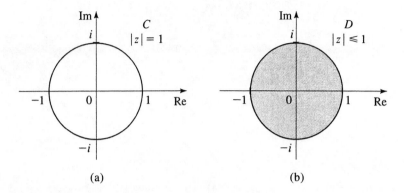

FIGURE 5 (a) (b) ■

Trigonometric Form of Complex Numbers

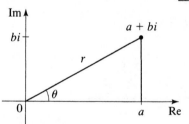

FIGURE 6

Let $z = a + bi$ be a complex number, and in the complex plane let's draw the line segment joining the origin to the point $a + bi$ (see Figure 6). The length of this line segment is denoted by $r = |z| = \sqrt{a^2 + b^2}$. If θ is an angle in standard position whose terminal side coincides with this line segment, then by the definitions of sine and cosine (see Section 4.2)

$$a = r \cos \theta \quad \text{and} \quad b = r \sin \theta$$

so $z = r \cos \theta + ir \sin \theta = r(\cos \theta + i \sin \theta)$. We have shown the following.

TRIGONOMETRIC FORM OF COMPLEX NUMBERS

A complex number $z = a + bi$ has the **trigonometric form**

$$z = r(\cos \theta + i \sin \theta)$$

where $r = |z| = \sqrt{a^2 + b^2}$ and $\tan \theta = b/a$. The number r is the **modulus** of z, and θ is an **argument** of z.

The argument of z is not unique, but any two arguments of z differ by a multiple of 2π.

EXAMPLE 5 ■ Writing Complex Numbers in Trigonometric Form

Write each of the following complex numbers in trigonometric form.

(a) $1 + i$ (b) $-1 + \sqrt{3}\, i$ (c) $-4\sqrt{3} - 4i$ (d) $3 + 4i$

SOLUTION

These complex numbers are graphed in Figure 7, which helps us find their arguments.

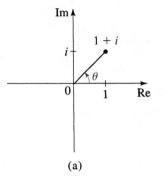

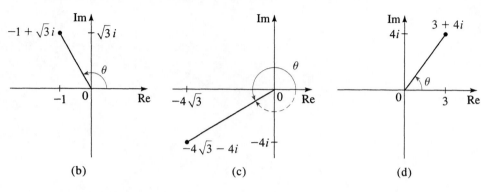

(a) (b) (c) (d)

FIGURE 7

$\tan \theta = \frac{1}{1} = 1$

$\theta = \frac{\pi}{4}$

(a) An argument is $\theta = \pi/4$ and $r = \sqrt{1 + 1} = \sqrt{2}$. Thus

$$1 + i = \sqrt{2}\left(\cos \frac{\pi}{4} + i \sin \frac{\pi}{4}\right)$$

$\tan \theta = \frac{\sqrt{3}}{-1} = -\sqrt{3}$

$\theta = \frac{2\pi}{3}$

(b) An argument is $\theta = 2\pi/3$ and $r = \sqrt{1 + 3} = 2$. Thus

$$-1 + \sqrt{3}\,i = 2\left(\cos \frac{2\pi}{3} + i \sin \frac{2\pi}{3}\right)$$

$\tan \theta = \frac{-4}{-4\sqrt{3}} = \frac{1}{\sqrt{3}}$

$\theta = \frac{7\pi}{6}$

(c) An argument is $\theta = 7\pi/6$ (or we could use $\theta = -5\pi/6$), and $r = \sqrt{48 + 16} = 8$. Thus

$$-4\sqrt{3} - 4i = 8\left(\cos \frac{7\pi}{6} + i \sin \frac{7\pi}{6}\right)$$

$\tan \theta = \frac{4}{3}$

$\theta = \tan^{-1}\frac{4}{3}$

(d) An argument is $\theta = \tan^{-1}\frac{4}{3}$ and $r = \sqrt{3^2 + 4^2} = 5$. So

$$3 + 4i = 5\left[\cos\left(\tan^{-1}\frac{4}{3}\right) + i \sin\left(\tan^{-1}\frac{4}{3}\right)\right]$$ ∎

The addition formulas for sine and cosine discussed in Section 7.2 greatly simplify the multiplication and division of complex numbers in trigonometric form. The following theorem shows how.

MULTIPLICATION AND DIVISION OF COMPLEX NUMBERS

If the two complex numbers z_1 and z_2 have the trigonometric forms

$$z_1 = r_1(\cos \theta_1 + i \sin \theta_1) \quad \text{and} \quad z_2 = r_2(\cos \theta_2 + i \sin \theta_2)$$

then

$$z_1 z_2 = r_1 r_2[\cos(\theta_1 + \theta_2) + i \sin(\theta_1 + \theta_2)] \qquad \text{Multiplication}$$

$$\frac{z_1}{z_2} = \frac{r_1}{r_2}[\cos(\theta_1 - \theta_2) + i \sin(\theta_1 - \theta_2)] \qquad (z_2 \neq 0) \qquad \text{Division}$$

This theorem says:

To multiply two complex numbers, multiply the moduli and add the arguments.

To divide two complex numbers, divide the moduli and subtract the arguments.

■ **Proof**   To prove the multiplication formula, we simply multiply the two complex numbers.

$$z_1 z_2 = r_1 r_2 (\cos \theta_1 + i \sin \theta_1)(\cos \theta_2 + i \sin \theta_2)$$

$$= r_1 r_2 [\cos \theta_1 \cos \theta_2 - \sin \theta_1 \sin \theta_2 + i(\sin \theta_1 \cos \theta_2 + \cos \theta_1 \sin \theta_2)]$$

$$= r_1 r_2 [\cos(\theta_1 + \theta_2) + i \sin(\theta_1 + \theta_2)]$$

In the last step we used the addition formulas for sine and cosine.   □

The proof of the division formula is left as an exercise.

EXAMPLE 6 ■ Multiplying and Dividing Complex Numbers

Let

$$z_1 = 2\left(\cos \frac{\pi}{4} + i \sin \frac{\pi}{4}\right) \quad \text{and} \quad z_2 = 5\left(\cos \frac{\pi}{3} + i \sin \frac{\pi}{3}\right)$$

Find (a) $z_1 z_2$ and (b) z_1/z_2.

SOLUTION

(a) By the multiplication formula

$$z_1 z_2 = (2)(5)\left[\cos\left(\frac{\pi}{4} + \frac{\pi}{3}\right) + i \sin\left(\frac{\pi}{4} + \frac{\pi}{3}\right)\right]$$

$$= 10\left(\cos \frac{7\pi}{12} + i \sin \frac{7\pi}{12}\right)$$

To approximate the answer, we use a calculator in radian mode and get

$$z_1 z_2 \approx 10(-0.2588 + 0.9659i) = -2.588 + 9.659i$$

(b) By the division formula

$$\frac{z_1}{z_2} = \frac{2}{5}\left[\cos\left(\frac{\pi}{4} - \frac{\pi}{3}\right) + i \sin\left(\frac{\pi}{4} - \frac{\pi}{3}\right)\right]$$

$$= \frac{2}{5}\left[\cos\left(-\frac{\pi}{12}\right) + i \sin\left(-\frac{\pi}{12}\right)\right]$$

$$= \frac{2}{5}\left(\cos \frac{\pi}{12} - i \sin \frac{\pi}{12}\right)$$

Using a calculator in radian mode, we get the approximate answer:

$$\frac{z_1}{z_2} \approx \frac{2}{5}(0.9659 - 0.2588i) = 0.3864 - 0.1035i$$

∎

DeMoivre's Theorem

Repeated use of the multiplication formula gives the following useful formula for raising a complex number to a power n for any positive integer n.

> **DeMOIVRE'S THEOREM**
>
> If $z = r(\cos \theta + i \sin \theta)$, then for any integer n
>
> $$z^n = r^n(\cos n\theta + i \sin n\theta)$$

This theorem says: *To take the nth power of a complex number, we take the nth power of the modulus and multiply the argument by n.*

■ **Proof**   By the multiplication formula

$$z^2 = zz = r^2[\cos(\theta + \theta) + i \sin(\theta + \theta)]$$

$$= r^2(\cos 2\theta + i \sin 2\theta)$$

Now we multiply z^2 by z to get

$$z^3 = z^2z = r^3[\cos(2\theta + \theta) + i \sin(2\theta + \theta)]$$

$$= r^3(\cos 3\theta + i \sin 3\theta)$$

Repeating this argument, we see that for any positive integer n

$$z^n = r^n(\cos n\theta + i \sin n\theta)$$

A similar argument using the division formula shows that this also holds for negative integers.   □

EXAMPLE 7 ■ Finding a Power Using DeMoivre's Theorem

Find $\left(\frac{1}{2} + \frac{1}{2}i\right)^{10}$.

SOLUTION

Since $\frac{1}{2} + \frac{1}{2}i = \frac{1}{2}(1 + i)$, it follows from Example 5(a) that

$$\frac{1}{2} + \frac{1}{2}i = \frac{\sqrt{2}}{2}\left(\cos \frac{\pi}{4} + i \sin \frac{\pi}{4}\right)$$

So by DeMoivre's Theorem,

$$\left(\frac{1}{2} + \frac{1}{2}i\right)^{10} = \left(\frac{\sqrt{2}}{2}\right)^{10}\left(\cos\frac{10\pi}{4} + i\sin\frac{10\pi}{4}\right)$$

$$= \frac{2^5}{2^{10}}\left(\cos\frac{5\pi}{2} + i\sin\frac{5\pi}{2}\right) = \frac{1}{32}i$$

*n*th Roots of Complex Numbers

DeMoivre's Theorem gives us a method for calculating the *n*th roots of any complex number.

---

*n*TH ROOTS OF COMPLEX NUMBERS

If $z = r(\cos\theta + i\sin\theta)$ and n is a positive integer, then z has the n distinct *n*th roots

$$w_k = r^{1/n}\left[\cos\left(\frac{\theta + 2k\pi}{n}\right) + i\sin\left(\frac{\theta + 2k\pi}{n}\right)\right]$$

for $k = 0, 1, 2, \ldots, n - 1$.

■ **Proof**   To find the *n*th roots of z, we need to find a complex number w such that

$$w^n = z$$

Let's write z in trigonometric form:

$$z = r(\cos\theta + i\sin\theta)$$

One *n*th root of z is

$$w = r^{1/n}\left(\cos\frac{\theta}{n} + i\sin\frac{\theta}{n}\right)$$

since by DeMoivre's Theorem, $w^n = z$. But the argument θ of z can be replaced by $\theta + 2k\pi$ for any integer k. Since this expression gives a different value of w for $k = 0, 1, 2, \ldots, n - 1$, we have proved the formula in the theorem.   □

The following observations help us use the preceding formula.

---

1. The modulus of each *n*th root is $r^{1/n}$.

2. The argument of the first root is θ/n.

3. We repeatedly add $2\pi/n$ to get the argument of each successive root.

These observations show that, when graphed, the *n*th roots of z are spaced equally on the circle of radius $r^{1/n}$.

EXAMPLE 8 ■ Finding Roots of a Complex Number

Find the six sixth roots of $z = -64$, and graph these roots in the complex plane.

SOLUTION

In trigonometric form, $z = 64(\cos \pi + i \sin \pi)$. Applying the formula for nth roots with $n = 6$, we get

$$w_k = 64^{1/6}\left[\cos\left(\frac{\pi + 2k\pi}{6}\right) + i \sin\left(\frac{\pi + 2k\pi}{6}\right)\right]$$

for $k = 0, 1, 2, 3, 4, 5$. Thus, the six sixth roots of -64 are

We add $2\pi/6 = \pi/3$ to each argument to get the argument of the next root.

$$w_0 = 64^{1/6}\left(\cos \frac{\pi}{6} + i \sin \frac{\pi}{6}\right) = \sqrt{3} + i$$

$$w_1 = 64^{1/6}\left(\cos \frac{\pi}{2} + i \sin \frac{\pi}{2}\right) = 2i$$

$$w_2 = 64^{1/6}\left(\cos \frac{5\pi}{6} + i \sin \frac{5\pi}{6}\right) = -\sqrt{3} + i$$

$$w_3 = 64^{1/6}\left(\cos \frac{7\pi}{6} + i \sin \frac{7\pi}{6}\right) = -\sqrt{3} - i$$

$$w_4 = 64^{1/6}\left(\cos \frac{3\pi}{2} + i \sin \frac{3\pi}{2}\right) = -2i$$

$$w_5 = 64^{1/6}\left(\cos \frac{11\pi}{6} + i \sin \frac{11\pi}{6}\right) = \sqrt{3} - i$$

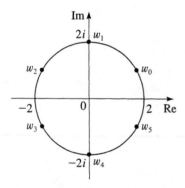

FIGURE 8
The six sixth roots of $z = -64$

All these points lie on the circle of radius 2, as shown in Figure 8.   ■

When finding roots of complex numbers, we sometimes write the argument θ of the complex number in degrees. In this case, the nth roots are obtained from the formula

$$w_k = r^{1/n}\left[\cos\left(\frac{\theta + 360°k}{n}\right) + i \sin\left(\frac{\theta + 360°k}{n}\right)\right]$$

for $k = 0, 1, 2, \ldots, n - 1$.

EXAMPLE 9 ■ Finding Cube Roots of a Complex Number

Find the three cube roots of $z = 2 + 2i$, and graph these roots in the complex plane.

SOLUTION

First we write z in trigonometric form using degrees. We have
$r = \sqrt{2^2 + 2^2} = 2\sqrt{2}$ and $\theta = 45°$. Thus

$$z = 2\sqrt{2}(\cos 45° + i \sin 45°)$$

Applying the formula for nth roots (in degrees) with $n = 3$, we find the cube roots of z are of the form

$$w_k = \left(2\sqrt{2}\right)^{1/3}\left[\cos\left(\frac{45° + 360°k}{3}\right) + i \sin\left(\frac{45° + 360°k}{3}\right)\right]$$

$(2\sqrt{2})^{1/3} = (2^{3/2})^{1/3} = 2^{1/2} = \sqrt{2}$

where $k = 0, 1, 2$. Thus, the three cube roots are

We add $360°/3 = 120°$ to each argument to get the argument of the next root.

$$w_0 = \sqrt{2}(\cos 15° + i \sin 15°) \approx 1.366 + 0.366i$$

$$w_1 = \sqrt{2}(\cos 135° + i \sin 135°) = -1 + i$$

$$w_2 = \sqrt{2}(\cos 255° + i \sin 255°) \approx -0.366 + 1.366i$$

The three cube roots of z are graphed in Figure 9. These roots are spaced equally on the circle of radius $\sqrt{2}$. ∎

EXAMPLE 10 ■ Solving an Equation Using the nth Roots Formula

Solve the equation $z^6 + 64 = 0$.

SOLUTION

This equation can be written as $z^6 = -64$. Thus, the solutions are the sixth roots of -64, which we found in Example 8. ∎

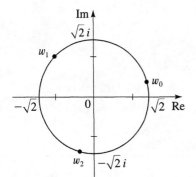

FIGURE 9
The three cube roots of $z = 2 + 2i$

7.6 EXERCISES

1–8 ■ Graph the complex number and find its modulus.

1. $4i$

2. -2

3. $5 + 2i$

4. $7 - 3i$

5. $\sqrt{3} + i$

6. $-1 - \dfrac{\sqrt{3}}{3}i$

7. $\dfrac{3 + 4i}{5}$

8. $\dfrac{-\sqrt{2} + i\sqrt{2}}{2}$

9–10 ■ Sketch the complex number z, and also sketch $2z$, $-z$, and $\frac{1}{2}z$ on the same complex plane.

9. $z = 1 + i$

10. $z = -1 + i\sqrt{3}$

11–12 ■ Sketch the complex number z and its complex conjugate $\bar{z}$ on the same complex plane.

11. $z = 8 + 2i$

12. $z = -5 + 6i$

13–14 ■ Sketch z_1, z_2, $z_1 + z_2$, and $z_1 z_2$ on the same complex plane.

13. $z_1 = 2 - i$, $z_2 = 2 + i$

14. $z_1 = -1 + i$, $z_2 = 2 - 3i$

15–22 ■ Sketch the set in the complex plane.

15. $\{z = a + bi \mid a \leq 0, b \geq 0\}$

16. $\{z = a + bi \mid a > 1, b > 1\}$

17. $\{z \mid |z| = 3\}$

18. $\{z \mid |z| \geq 1\}$

19. $\{z \mid |z| < 2\}$

20. $\{z \mid 2 \leq |z| \leq 5\}$

21. $\{z = a + bi \mid a + b < 2\}$

22. $\{z = a + bi \mid a \geq b\}$

23–46 ■ Write the complex number in trigonometric form with argument θ between 0 and 2π.

23. $1 + i$

24. $1 + \sqrt{3}\, i$

25. $\sqrt{2} - \sqrt{2}\, i$

26. $1 - i$

27. $2\sqrt{3} - 2i$

28. $-1 + i$

29. $-3i$

30. $-3 - 3\sqrt{3}\, i$

31. $5 + 5i$

32. 4

33. $4\sqrt{3} - 4i$

34. $8i$

35. -20

36. $\sqrt{3} + i$

37. $3 + 4i$

38. $i(2 - 2i)$

39. $3i(1 + i)$

40. $2(1 - i)$

41. $4(\sqrt{3} + i)$

42. $-3 - 3i$

43. $2 + i$

44. $3 + \sqrt{3}\, i$

45. $\sqrt{2} + \sqrt{2}\, i$

46. $-\pi i$

47–54 ■ Find the product $z_1 z_2$ and the quotient z_1/z_2. Express your answer in trigonometric form.

47. $z_1 = \cos \pi + i \sin \pi, \quad z_2 = \cos \dfrac{\pi}{3} + i \sin \dfrac{\pi}{3}$

48. $z_1 = \cos \dfrac{\pi}{4} + i \sin \dfrac{\pi}{4}, \quad z_2 = \cos \dfrac{3\pi}{4} + i \sin \dfrac{3\pi}{4}$

49. $z_1 = 3\left(\cos \dfrac{\pi}{6} + i \sin \dfrac{\pi}{6}\right), \quad z_2 = 5\left(\cos \dfrac{4\pi}{3} + i \sin \dfrac{4\pi}{3}\right)$

50. $z_1 = 7\left(\cos \dfrac{9\pi}{8} + i \sin \dfrac{9\pi}{8}\right), \quad z_2 = 2\left(\cos \dfrac{\pi}{8} + i \sin \dfrac{\pi}{8}\right)$

51. $z_1 = 4(\cos 120° + i \sin 120°),$
$z_2 = 2(\cos 30° + i \sin 30°)$

52. $z_1 = \sqrt{2}\,(\cos 75° + i \sin 75°),$
$z_2 = 3\sqrt{2}\,(\cos 60° + i \sin 60°)$

53. $z_1 = 4(\cos 200° + i \sin 200°),$
$z_2 = 25(\cos 150° + i \sin 150°)$

54. $z_1 = \frac{4}{5}(\cos 25° + i \sin 25°),$
$z_2 = \frac{1}{5}(\cos 155° + i \sin 155°)$

55–62 ■ Write z_1 and z_2 in trigonometric form, and then find the product $z_1 z_2$ and the quotients z_1/z_2 and $1/z_1$.

55. $z_1 = \sqrt{3} + i, \quad z_2 = 1 + \sqrt{3}\, i$

56. $z_1 = \sqrt{2} - \sqrt{2}\, i, \quad z_2 = 1 - i$

57. $z_1 = 2\sqrt{3} - 2i, \quad z_2 = -1 + i$

58. $z_1 = -\sqrt{2}\, i, \quad z_2 = -3 - 3\sqrt{3}\, i$

59. $z_1 = 5 + 5i, \quad z_2 = 4$

60. $z_1 = 4\sqrt{3} - 4i, \quad z_2 = 8i$

61. $z_1 = -20, \quad z_2 = \sqrt{3} + i$

62. $z_1 = 3 + 4i, \quad z_2 = 2 - 2i$

63–74 ■ Find the indicated power using DeMoivre's Theorem.

63. $(1 + i)^{20}$

64. $\left(1 - \sqrt{3}\, i\right)^5$

65. $\left(2\sqrt{3} + 2i\right)^5$

66. $(1 - i)^8$

67. $\left(\dfrac{\sqrt{2}}{2} + \dfrac{\sqrt{2}}{2} i\right)^{12}$

68. $\left(\sqrt{3} - i\right)^{-10}$

69. $(2 - 2i)^8$

70. $\left(-\dfrac{1}{2} - \dfrac{\sqrt{3}}{2} i\right)^{15}$

71. $(-1 - i)^7$

72. $\left(3 + \sqrt{3}\, i\right)^4$

73. $\left(2\sqrt{3} + 2i\right)^{-5}$

74. $(1 - i)^{-8}$

75–84 ■ Find the indicated roots, and graph the roots in the complex plane.

75. The square roots of $4\sqrt{3} + 4i$

76. The cube roots of $4\sqrt{3} + 4i$

77. The fourth roots of $-81i$

78. The fifth roots of 32

79. The eighth roots of 1

80. The cube roots of $1 + i$

81. The cube roots of i

82. The fifth roots of i

83. The fourth roots of -1

84. The fifth roots of $-16 - 16\sqrt{3}\, i$

85–90 ■ Solve the equation.

85. $z^4 + 1 = 0$

86. $z^8 - i = 0$

87. $z^3 - 4\sqrt{3} - 4i = 0$

88. $z^6 - 1 = 0$

89. $z^3 + 1 = -i$

90. $z^3 - 1 = 0$

91. (a) Let $w = \cos \dfrac{2\pi}{n} + i \sin \dfrac{2\pi}{n}$ where n is a positive integer. Show that $1, w, w^2, w^3, \ldots, w^{n-1}$ are the n distinct nth roots of 1.

(b) If $z \neq 0$ is any complex number and $s^n = z$, show that the n distinct nth roots of z are

$$s, sw, sw^2, sw^3, \ldots, sw^{n-1}$$

DISCOVERY · DISCUSSION

92. Sums of Roots of Unity Find the exact values of all three cube roots of 1 (see Exercise 91) and then add them.

Do the same for the fourth, fifth, sixth, and eighth roots of 1. What do you think is the sum of the nth roots of 1, for any n?

93. Products of Roots of Unity   Find the product of the three cube roots of 1 (see Exercise 91). Do the same for the fourth, fifth, sixth, and eighth roots of 1. What do you think is the product of the nth roots of 1, for any n?

94. Complex Coefficients and the Quadratic Formula
The quadratic formula works whether the coefficients of the equation are real or complex. Solve these equations using the quadratic formula, and, if necessary, DeMoivre's Theorem.

(a) $z^2 + (1 + i)z + i = 0$

(b) $z^2 - iz + 1 = 0$

(c) $z^2 - (2 - i)z - \frac{1}{4}i = 0$

7.7   VECTORS

In applications of mathematics, certain quantities are determined completely by their magnitude—for example, length, mass, area, temperature, and energy. We speak of a length of 5 m or a mass of 3 kg; only one number is needed to describe each of these quantities. Such a quantity is called a **scalar**.

On the other hand, to describe the displacement of an object, two numbers are required: the *magnitude* and the *direction* of the displacement. To describe the velocity of a moving object, we must specify both the *speed* and the *direction* of travel. Quantities such as displacement, velocity, acceleration, and force that involve magnitude as well as direction are called *directed quantities*. One way to represent such quantities mathematically is through the use of *vectors*.

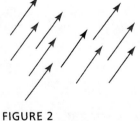

$\mathbf{u} = \overrightarrow{AB}$

FIGURE 1

Geometric Description of Vectors

A **vector** in the plane is a line segment with an assigned direction. We sketch a vector as shown in Figure 1 with an arrow to specify the direction. We denote this vector by $\overrightarrow{AB}$. Point A is the **initial point**, and B is the **terminal point** of the vector $\overrightarrow{AB}$. The length of the line segment AB is called the **magnitude** or **length** of the vector and is denoted by $|\overrightarrow{AB}|$. We use boldface letters to denote vectors. Thus, we write $\mathbf{u} = \overrightarrow{AB}$.

Two vectors are considered **equal** if they have equal magnitude and the same direction. Thus, all the vectors in Figure 2 are equal. This definition of equality makes sense if we think of a vector as representing a displacement. Two such displacements are the same if they have equal magnitudes and the same direction. So the vectors in Figure 2 can be thought of as the *same* displacement applied to objects in different locations in the plane.

FIGURE 2

If the displacement $\mathbf{u} = \overrightarrow{AB}$ is followed by the displacement $\mathbf{v} = \overrightarrow{BC}$, then the resulting displacement is $\overrightarrow{AC}$ as shown in Figure 3. In other words, the single displacement represented by the vector $\overrightarrow{AC}$ has the same effect as the other two displacements together. We call the vector $\overrightarrow{AC}$ the **sum** of the vectors $\overrightarrow{AB}$ and $\overrightarrow{BC}$ and we write $\overrightarrow{AC} = \overrightarrow{AB} + \overrightarrow{BC}$. (The **zero vector**, denoted by $\mathbf{0}$, represents no displacement). Thus, to find the sum of any two vectors $\mathbf{u}$ and $\mathbf{v}$, we sketch vectors equal to $\mathbf{u}$ and $\mathbf{v}$ with the initial point of one at the terminal point of the other

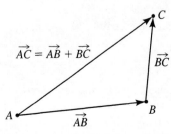

$\overrightarrow{AC} = \overrightarrow{AB} + \overrightarrow{BC}$

FIGURE 3

[see Figure 4(a)]. If we draw **u** and **v** starting at the same point, then **u** + **v** is the vector that is the diagonal of the parallelogram formed by **u** and **v**, as shown in Figure 4(b).

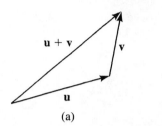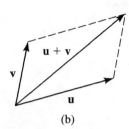

FIGURE 4

Addition of vectors

(a)   (b)

If a is a real number and **v** is a vector, we define a new vector a**v** as follows: The vector a**v** has magnitude $|a||\mathbf{v}|$ and has the same direction as **v** if $a > 0$, or the opposite direction if $a < 0$. If $a = 0$, then $a\mathbf{v} = \mathbf{0}$, the zero vector. This process is called **multiplication of a vector by a scalar**. Multiplying a vector by a scalar has the effect of stretching or shrinking the vector. Figure 5 shows graphs of the vector a**v** for different values of a. We write the vector $(-1)\mathbf{v}$ as $-\mathbf{v}$. Thus, $-\mathbf{v}$ is the vector with the same length as **v** but with the opposite direction.

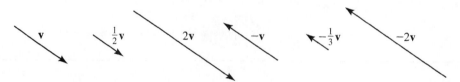

FIGURE 5

Multiplication of a vector by a scalar

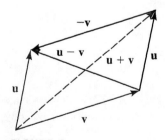

FIGURE 6

Subtraction of vectors

The **difference** of two vectors **u** and **v** is defined by $\mathbf{u} - \mathbf{v} = \mathbf{u} + (-\mathbf{v})$. Figure 6 shows that the vector $\mathbf{u} - \mathbf{v}$ is the other diagonal of the parallelogram formed by **u** and **v**.

■ Analytic Description of Vectors

So far we've discussed vectors geometrically. By placing a vector in a coordinate plane, we can describe it analytically (that is, by using components). In Figure 7(a), to go from the initial point of the vector **v** to the terminal point, we move a units to the right and b units upward. We represent **v** as an ordered pair of real numbers.

Note the distinction between the *vector* $\langle a, b \rangle$ and the *point* (a, b).

$$\mathbf{v} = \langle a, b \rangle$$

where a is the **horizontal component** of **v** and b is the **vertical component** of **v**. Remember that a vector represents a magnitude and a direction, not a particular arrow in the plane. Thus, the vector $\langle a, b \rangle$ has many different representations, depending on its initial point [see Figure 7(b)].

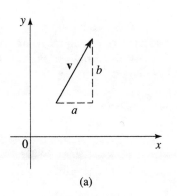

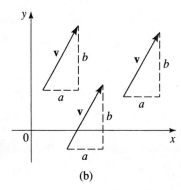

FIGURE 7   (a)   (b)

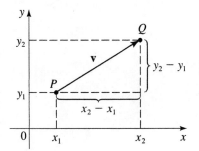

FIGURE 8

Using Figure 8, the relationship between a geometric representation of a vector and the analytic one can be stated as follows.

COMPONENT FORM OF A VECTOR

If a vector $\mathbf{v}$ is represented in the plane with initial point $P(x_1, y_1)$ and terminal point $Q(x_2, y_2)$, then

$$\mathbf{v} = \langle x_2 - x_1, y_2 - y_1 \rangle$$

EXAMPLE 1 ■ Describing Vectors in Component Form

(a) Find the component form of the vector $\mathbf{u}$ with initial point $(-2, 5)$ and terminal point $(3, 7)$.

(b) If the vector $\mathbf{v} = \langle 3, 7 \rangle$ is sketched with initial point $(2, 4)$, what is its terminal point?

(c) Sketch representations of the vector $\mathbf{w} = \langle 2, 3 \rangle$ with initial points at $(0, 0)$, $(2, 2)$, $(-2, -1)$, and $(1, 4)$.

SOLUTION

(a) The desired vector is

$$\mathbf{u} = \langle 3 - (-2), 7 - 5 \rangle = \langle 5, 2 \rangle$$

(b) Let the terminal point of $\mathbf{v}$ be (x, y). Then

$$\langle x - 2, y - 4 \rangle = \langle 3, 7 \rangle$$

So $x - 2 = 3$ and $y - 4 = 7$, or $x = 5$ and $y = 11$. The terminal point is $(5, 11)$.

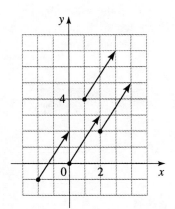

FIGURE 9

(c) Representations of the vector $\mathbf{w}$ are sketched in Figure 9. ■

We now give analytic definitions of the various operations on vectors that we have described geometrically. Let's start with equality of vectors. We've said that two vectors are equal if they have equal magnitude and the same direction. For the

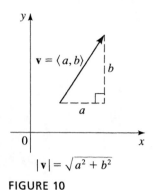

$$|\mathbf{v}| = \sqrt{a^2 + b^2}$$

FIGURE 10

vectors $\mathbf{u} = \langle a_1, b_1 \rangle$ and $\mathbf{v} = \langle a_2, b_2 \rangle$, this means that $a_1 = a_2$ and $b_1 = b_2$. In other words, two vectors are **equal** if and only if their corresponding components are equal. Thus, all the arrows in Figure 7(b) represent the same vector, as do all the arrows in Figure 9.

Applying the Pythagorean Theorem to the triangle in Figure 10, we obtain the following formula for the magnitude of a vector.

MAGNITUDE OF A VECTOR

The **magnitude** or **length** of a vector $\mathbf{v} = \langle a, b \rangle$ is

$$|\mathbf{v}| = \sqrt{a^2 + b^2}$$

EXAMPLE 2 ■ Magnitudes of Vectors

Find the magnitude of each vector.

(a) $\mathbf{u} = \langle 2, -3 \rangle$ (b) $\mathbf{v} = \langle 5, 0 \rangle$ (c) $\mathbf{w} = \left\langle \frac{3}{5}, \frac{4}{5} \right\rangle$

SOLUTION

(a) $|\mathbf{u}| = \sqrt{2^2 + (-3)^2} = \sqrt{13}$

(b) $|\mathbf{v}| = \sqrt{5^2 + 0^2} = \sqrt{25} = 5$

(c) $|\mathbf{w}| = \sqrt{\left(\frac{3}{5}\right)^2 + \left(\frac{4}{5}\right)^2} = \sqrt{\frac{9}{25} + \frac{16}{25}} = 1$ ■

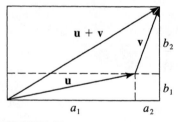

FIGURE 11

The following definitions of addition, subtraction, and scalar multiplication of vectors correspond to the geometric descriptions given earlier. Figure 11 shows how the analytic definition of addition corresponds to the geometric one.

ALGEBRAIC OPERATIONS ON VECTORS

If $\mathbf{u} = \langle a_1, b_1 \rangle$ and $\mathbf{v} = \langle a_2, b_2 \rangle$, then

$$\mathbf{u} + \mathbf{v} = \langle a_1 + a_2, b_1 + b_2 \rangle$$

$$\mathbf{u} - \mathbf{v} = \langle a_1 - a_2, b_1 - b_2 \rangle$$

$$c\mathbf{u} = \langle ca_1, cb_1 \rangle, \qquad c \in \mathbb{R}$$

EXAMPLE 3 ■ Operations with Vectors

If $\mathbf{u} = \langle 2, -3 \rangle$ and $\mathbf{v} = \langle -1, 2 \rangle$, find $\mathbf{u} + \mathbf{v}$, $\mathbf{u} - \mathbf{v}$, $2\mathbf{u}$, $-3\mathbf{v}$, and $2\mathbf{u} + 3\mathbf{v}$.

SOLUTION

By the definitions of the vector operations, we have

$$\mathbf{u} + \mathbf{v} = \langle 2, -3 \rangle + \langle -1, 2 \rangle = \langle 1, -1 \rangle$$

$$\mathbf{u} - \mathbf{v} = \langle 2, -3 \rangle - \langle -1, 2 \rangle = \langle 3, -5 \rangle$$

$$2\mathbf{u} = 2\langle 2, -3 \rangle = \langle 4, -6 \rangle$$

$$-3\mathbf{v} = -3\langle -1, 2 \rangle = \langle 3, -6 \rangle$$

$$2\mathbf{u} + 3\mathbf{v} = 2\langle 2, -3 \rangle + 3\langle -1, 2 \rangle = \langle 4, -6 \rangle + \langle -3, 6 \rangle = \langle 1, 0 \rangle \quad \blacksquare$$

The following properties for vector operations can be easily proved from the definitions. The **zero vector** is the vector $\mathbf{0} = \langle 0, 0 \rangle$. It plays the same role for addition of vectors as the number 0 does for addition of real numbers.

PROPERTIES OF VECTORS

Vector addition	Multiplication by a scalar
$\mathbf{u} + \mathbf{v} = \mathbf{v} + \mathbf{u}$	$c(\mathbf{u} + \mathbf{v}) = c\mathbf{u} + c\mathbf{v}$
$\mathbf{u} + (\mathbf{v} + \mathbf{w}) = (\mathbf{u} + \mathbf{v}) + \mathbf{w}$	$(c + d)\mathbf{u} = c\mathbf{u} + d\mathbf{u}$
$\mathbf{u} + \mathbf{0} = \mathbf{u}$	$(cd)\mathbf{u} = c(d\mathbf{u}) = d(c\mathbf{u})$
$\mathbf{u} + (-\mathbf{u}) = \mathbf{0}$	$1\mathbf{u} = \mathbf{u}$
Length of a vector	$0\mathbf{u} = \mathbf{0}$
$|c\mathbf{u}| = |c|\,|\mathbf{u}|$	$c\mathbf{0} = \mathbf{0}$

A vector of length 1 is called a **unit vector**. For instance, in Example 2(c), the vector $\mathbf{w} = \langle \frac{3}{5}, \frac{4}{5} \rangle$ is a unit vector. Two useful unit vectors are $\mathbf{i}$ and $\mathbf{j}$, defined by

$$\mathbf{i} = \langle 1, 0 \rangle \qquad \mathbf{j} = \langle 0, 1 \rangle$$

These vectors are special because any vector can be expressed in terms of them.

VECTORS IN TERMS OF i AND j

The vector $\mathbf{v} = \langle a, b \rangle$ can be expressed in terms of $\mathbf{i}$ and $\mathbf{j}$ by

$$\mathbf{v} = \langle a, b \rangle = a\mathbf{i} + b\mathbf{j}$$

EXAMPLE 4 ■ Vectors in Terms of i and j

(a) Write the vector $\mathbf{u} = \langle 5, -8 \rangle$ in terms of $\mathbf{i}$ and $\mathbf{j}$.
(b) If $\mathbf{u} = 3\mathbf{i} + 2\mathbf{j}$ and $\mathbf{v} = -\mathbf{i} + 6\mathbf{j}$, write $2\mathbf{u} + 5\mathbf{v}$ in terms of $\mathbf{i}$ and $\mathbf{j}$.

SOLUTION

(a) $\mathbf{u} = 5\mathbf{i} + (-8)\mathbf{j} = 5\mathbf{i} - 8\mathbf{j}$

(b) The properties of addition and scalar multiplication of vectors show that we can manipulate vectors in the same way as algebraic expressions. Thus

$$2\mathbf{u} + 5\mathbf{v} = 2(3\mathbf{i} + 2\mathbf{j}) + 5(-\mathbf{i} + 6\mathbf{j})$$

$$= (6\mathbf{i} + 4\mathbf{j}) + (-5\mathbf{i} + 30\mathbf{j})$$

$$= \mathbf{i} + 34\mathbf{j} \qquad\blacksquare$$

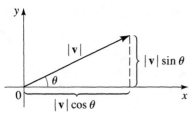

FIGURE 12

Let $\mathbf{v}$ be a vector in the plane with its initial point at the origin. The **direction** of $\mathbf{v}$ is θ, the smallest positive angle in standard position formed by the positive x-axis and $\mathbf{v}$ (see Figure 12). If we know the magnitude and direction of a vector, then Figure 12 shows that we can find the horizontal and vertical components of the vector.

HORIZONTAL AND VERTICAL COMPONENTS OF A VECTOR

Let $\mathbf{v}$ be a vector with magnitude $|\mathbf{v}|$ and direction θ.
Then $\mathbf{v} = \langle a, b \rangle = a\mathbf{i} + b\mathbf{j}$, where

$$a = |\mathbf{v}| \cos \theta \qquad \text{and} \qquad b = |\mathbf{v}| \sin \theta$$

EXAMPLE 5 ■ Components and Direction of a Vector

(a) A vector $\mathbf{v}$ has length 8 and direction $\pi/3$. Find the horizontal and vertical components, and write $\mathbf{v}$ in terms of $\mathbf{i}$ and $\mathbf{j}$.

(b) Find the direction of the vector $\mathbf{u} = -\sqrt{3}\,\mathbf{i} + \mathbf{j}$.

SOLUTION

(a) We have $\mathbf{v} = \langle a, b \rangle$, where the components are given by

$$a = 8 \cos \frac{\pi}{3} = 4 \qquad \text{and} \qquad b = 8 \sin \frac{\pi}{3} = 4\sqrt{3}$$

Thus, $\mathbf{v} = \langle 4, 4\sqrt{3} \rangle = 4\mathbf{i} + 4\sqrt{3}\,\mathbf{j}$.

(b) From Figure 13 we see that the direction θ has the property that

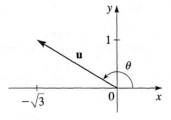

FIGURE 13

$$\tan \theta = \frac{1}{-\sqrt{3}} = -\frac{\sqrt{3}}{3}$$

Thus, the reference angle for θ is $\pi/6$. Since the terminal point of the vector $\mathbf{u}$ is in quadrant II, it follows that $\theta = 5\pi/6$. $\qquad\blacksquare$

Using Vectors to Model Velocity and Force

The use of bearings (such as N 30° E) to describe directions is explained on page 515 in Section 6.5.

The **velocity** of a moving object is modeled by a vector whose direction is the direction of motion and whose magnitude is the speed. Figure 14 shows some vectors **u**, representing the velocity of wind flowing in the direction N 30° E, and a vector **v**, representing the velocity of an airplane flying through this wind at the point P. It's obvious from our experience that wind affects both the speed and the direction of an airplane. Figure 15 indicates that the true velocity of the plane (relative to the ground) is given by the vector **w** = **u** + **v**.

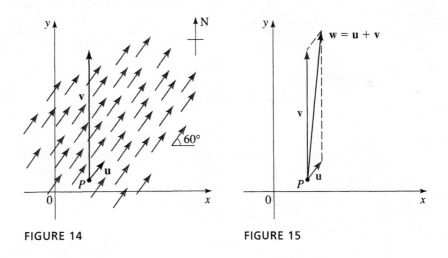

FIGURE 14   FIGURE 15

EXAMPLE 6 ■ The True Speed and Direction of an Airplane

An airplane heads due north at 300 mi/h. It experiences a 40 mi/h crosswind flowing in the direction N 30° E, as shown in Figure 14.

(a) Express the velocity **v** of the airplane relative to the air, and the velocity **u** of the wind, in component form.

(b) Find the true velocity of the airplane as a vector.

(c) Find the true speed and direction of the airplane.

SOLUTION

(a) The velocity of the airplane relative to the air is **v** = 0**i** + 300**j** = 300**j**.

By the formulas for the components of a vector, we find that the velocity of the wind is

$$\mathbf{u} = (40 \cos 60°)\mathbf{i} + (40 \sin 60°)\mathbf{j}$$

$$= 20\mathbf{i} + 20\sqrt{3}\,\mathbf{j}$$

$$\approx 20\mathbf{i} + 34.64\,\mathbf{j}$$

(b) The true velocity of the airplane is given by the vector $\mathbf{w} = \mathbf{u} + \mathbf{v}$.

$$\mathbf{w} = \mathbf{u} + \mathbf{v} = (20\mathbf{i} + 20\sqrt{3}\,\mathbf{j}) + (300\mathbf{j})$$
$$= 20\mathbf{i} + (20\sqrt{3} + 300)\mathbf{j}$$
$$\approx 20\mathbf{i} + 334.64\,\mathbf{j}$$

(c) The true speed of the airplane is given by the magnitude of $\mathbf{w}$.

$$|\mathbf{w}| \approx \sqrt{(20)^2 + (334.64)^2} \approx 335.2 \text{ mi/h}$$

The direction of the airplane is the direction θ of the vector $\mathbf{w}$. The angle θ has the property that $\tan\theta \approx 334.64/20 = 16.732$ and so $\theta \approx 86.6°$. Thus, the airplane is heading in the direction N 3.4° E.   ∎

EXAMPLE 7 ■ Calculating a Heading

A woman launches a boat from one shore of a straight river and wants to land at the point directly on the opposite shore. If the speed of the boat (relative to the water) is 10 mi/h and the river is flowing east at the rate of 5 mi/h, in what direction should she head the boat in order to arrive at the desired landing point?

SOLUTION

We choose a coordinate system with the origin at the initial position of the boat as shown in Figure 16. Let $\mathbf{u}$ and $\mathbf{v}$ represent the velocities of the river and the boat, respectively. Clearly, $\mathbf{u} = 5\mathbf{i}$ and, since the speed of the boat is 10 mi/h, we have $|\mathbf{v}| = 10$, so

$$\mathbf{v} = (10\cos\theta)\mathbf{i} + (10\sin\theta)\mathbf{j}$$

where the angle θ is as shown in Figure 16. The true course of the boat is given by the vector $\mathbf{w} = \mathbf{u} + \mathbf{v}$. We have

$$\mathbf{w} = \mathbf{u} + \mathbf{v} = 5\mathbf{i} + (10\cos\theta)\mathbf{i} + (10\sin\theta)\mathbf{j}$$
$$= (5 + 10\cos\theta)\mathbf{i} + (10\sin\theta)\mathbf{j}$$

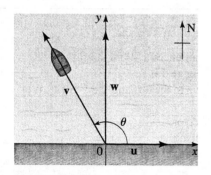

FIGURE 16

Since the woman wants to land at a point directly across the river, her direction should have horizontal component 0. In other words, she should choose θ in such a way that

$$5 + 10\cos\theta = 0$$
$$\cos\theta = -\tfrac{1}{2}$$
$$\theta = 120°$$

Thus, she should head the boat in the direction $\theta = 120°$ (or N 30° W).   ∎

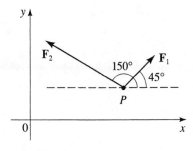

FIGURE 17

Force is also represented by a vector. Intuitively, we can think of force as describing a push or a pull on an object, for example, a horizontal push of a book across a table or the downward pull of the earth's gravity on a ball. Force is measured in pounds (or in newtons, in the metric system). For instance, a man weighing 200 lb exerts a force of 200 lb downward on the ground. If several forces are acting on an object, the **resultant force** experienced by the object is the vector sum of these forces.

EXAMPLE 8 ■ Resultant Force

Two forces $\mathbf{F}_1$ and $\mathbf{F}_2$ with magnitudes 10 and 20 lb, respectively, act on an object at a point P as shown in Figure 17. Find the resultant force acting at P.

SOLUTION

We write $\mathbf{F}_1$ and $\mathbf{F}_2$ in component form:

$$\mathbf{F}_1 = (10 \cos 45°)\mathbf{i} + (10 \sin 45°)\mathbf{j} = 10 \frac{\sqrt{2}}{2}\mathbf{i} + 10 \frac{\sqrt{2}}{2}\mathbf{j} = 5\sqrt{2}\,\mathbf{i} + 5\sqrt{2}\,\mathbf{j}$$

$$\mathbf{F}_2 = (20 \cos 150°)\mathbf{i} + (20 \sin 150°)\mathbf{j} = -20 \frac{\sqrt{3}}{2}\mathbf{i} + 20\left(\frac{1}{2}\right)\mathbf{j}$$

$$= -10\sqrt{3}\,\mathbf{i} + 10\mathbf{j}$$

So the resultant force $\mathbf{F}$ is

$$\mathbf{F} = \mathbf{F}_1 + \mathbf{F}_2$$
$$= \left(5\sqrt{2}\,\mathbf{i} + 5\sqrt{2}\,\mathbf{j}\right) + \left(-10\sqrt{3}\,\mathbf{i} + 10\mathbf{j}\right)$$
$$= \left(5\sqrt{2} - 10\sqrt{3}\right)\mathbf{i} + \left(5\sqrt{2} + 10\right)\mathbf{j}$$
$$\approx -10\mathbf{i} + 17\mathbf{j}$$

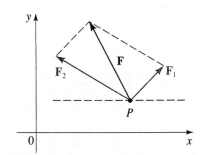

FIGURE 18

The resultant force $\mathbf{F}$ is shown in Figure 18.   ■

7.7   EXERCISES

1–6 ■ Sketch the vector indicated. (The vectors $\mathbf{u}$ and $\mathbf{v}$ are shown in the figure.)

1. $2\mathbf{u}$

2. $-\mathbf{v}$

3. $\mathbf{u} + \mathbf{v}$

4. $\mathbf{u} - \mathbf{v}$

5. $\mathbf{v} - 2\mathbf{u}$

6. $2\mathbf{u} + \mathbf{v}$

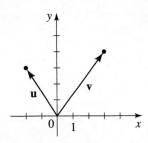

7–16 ■ Express the vector with initial point P and terminal point Q in component form.

7.

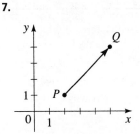

8.

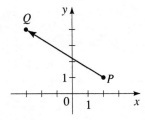

9.

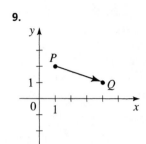

10.

11. $P(3, 2)$, $Q(8, 9)$ **12.** $P(1, 1)$, $Q(9, 9)$

13. $P(5, 3)$, $Q(1, 0)$ **14.** $P(-1, 3)$, $Q(-6, -1)$

15. $P(-1, -1)$, $Q(-1, 1)$ **16.** $P(-8, -6)$, $Q(-1, -1)$

17–22 ■ Find $2\mathbf{u}$, $-3\mathbf{v}$, $\mathbf{u} + \mathbf{v}$, and $3\mathbf{u} - 4\mathbf{v}$ for the given vectors $\mathbf{u}$ and $\mathbf{v}$.

17. $\mathbf{u} = \langle 2, 7 \rangle$, $\mathbf{v} = \langle 3, 1 \rangle$ **18.** $\mathbf{u} = \langle -2, 5 \rangle$, $\mathbf{v} = \langle 2, -8 \rangle$

19. $\mathbf{u} = \langle 0, -1 \rangle$, $\mathbf{v} = \langle -2, 0 \rangle$

20. $\mathbf{u} = \mathbf{i}$, $\mathbf{v} = -2\mathbf{j}$

21. $\mathbf{u} = 2\mathbf{i}$, $\mathbf{v} = 3\mathbf{i} - 2\mathbf{j}$ **22.** $\mathbf{u} = \mathbf{i} + \mathbf{j}$, $\mathbf{v} = \mathbf{i} - \mathbf{j}$

23–26 ■ Find $|\mathbf{u}|$, $|\mathbf{v}|$, $|2\mathbf{u}|$, $\left|\frac{1}{2}\mathbf{v}\right|$, $|\mathbf{u} + \mathbf{v}|$, $|\mathbf{u} - \mathbf{v}|$, and $|\mathbf{u}| - |\mathbf{v}|$.

23. $\mathbf{u} = 2\mathbf{i} + \mathbf{j}$, $\mathbf{v} = 3\mathbf{i} - 2\mathbf{j}$

24. $\mathbf{u} = -2\mathbf{i} + 3\mathbf{j}$, $\mathbf{v} = \mathbf{i} - 2\mathbf{j}$

25. $\mathbf{u} = \langle 10, -1 \rangle$, $\mathbf{v} = \langle -2, -2 \rangle$

26. $\mathbf{u} = \langle -6, 6 \rangle$, $\mathbf{v} = \langle -2, -1 \rangle$

27–32 ■ Find the horizontal and vertical components of the vector with given length and direction, and write the vector in terms of the vectors $\mathbf{i}$ and $\mathbf{j}$.

27. $|\mathbf{v}| = 40$, $\theta = 30°$ **28.** $|\mathbf{v}| = 50$, $\theta = 120°$

29. $|\mathbf{v}| = 1$, $\theta = 225°$ **30.** $|\mathbf{v}| = 800$, $\theta = 125°$

31. $|\mathbf{v}| = 4$, $\theta = 10°$ **32.** $|\mathbf{v}| = \sqrt{3}$, $\theta = 300°$

33. A man pushes a lawn mower with a force of 30 lb exerted at an angle of 30° to the ground. Find the horizontal and vertical components of the force.

34. A jet is flying in a direction N 20° E with a speed of 500 mi/h. Find the north and east components of the velocity.

35–40 ■ Find the magnitude and direction (in degrees) of the vector.

35. $\mathbf{v} = \langle 3, 4 \rangle$ **36.** $\mathbf{v} = \left\langle -\dfrac{\sqrt{2}}{2}, -\dfrac{\sqrt{2}}{2} \right\rangle$

37. $\mathbf{v} = \langle -12, 5 \rangle$ **38.** $\mathbf{v} = \langle 40, 9 \rangle$

39. $\mathbf{v} = \mathbf{i} + \sqrt{3}\,\mathbf{j}$ **40.** $\mathbf{v} = \mathbf{i} + \mathbf{j}$

41. A river flows due south at 3 mi/h. A swimmer attempting to cross the river heads due east swimming at 2 mi/h relative to the water. Find the true velocity of the swimmer.

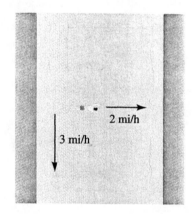

42. A migrating salmon heads in the direction N 45° E, swimming at 5 mi/h relative to the water. The prevailing ocean currents flow due east at 3 mi/h. Find the true velocity of the fish.

43. A pilot heads his jet due east. The jet has a speed of 425 mi/h relative to the air. The wind is blowing due north with a speed of 40 mi/h.
(a) Express the velocity of the wind as a vector in component form.
(b) Express the velocity of the jet relative to the air as a vector in component form.
(c) Find the true velocity of the jet.
(d) Find the true speed and direction of the jet.

44. A jet is flying through a wind that is blowing with a speed of 55 mi/h in the direction N 30° E (see the figure). The jet has a speed of 765 mi/h relative to the air, and the pilot heads the jet in the direction N 45° E.
(a) Express the velocity of the wind as a vector in component form.
(b) Express the velocity of the jet relative to the air as a vector in component form.
(c) Find the true velocity of the jet.

(d) Find the true speed and direction of the jet.

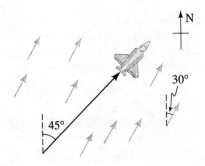

45. Find the true speed and direction of the jet in Exercise 44 if the pilot heads the plane in the direction N 30° W.

46. In what direction should the pilot in Exercise 44 head the plane for the true course to be due north?

47. A straight river flows east at a speed of 10 mi/h. A boater starts at the south shore of the river and heads in a direction 60° from the shore (see the figure). The motorboat has a speed of 20 mi/h relative to the water.
 (a) Express the velocity of the river as a vector in component form.
 (b) Express the velocity of the motorboat relative to the water as a vector in component form.
 (c) Find the true velocity of the motorboat.
 (d) Find the true speed and direction of the motorboat.

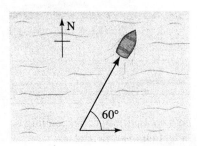

48. The boater in Exercise 47 wants to arrive at a point on the north shore of the river directly opposite the starting point. In what direction should the boat be headed?

49. A boat heads in the direction N 72° E. The speed of the boat relative to the water is 24 mi/h. The water is flowing directly south. It is observed that the true direction of the boat is directly east.
 (a) Express the velocity of the boat relative to the water as a vector in component form.
 (b) Find the speed of the water and the true speed of the boat.

50. A woman walks due west on the deck of an ocean liner at 2 mi/h. The ocean liner is moving due north at a speed of 25 mi/h. Find the speed and direction of the woman relative to the surface of the water.

51–56 ■ The forces $F_1, F_2, \ldots, F_n$ acting at the same point P are said to be in equilibrium if the resultant force is zero, that is, if $F_1 + F_2 + \cdots + F_n = 0$. Find (a) the resultant forces acting at P, and (b) the additional force required (if any) for the forces to be in equilibrium.

51. $F_1 = \langle 2, 5 \rangle$, $F_2 = \langle 3, -8 \rangle$

52. $F_1 = \langle 3, -7 \rangle$, $F_2 = \langle 4, -2 \rangle$, $F_3 = \langle -7, 9 \rangle$

53. $F_1 = 4i - j$, $F_2 = 3i - 7j$,
   $F_3 = -8i + 3j$, $F_4 = i + j$

54. $F_1 = i - j$, $F_2 = i + j$, $F_3 = -2i + j$

55.

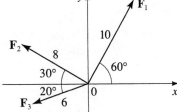

56.

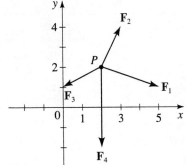

57. A 100-lb weight hangs from a string as shown in the figure. Find the tensions T_1 and T_2 in the string.

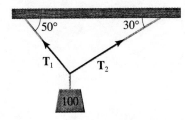

58. The cranes in the figure are lifting an object that weighs 18,278 lb. Find the tensions T_1 and T_2.

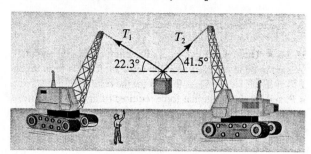

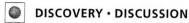

59. Vectors That Form a Polygon Suppose that n vectors can be placed head to tail in the plane so that they form a polygon. (The figure shows the case of a hexagon.) Explain why the sum of these vectors is **0**.

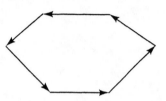

7.8 THE DOT PRODUCT

In this section we define an operation on vectors called the dot product. This concept is very useful in calculus and in applications of vectors to physics and engineering.

The Dot Product of Vectors

We begin by defining the dot product of two vectors.

> **DEFINITION OF THE DOT PRODUCT**
>
> If $\mathbf{u} = \langle a_1, b_1 \rangle$ and $\mathbf{v} = \langle a_2, b_2 \rangle$ are vectors, then their **dot product**, denoted by $\mathbf{u} \cdot \mathbf{v}$, is defined by
>
> $$\mathbf{u} \cdot \mathbf{v} = a_1 a_2 + b_1 b_2$$

Thus, to find the dot product of $\mathbf{u}$ and $\mathbf{v}$ we multiply corresponding components and add. The result is *not* a vector; it is a real number, or scalar.

EXAMPLE 1 ■ **Calculating Dot Products**

(a) If $\mathbf{u} = \langle 3, -2 \rangle$ and $\mathbf{v} = \langle 4, 5 \rangle$, then

$$\mathbf{u} \cdot \mathbf{v} = (3)(4) + (-2)(5) = 2$$

(b) If $\mathbf{u} = 2\mathbf{i} + \mathbf{j}$ and $\mathbf{v} = 5\mathbf{i} - 6\mathbf{j}$, then

$$\mathbf{u} \cdot \mathbf{v} = (2)(5) + (1)(-6) = 4$$ ■

The proofs of the following properties of the dot product follow easily from the definition.

PROPERTIES OF THE DOT PRODUCT

$$\mathbf{u} \cdot \mathbf{v} = \mathbf{v} \cdot \mathbf{u}$$

$$(a\mathbf{u}) \cdot \mathbf{v} = a(\mathbf{u} \cdot \mathbf{v}) = \mathbf{u} \cdot (a\mathbf{v})$$

$$(\mathbf{u} + \mathbf{v}) \cdot \mathbf{w} = \mathbf{u} \cdot \mathbf{w} + \mathbf{v} \cdot \mathbf{w}$$

$$|\mathbf{u}|^2 = \mathbf{u} \cdot \mathbf{u}$$

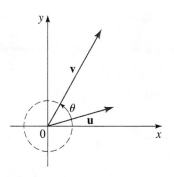

FIGURE 1

■ **Proof** We prove only the last property. The proofs of the others are left as exercises. Let $\mathbf{u} = \langle a\ b \rangle$. Then

$$\mathbf{u} \cdot \mathbf{u} = \langle a, b \rangle \cdot \langle a, b \rangle = a^2 + b^2 = |\mathbf{u}|^2 \qquad \square$$

Let $\mathbf{u}$ and $\mathbf{v}$ be vectors and sketch them with initial points at the origin. We define the **angle θ between u and v** to be the smaller of the angles formed by these representations of $\mathbf{u}$ and $\mathbf{v}$ (see Figure 1). Thus, $0 \le \theta \le \pi$. The next theorem relates the angle between two vectors to their dot product.

THE DOT PRODUCT THEOREM

If θ is the angle between two nonzero vectors $\mathbf{u}$ and $\mathbf{v}$, then

$$\mathbf{u} \cdot \mathbf{v} = |\mathbf{u}|\,|\mathbf{v}| \cos \theta$$

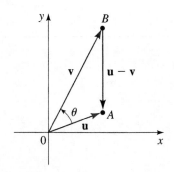

FIGURE 2

■ **Proof** The proof is a nice application of the Law of Cosines. Applying the Law of Cosines to triangle AOB in Figure 2 gives

$$|\mathbf{u} - \mathbf{v}|^2 = |\mathbf{u}|^2 + |\mathbf{v}|^2 - 2|\mathbf{u}|\,|\mathbf{v}| \cos \theta$$

Using the properties of the dot product, we write the left-hand side as follows:

$$|\mathbf{u} - \mathbf{v}|^2 = (\mathbf{u} - \mathbf{v}) \cdot (\mathbf{u} - \mathbf{v})$$

$$= \mathbf{u} \cdot \mathbf{u} - \mathbf{u} \cdot \mathbf{v} - \mathbf{v} \cdot \mathbf{u} + \mathbf{v} \cdot \mathbf{v}$$

$$= |\mathbf{u}|^2 - 2(\mathbf{u} \cdot \mathbf{v}) + |\mathbf{v}|^2$$

Equating the right-hand sides of the displayed equations, we get

$$|\mathbf{u}|^2 - 2(\mathbf{u} \cdot \mathbf{v}) + |\mathbf{v}|^2 = |\mathbf{u}|^2 + |\mathbf{v}|^2 - 2|\mathbf{u}|\,|\mathbf{v}| \cos \theta$$

$$-2(\mathbf{u} \cdot \mathbf{v}) = -2|\mathbf{u}|\,|\mathbf{v}| \cos \theta$$

$$\mathbf{u} \cdot \mathbf{v} = |\mathbf{u}|\,|\mathbf{v}| \cos \theta$$

This proves the theorem. $\qquad \square$

The Dot Product Theorem is useful because it allows us to find the angle between two vectors if we know the components of the vectors. The angle is obtained simply by solving the equation in the Dot Product Theorem for $\cos \theta$. We state this important result explicitly.

> **ANGLE BETWEEN TWO VECTORS**
>
> If θ is the angle between two nonzero vectors $\mathbf{u}$ and $\mathbf{v}$, then
>
> $$\cos \theta = \frac{\mathbf{u} \cdot \mathbf{v}}{|\mathbf{u}||\mathbf{v}|}$$

EXAMPLE 2 ■ Finding the Angle between Two Vectors

Find the angle between the vectors $\mathbf{u} = \langle 2, 5 \rangle$ and $\mathbf{v} = \langle 4, -3 \rangle$.

SOLUTION

By the formula for the angle between two vectors, we have

$$\cos \theta = \frac{\mathbf{u} \cdot \mathbf{v}}{|\mathbf{u}||\mathbf{v}|} = \frac{(2)(4) + (5)(-3)}{\sqrt{4 + 25}\sqrt{16 + 9}} = \frac{-7}{5\sqrt{29}}$$

Thus, the angle between $\mathbf{u}$ and $\mathbf{v}$ is

$$\theta = \cos^{-1}\left(\frac{-7}{5\sqrt{29}}\right) \approx 105.1° \qquad ■$$

Two nonzero vectors $\mathbf{u}$ and $\mathbf{v}$ are called **perpendicular**, or **orthogonal**, if the angle between them is $\pi/2$. The following theorem shows that we can determine if two vectors are perpendicular by finding their dot product.

> **ORTHOGONAL VECTORS**
>
> Two nonzero vectors $\mathbf{u}$ and $\mathbf{v}$ are perpendicular if and only if $\mathbf{u} \cdot \mathbf{v} = 0$.

■ **Proof** If $\mathbf{u}$ and $\mathbf{v}$ are perpendicular, then the angle between them is $\pi/2$ and so

$$\mathbf{u} \cdot \mathbf{v} = |\mathbf{u}||\mathbf{v}| \cos \frac{\pi}{2} = 0$$

Conversely, if $\mathbf{u} \cdot \mathbf{v} = 0$, then

$$|\mathbf{u}||\mathbf{v}| \cos \theta = 0$$

Since $\mathbf{u}$ and $\mathbf{v}$ are nonzero vectors, we conclude that $\cos \theta = 0$, and so $\theta = \pi/2$. Thus, $\mathbf{u}$ and $\mathbf{v}$ are orthogonal. ☐

EXAMPLE 3 ■ Checking Vectors for Perpendicularity

Determine whether the vectors in each pair are perpendicular.

(a) $\mathbf{u} = \langle 3, 5 \rangle$ and $\mathbf{v} = \langle 2, -8 \rangle$ (b) $\mathbf{u} = \langle 2, 1 \rangle$ and $\mathbf{v} = \langle -1, 2 \rangle$

SOLUTION

(a) $\mathbf{u} \cdot \mathbf{v} = (3)(2) + (5)(-8) = -34 \neq 0$, so $\mathbf{u}$ and $\mathbf{v}$ are not perpendicular.

(b) $\mathbf{u} \cdot \mathbf{v} = (2)(-1) + (1)(2) = 0$, so $\mathbf{u}$ and $\mathbf{v}$ are perpendicular. ■

▊ The Component of u Along v

The **component of u along v** (or the **component of u in the direction of v**) is defined to be

Note that the component of **u** along **v** is a scalar, not a vector.

$$|\mathbf{u}| \cos \theta$$

where θ is the angle between $\mathbf{u}$ and $\mathbf{v}$. Figure 3 gives a geometric interpretation of this concept. Intuitively, the component of $\mathbf{u}$ along $\mathbf{v}$ is the magnitude of the portion of $\mathbf{u}$ that points in the direction of $\mathbf{v}$. Notice that the component of $\mathbf{u}$ along $\mathbf{v}$ is negative if $\pi/2 < \theta \leq \pi$.

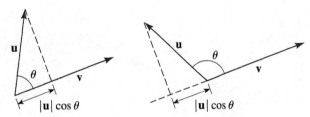

FIGURE 3

When analyzing forces in physics and engineering, it's often helpful to express a vector as a sum of two vectors lying in perpendicular directions. For example, suppose a car is parked on an inclined driveway as in Figure 4. The weight of the car is a vector $\mathbf{w}$ that points directly downward. We can write

$$\mathbf{w} = \mathbf{u} + \mathbf{v}$$

where $\mathbf{u}$ is parallel to the driveway and $\mathbf{v}$ is perpendicular to the driveway. The vector $\mathbf{u}$ is the force that tends to roll the car down the driveway, and $\mathbf{v}$ is the force experienced by the surface of the driveway. The magnitudes of these forces are the components of $\mathbf{w}$ along $\mathbf{u}$ and $\mathbf{v}$, respectively.

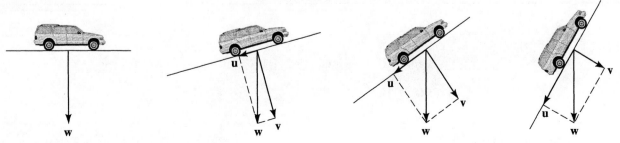

FIGURE 4

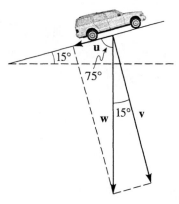

FIGURE 5

EXAMPLE 4 ■ Resolving a Force into Components

A car weighing 3000 lb is parked on a driveway that is inclined 15° to the horizontal, as shown in Figure 5.

(a) Find the magnitude of the force required to prevent the car from rolling down the driveway.
(b) Find the magnitude of the force experienced by the driveway due to the weight of the car.

SOLUTION

The car exerts a force **w** of 3000 lb directly downward. We resolve **w** into the sum of two vectors **u** and **v**, one parallel to the surface of the driveway and the other perpendicular to it, as shown in Figure 5.

(a) The magnitude of the part of the force **w** that causes the car to roll down the driveway is

$$|\mathbf{u}| = \text{component of } \mathbf{w} \text{ along } \mathbf{u} = 3000 \cos 75° \approx 776$$

Thus, the force needed to prevent the car from rolling down the driveway is about 776 lb.

(b) The magnitude of the force exerted by the car on the driveway is

$$|\mathbf{v}| = \text{component of } \mathbf{w} \text{ along } \mathbf{v} = 3000 \cos 15° \approx 2898$$

The force experienced by the driveway is about 2898 lb. ■

The component of **u** along **v** can be computed using dot products:

$$|\mathbf{u}| \cos \theta = \frac{|\mathbf{v}| \, |\mathbf{u}| \cos \theta}{|\mathbf{v}|} = \frac{\mathbf{u} \cdot \mathbf{v}}{|\mathbf{v}|}$$

We have shown the following.

CALCULATING COMPONENTS

The component of **u** along **v** is $\dfrac{\mathbf{u} \cdot \mathbf{v}}{|\mathbf{v}|}$

EXAMPLE 5 ■ Finding Components

Let $\mathbf{u} = \langle 1, 4 \rangle$ and $\mathbf{v} = \langle -2, 1 \rangle$. Find the component of **u** along **v**.

SOLUTION

We have

$$\text{component of } \mathbf{u} \text{ along } \mathbf{v} = \frac{\mathbf{u} \cdot \mathbf{v}}{|\mathbf{v}|} = \frac{(1)(-2) + (4)(1)}{\sqrt{4 + 1}} = \frac{2}{\sqrt{5}}$$

■

The Projection of u onto v

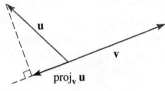

FIGURE 6

Figure 6 shows representations of the vectors **u** and **v**. The projection of **u** onto **v**, denoted by proj$_v$ **u**, is the vector whose *direction* is the same as **v** and whose *length* is the component of **u** along **v**. To find an expression for proj$_v$ **u**, we first find a unit vector in the direction of **v** and then multiply it by the component of **u** along **v**.

$$\text{proj}_v\ \mathbf{u} = (\text{component of } \mathbf{u} \text{ along } \mathbf{v})(\text{unit vector in direction of } \mathbf{v})$$

$$= \left(\frac{\mathbf{u}\cdot\mathbf{v}}{|\mathbf{v}|}\right)\frac{\mathbf{v}}{|\mathbf{v}|} = \left(\frac{\mathbf{u}\cdot\mathbf{v}}{|\mathbf{v}|^2}\right)\mathbf{v}$$

We often need to **resolve** a vector **u** into the sum of two vectors, one parallel to **v** and one orthogonal to **v**. That is, we want to write $\mathbf{u} = \mathbf{u}_1 + \mathbf{u}_2$ where $\mathbf{u}_1$ is parallel to **v** and $\mathbf{u}_2$ is orthogonal to **v**. In this case, $\mathbf{u}_1 = \text{proj}_v\ \mathbf{u}$ and $\mathbf{u}_2 = \mathbf{u} - \text{proj}_v\ \mathbf{u}$ (see Exercise 45).

CALCULATING PROJECTIONS

The **projection of u onto v** is the vector proj$_v$ **u** given by

$$\text{proj}_v\ \mathbf{u} = \left(\frac{\mathbf{u}\cdot\mathbf{v}}{|\mathbf{v}|^2}\right)\mathbf{v}$$

If the vector **u** is **resolved** into $\mathbf{u}_1$ and $\mathbf{u}_2$, where $\mathbf{u}_1$ is parallel to **v** and $\mathbf{u}_2$ is orthogonal to **v**, then

$$\mathbf{u}_1 = \text{proj}_v\ \mathbf{u} \qquad \text{and} \qquad \mathbf{u}_2 = \mathbf{u} - \text{proj}_v\ \mathbf{u}$$

EXAMPLE 6 ■ Resolving a Vector into Orthogonal Vectors

Let $\mathbf{u} = \langle -2, 9\rangle$ and $\mathbf{v} = \langle -1, 2\rangle$.
(a) Find proj$_v$ **u**.
(b) Resolve **u** into $\mathbf{u}_1$ and $\mathbf{u}_2$, where $\mathbf{u}_1$ is parallel to **v** and $\mathbf{u}_2$ is orthogonal to **v**.

SOLUTION

(a) By the formula for the projection of one vector onto another we have

$$\text{proj}_v\ \mathbf{u} = \left(\frac{\mathbf{u}\cdot\mathbf{v}}{|\mathbf{v}|^2}\right)\mathbf{v} \qquad \text{Formula for projection}$$

$$= \left(\frac{\langle -2, 9\rangle\cdot\langle -1, 2\rangle}{(-1)^2 + 2^2}\right)\langle -1, 2\rangle \qquad \text{Definition of } \mathbf{u} \text{ and } \mathbf{v}$$

$$= 4\langle -1, 2\rangle = \langle -4, 8\rangle$$

(b) By the formula in the preceding box we have $\mathbf{u} = \mathbf{u}_1 + \mathbf{u}_2$, where

$$\mathbf{u}_1 = \text{proj}_v\ \mathbf{u} = \langle -4, 8\rangle \qquad \text{From part (a)}$$

$$\mathbf{u}_2 = \mathbf{u} - \text{proj}_v\ \mathbf{u} = \langle -2, 9\rangle - \langle -4, 8\rangle = \langle 2, 1\rangle$$

■

Work

One use of the dot product occurs in calculating work. In everyday use, the term *work* means the total amount of effort required to perform a task. In physics, *work* has a technical meaning that conforms to this intuitive meaning. If a constant force of magnitude F moves an object through a distance d along a straight line, then the **work** done is

$$W = Fd \qquad \text{or} \qquad \text{work} = \text{force} \times \text{distance}$$

If F is measured in pounds and d in feet, then the unit of work is a foot-pound (ft-lb). For example, how much work is done in lifting a 20-lb weight 6 ft off the ground? Since a force of 20 lb is required to lift this weight and since the weight moves through a distance of 6 ft, the amount of work done is

$$W = Fd = (20)(6) = 120 \text{ ft-lb}$$

This formula applies only when the force is directed along the direction of motion. In the general case, if the force $\mathbf{F}$ moves an object from P to Q, as in Figure 7, then only the component of the force in the direction of $\mathbf{D} = \overrightarrow{PQ}$ affects the object. Thus, the effective magnitude of the force on the object is

$$\text{component of } \mathbf{F} \text{ along } \mathbf{D} = |\mathbf{F}| \cos \theta$$

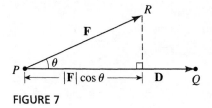

FIGURE 7

So, the work done is

$$W = \text{force} \times \text{distance} = (|\mathbf{F}| \cos \theta)\,|\mathbf{D}| = |\mathbf{F}|\,|\mathbf{D}| \cos \theta = \mathbf{F} \cdot \mathbf{D}$$

We have derived the following simple formula for calculating work.

> **WORK**
>
> The **work** W done by a force $\mathbf{F}$ in moving along a vector $\mathbf{D}$ is
>
> $$W = \mathbf{F} \cdot \mathbf{D}$$

EXAMPLE 7 ■ Calculating Work

A force is given by the vector $\mathbf{F} = \langle 2, 3 \rangle$ and moves an object from the point $(1, 3)$ to the point $(5, 9)$. Find the work done.

SOLUTION

The displacement vector is

$$\mathbf{D} = \langle 5 - 1, 9 - 3 \rangle = \langle 4, 6 \rangle$$

So the work done is

$$W = \mathbf{F} \cdot \mathbf{D} = \langle 2, 3 \rangle \cdot \langle 4, 6 \rangle = 26$$

If the unit of force is pounds and the distance is measured in feet, then the work done is 26 ft-lb.

■

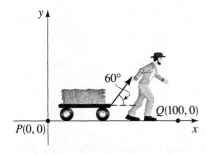

y

60°

$Q(100, 0)$

$P(0, 0)$

x

FIGURE 8

EXAMPLE 8 ■ Calculating Work

A man pulls a wagon horizontally by exerting a force of 20 lb on the handle. If the handle makes an angle of 60° with the horizontal, find the work done in moving the wagon 100 ft.

SOLUTION

We choose a coordinate system with the origin at the initial position of the wagon (see Figure 8). That is, the wagon moves from the point $P(0, 0)$ to the point $Q(100, 0)$. The vector that represents this displacement is

$$\mathbf{D} = 100\,\mathbf{i}$$

The force on the handle can be written in terms of components (see Section 7.7) as

$$\mathbf{F} = (20 \cos 60°)\,\mathbf{i} + (20 \sin 60°)\,\mathbf{j} = 10\,\mathbf{i} + 10\sqrt{3}\,\mathbf{j}$$

Thus, the work done is

$$W = \mathbf{F} \cdot \mathbf{D} = (10\,\mathbf{i} + 10\sqrt{3}\,\mathbf{j}) \cdot (100\,\mathbf{i}) = 1000 \text{ ft-lb} \quad ■$$

7.8 EXERCISES

1–8 ■ Find (a) $\mathbf{u} \cdot \mathbf{v}$ and (b) the angle between $\mathbf{u}$ and $\mathbf{v}$ to the nearest degree.

1. $\mathbf{u} = \langle 2, 0 \rangle, \quad \mathbf{v} = \langle 1, 1 \rangle$

2. $\mathbf{u} = \mathbf{i} + \sqrt{3}\,\mathbf{j}, \quad \mathbf{v} = -\sqrt{3}\,\mathbf{i} + \mathbf{j}$

3. $\mathbf{u} = \langle 2, 7 \rangle, \quad \mathbf{v} = \langle 3, 1 \rangle$

4. $\mathbf{u} = \langle -6, 6 \rangle, \quad \mathbf{v} = \langle 1, -1 \rangle$

5. $\mathbf{u} = \langle 3, -2 \rangle, \quad \mathbf{v} = \langle 1, 2 \rangle$

6. $\mathbf{u} = 2\mathbf{i} + \mathbf{j}, \quad \mathbf{v} = 3\mathbf{i} - 2\mathbf{j}$

7. $\mathbf{u} = -5\mathbf{j}, \quad \mathbf{v} = -\mathbf{i} - \sqrt{3}\,\mathbf{j}$

8. $\mathbf{u} = \mathbf{i} + \mathbf{j}, \quad \mathbf{v} = \mathbf{i} - \mathbf{j}$

9–14 ■ Determine whether the given vectors are orthogonal.

9. $\mathbf{u} = \langle 6, 4 \rangle, \quad \mathbf{v} = \langle -2, 3 \rangle$

10. $\mathbf{u} = \langle 0, -5 \rangle, \quad \mathbf{v} = \langle 4, 0 \rangle$

11. $\mathbf{u} = \langle -2, 6 \rangle, \quad \mathbf{v} = \langle 4, 2 \rangle$

12. $\mathbf{u} = 2\mathbf{i}, \quad \mathbf{v} = -7\mathbf{j}$

13. $\mathbf{u} = 2\mathbf{i} - 8\mathbf{j}, \quad \mathbf{v} = -12\mathbf{i} - 3\mathbf{j}$

14. $\mathbf{u} = 4\mathbf{i}, \quad \mathbf{v} = -\mathbf{i} + 3\mathbf{j}$

15–18 ■ Find the indicated quantity, assuming $\mathbf{u} = 2\mathbf{i} + \mathbf{j}$, $\mathbf{v} = \mathbf{i} - 3\mathbf{j}$, and $\mathbf{w} = 3\mathbf{i} + 4\mathbf{j}$.

15. $\mathbf{u} \cdot \mathbf{v} + \mathbf{u} \cdot \mathbf{w}$

16. $\mathbf{u} \cdot (\mathbf{v} + \mathbf{w})$

17. $(\mathbf{u} + \mathbf{v}) \cdot (\mathbf{u} - \mathbf{v})$

18. $(\mathbf{u} \cdot \mathbf{v})(\mathbf{u} \cdot \mathbf{w})$

19–22 ■ Find the component of $\mathbf{u}$ along $\mathbf{v}$.

19. $\mathbf{u} = \langle 4, 6 \rangle, \quad \mathbf{v} = \langle 3, -4 \rangle$

20. $\mathbf{u} = \langle -3, 5 \rangle, \quad \mathbf{v} = \langle 1/\sqrt{2}, 1/\sqrt{2} \rangle$

21. $\mathbf{u} = 7\mathbf{i} - 24\mathbf{j}, \quad \mathbf{v} = \mathbf{j}$

22. $\mathbf{u} = 7\mathbf{i}, \quad \mathbf{v} = 8\mathbf{i} + 6\mathbf{j}$

23–28 ■ (a) Calculate $\text{proj}_{\mathbf{v}}\,\mathbf{u}$. (b) Resolve $\mathbf{u}$ into $\mathbf{u}_1$ and $\mathbf{u}_2$, where $\mathbf{u}_1$ is parallel to $\mathbf{v}$ and $\mathbf{u}_2$ is orthogonal to $\mathbf{v}$.

23. $\mathbf{u} = \langle -2, 4 \rangle, \quad \mathbf{v} = \langle 1, 1 \rangle$

24. $\mathbf{u} = \langle 7, -4 \rangle, \quad \mathbf{v} = \langle 2, 1 \rangle$

25. $\mathbf{u} = \langle 1, 2 \rangle, \quad \mathbf{v} = \langle 1, -3 \rangle$

26. $\mathbf{u} = \langle 11, 3 \rangle, \quad \mathbf{v} = \langle -3, -2 \rangle$

27. $\mathbf{u} = \langle 2, 9 \rangle, \quad \mathbf{v} = \langle -3, 4 \rangle$

28. $\mathbf{u} = \langle 1, 1 \rangle, \quad \mathbf{v} = \langle 2, -1 \rangle$

29–32 ■ Find the work done by the force **F** in moving an object from P to Q.

29. $\mathbf{F} = 4\mathbf{i} - 5\mathbf{j}$; $P(0, 0)$, $Q(3, 8)$

30. $\mathbf{F} = 400\mathbf{i} + 50\mathbf{j}$; $P(-1, 1)$, $Q(200, 1)$

31. $\mathbf{F} = 10\mathbf{i} + 3\mathbf{j}$; $P(2, 3)$, $Q(6, -2)$

32. $\mathbf{F} = -4\mathbf{i} + 20\mathbf{j}$; $P(0, 10)$, $Q(5, 25)$

33. The force $\mathbf{F} = 4\mathbf{i} - 7\mathbf{j}$ moves an object 4 ft along the x-axis in the positive direction. Find the work done if the unit of force is the pound.

34. A constant force $\mathbf{F} = \langle 2, 8 \rangle$ moves an object along a straight line from the point $(2, 5)$ to the point $(11, 13)$. Find the work done if the distance is measured in feet and the force is measured in pounds.

35. A lawn mower is pushed a distance of 200 ft along a horizontal path by a constant force of 50 lb. The handle of the lawn mower is held at an angle of 30° from the horizontal (see the figure). Find the work done.

36. A car drives 500 ft on a road that is inclined 12° to the horizontal, as shown in the figure. The car weighs 2500 lb. Thus, gravity acts straight down on the car with a constant force $\mathbf{F} = -2500\mathbf{j}$. Find the work done by the car in overcoming gravity.

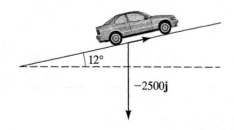

37. A car is on a driveway that is inclined 25° to the horizontal. If the car weighs 2755 lb, find the force required to keep it from rolling down the driveway.

38. A car is on a driveway that is inclined 10° to the horizontal. A force of 490 lb is required to keep the car from rolling down the driveway.

(a) Find the weight of the car.

(b) Find the force the car exerts against the driveway.

39. A package that weighs 200 lb is placed on an inclined plane. If a force of 80 lb is just sufficient to keep the package from sliding, find the angle of inclination of the plane. (Ignore the effects of friction.)

40. A sailboat has its sail inclined in the direction N 20° E. The wind is blowing into the sail in the direction S 45° W with a force of 220 lb (see the figure).

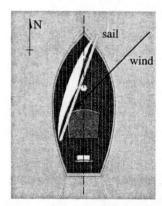

(a) Find the effective force of the wind on the sail. [*Hint:* Find the components of the wind parallel to the sail and perpendicular to the sail. The component of the wind parallel to the sail slips by and does not push on the sail.]

(b) If the keel of the ship is aligned due north, find the effective force of the wind that drives the boat forward. [*Hint:* Only the component of the force found in part (a) that is parallel to the keel drives the boat forward.]

41–44 ■ Let **u**, **v**, and **w** be vectors and let a be a scalar. Prove the given property.

41. $\mathbf{u} \cdot \mathbf{v} = \mathbf{v} \cdot \mathbf{u}$

42. $(a\mathbf{u}) \cdot \mathbf{v} = a(\mathbf{u} \cdot \mathbf{v}) = \mathbf{u} \cdot (a\mathbf{v})$

43. $(\mathbf{u} + \mathbf{v}) \cdot \mathbf{w} = \mathbf{u} \cdot \mathbf{w} + \mathbf{v} \cdot \mathbf{w}$

44. $(\mathbf{u} - \mathbf{v}) \cdot (\mathbf{u} + \mathbf{v}) = |\mathbf{u}|^2 - |\mathbf{v}|^2$

45. Show that the vectors $\text{proj}_\mathbf{v}\, \mathbf{u}$ and $\mathbf{u} - \text{proj}_\mathbf{v}\, \mathbf{u}$ are orthogonal.

📦 DISCOVERY · DISCUSSION

46. Distance from a Point to a Line   Let L be the line $2x + 4y = 8$ and let P be the point $(3, 4)$.

(a) Show that the points $Q(0, 2)$ and $R(2, 1)$ lie on L.

(b) Let $\mathbf{u} = \overrightarrow{QP}$ and $\mathbf{v} = \overrightarrow{QR}$, as shown in the figure. Find $\mathbf{w} = \text{proj}_{\mathbf{v}} \mathbf{u}$.

(c) Sketch a graph that explains why $|\mathbf{u} - \mathbf{w}|$ is the distance from P to L. Find this distance.

(d) Write a short paragraph describing the steps you would take to find the distance from a given point to a given line.

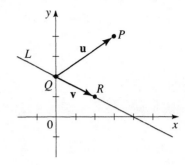

---

7 REVIEW

CONCEPT CHECK

1. (a) State the reciprocal identities.
 (b) State the Pythagorean identities.
 (c) State the even-odd identities.
 (d) State the cofunction identities.

2. Explain the difference between an equation and an identity.

3. How do you prove a trigonometric identity?

4. (a) State the addition formulas for sine, cosine, and tangent.
 (b) State the subtraction formulas for sine, cosine, and tangent.

5. (a) State the double-angle formulas for sine, cosine, and tangent.
 (b) State the formulas for lowering powers.
 (c) State the half-angle formulas.

6. (a) State the product-to-sum formulas.
 (b) State the sum-to-product formulas.

7. (a) Define the inverse sine function $\sin^{-1}$. What are its domain and range?
 (b) For what values of x is the equation $\sin(\sin^{-1}x) = x$ true?
 (c) For what values of x is the equation $\sin^{-1}(\sin x) = x$ true?

8. (a) Define the inverse cosine function $\cos^{-1}$. What are its domain and range?
 (b) For what values of x is the equation $\cos(\cos^{-1}x) = x$ true?
 (c) For what values of x is the equation $\cos^{-1}(\cos x) = x$ true?

9. (a) Define the inverse tangent function $\tan^{-1}$. What are its domain and range?
 (b) For what values of x is the equation $\tan(\tan^{-1}x) = x$ true?
 (c) For what values of x is the equation $\tan^{-1}(\tan x) = x$ true?

10. How do you graph a complex number z? What is the trigonometric form of a complex number z? What is the modulus of z? What is the argument of z?

11. (a) How do you multiply two complex numbers if they are given in trigonometric form?
 (b) How do you divide two such numbers?

12. (a) State DeMoivre's Theorem.
 (b) How do you find the nth roots of a complex number?

13. (a) What is the difference between a scalar and a vector?
 (b) Draw a diagram to show how to add two vectors.
 (c) Draw a diagram to show how to subtract two vectors.
 (d) Draw a diagram to show how to multiply a vector by the scalars 2, $\frac{1}{2}$, -2, and $-\frac{1}{2}$.

14. If $\mathbf{u} = \langle a_1, b_1 \rangle$, $\mathbf{v} = \langle a_2, b_2 \rangle$ and c is a scalar, write expressions for $\mathbf{u} + \mathbf{v}$, $\mathbf{u} - \mathbf{v}$, $c\mathbf{u}$, and $|\mathbf{u}|$.

15. (a) If $\mathbf{v} = \langle a, b \rangle$, write $\mathbf{v}$ in terms of $\mathbf{i}$ and $\mathbf{j}$.
 (b) Write the components of $\mathbf{v}$ in terms of the magnitude and direction of $\mathbf{v}$.

16. If $\mathbf{u} = \langle a_1, b_1 \rangle$ and $\mathbf{v} = \langle a_2, b_2 \rangle$, what is the dot product $\mathbf{u} \cdot \mathbf{v}$?

17. (a) How do you use the dot product to find the angle between two vectors?

(b) How do you use the dot product to determine whether two vectors are perpendicular?

18. What is the component of **u** along **v**, and how do you calculate it?

19. What is the projection of **u** onto **v**, and how do you calculate it?

20. How much work is done by the force **F** in moving an object along a displacement **D**?

EXERCISES

1–24 ■ Verify the identity.

1. $\sin \theta (\cot \theta + \tan \theta) = \sec \theta$

2. $(\sec \theta - 1)(\sec \theta + 1) = \tan^2 \theta$

3. $\cos^2 x \csc x - \csc x = -\sin x$

4. $\dfrac{1}{1 - \sin^2 x} = 1 + \tan^2 x$

5. $\dfrac{\cos^2 x - \tan^2 x}{\sin^2 x} = \cot^2 x - \sec^2 x$

6. $\dfrac{1 + \sec x}{\sec x} = \dfrac{\sin^2 x}{1 - \cos x}$ **7.** $\dfrac{\cos^2 x}{1 - \sin x} = \dfrac{\cos x}{\sec x - \tan x}$

8. $(1 - \tan x)(1 - \cot x) = 2 - \sec x \csc x$

9. $\sin^2 x \cot^2 x + \cos^2 x \tan^2 x = 1$

10. $(\tan x + \cot x)^2 = \csc^2 x \sec^2 x$

11. $\dfrac{\sin 2x}{1 + \cos 2x} = \tan x$

12. $\dfrac{\cos(x + y)}{\cos x \sin y} = \cot y - \tan x$

13. $\tan \dfrac{x}{2} = \csc x - \cot x$

14. $\dfrac{\sin(x + y) + \sin(x - y)}{\cos(x + y) + \cos(x - y)} = \tan x$

15. $\sin(x + y) \sin(x - y) = \sin^2 x - \sin^2 y$

16. $\csc x - \tan \dfrac{x}{2} = \cot x$ **17.** $1 + \tan x \tan \dfrac{x}{2} = \sec x$

18. $\dfrac{\sin 3x + \cos 3x}{\cos x - \sin x} = 1 + 2 \sin 2x$

19. $\left(\cos \dfrac{x}{2} - \sin \dfrac{x}{2}\right)^2 = 1 - \sin x$

20. $\dfrac{\cos 3x - \cos 7x}{\sin 3x + \sin 7x} = \tan 2x$ **21.** $\dfrac{\sin 2x}{\sin x} - \dfrac{\cos 2x}{\cos x} = \sec x$

22. $(\cos x + \cos y)^2 + (\sin x - \sin y)^2 = 2 + 2 \cos(x + y)$

23. $\tan\left(x + \dfrac{\pi}{4}\right) = \dfrac{1 + \tan x}{1 - \tan x}$ **24.** $\dfrac{\sec x - 1}{\sin x \sec x} = \tan \dfrac{x}{2}$

25–28 ■ (a) Graph f and g. (b) Do the graphs suggest that the equation $f(x) = g(x)$ is an identity? Prove your answer.

25. $f(x) = 1 - \left(\cos \dfrac{x}{2} - \sin \dfrac{x}{2}\right)^2$, $g(x) = \sin x$

26. $f(x) = \sin x + \cos x$, $g(x) = \sqrt{\sin^2 x + \cos^2 x}$

27. $f(x) = \tan x \tan \dfrac{x}{2}$, $g(x) = \dfrac{1}{\cos x}$

28. $f(x) = 1 - 8 \sin^2 x + 8 \sin^4 x$, $g(x) = \cos 4x$

29–30 ■ (a) Graph the function(s) and make a conjecture, and (b) prove your conjecture.

29. $f(x) = 2 \sin^2 3x + \cos 6x$

30. $f(x) = \sin x \cot \dfrac{x}{2}$, $g(x) = \cos x$

31–46 ■ Solve the equation in the interval $[0, 2\pi)$.

31. $\cos x \sin x - \sin x = 0$ **32.** $\sin x - 2 \sin^2 x = 0$

33. $2 \sin^2 x - 5 \sin x + 2 = 0$

34. $\sin x - \cos x - \tan x = -1$

35. $2 \cos^2 x - 7 \cos x + 3 = 0$ **36.** $4 \sin^2 x + 2 \cos^2 x = 3$

37. $\dfrac{1 - \cos x}{1 + \cos x} = 3$ **38.** $\sin x = \cos 2x$

39. $\tan^3 x + \tan^2 x - 3 \tan x - 3 = 0$

40. $\cos 2x \csc^2 x = 2 \cos 2x$ **41.** $\tan \frac{1}{2} x + 2 \sin 2x = \csc x$

42. $\cos 3x + \cos 2x + \cos x = 0$

43. $\tan x + \sec x = \sqrt{3}$ **44.** $2 \cos x - 3 \tan x = 0$

45. $\cos x = x^2 - 1$ **46.** $e^{\sin x} = x$

47. If a projectile is fired with velocity v_0 at an angle θ, then the maximum height it reaches (in feet) is modeled by the function

$$M(\theta) = \dfrac{v_0^2 \sin^2 \theta}{64}$$

Suppose $v_0 = 400$ ft/s.
(a) At what angle θ should the projectile be fired so that the maximum height it reaches is 2000 ft?

(b) Is it possible for the projectile to reach a height of 3000 ft?

(c) Find the angle θ for which the projectile will travel highest.

48. The displacement of an automobile shock absorber is modeled by the function

$$f(t) = e^{-0.2t} \sin 4\pi t$$

Find the times when the shock absorber is at its equilibrium position (that is, when $f(t) = 0$).

49–58 ■ Find the exact value of the expression.

49. $\cos 15°$

50. $\sin \dfrac{5\pi}{12}$

51. $\tan \dfrac{\pi}{8}$

52. $2 \sin \dfrac{\pi}{12} \cos \dfrac{\pi}{12}$

53. $\sin 5° \cos 40° + \cos 5° \sin 40°$

54. $\dfrac{\tan 66° - \tan 6°}{1 + \tan 66° \tan 6°}$

55. $\cos^2 \dfrac{\pi}{8} - \sin^2 \dfrac{\pi}{8}$

56. $\dfrac{1}{2} \cos \dfrac{\pi}{12} + \dfrac{\sqrt{3}}{2} \sin \dfrac{\pi}{12}$

57. $\cos 37.5° \cos 7.5°$

58. $\cos 67.5° + \cos 22.5°$

59–64 ■ Find the exact value of the expression given that $\sec x = \frac{3}{2}$, $\csc y = 3$, and x and y are in quadrant I.

59. $\sin(x + y)$

60. $\cos(x - y)$

61. $\tan(x + y)$

62. $\sin 2x$

63. $\cos \dfrac{y}{2}$

64. $\tan \dfrac{y}{2}$

65–72 ■ Find the exact value of the expression.

65. $\sin^{-1}(\sqrt{3}/2)$

66. $\tan^{-1}(\sqrt{3}/3)$

67. $\cos(\tan^{-1}\sqrt{3})$

68. $\sin(\cos^{-1}(\sqrt{3}/2))$

69. $\tan\left(\sin^{-1}\frac{2}{5}\right)$

70. $\sin\left(\cos^{-1}\frac{3}{8}\right)$

71. $\cos\left(2 \sin^{-1}\frac{1}{3}\right)$

72. $\cos\left(\sin^{-1}\frac{5}{13} - \cos^{-1}\frac{4}{5}\right)$

73–74 ■ Rewrite the expression as an algebraic function of x.

73. $\sin(\tan^{-1}x)$

74. $\sec(\sin^{-1}x)$

75–76 ■ Express θ in terms of x.

75.

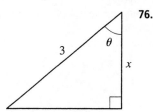

76.

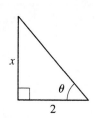

77. A 10-ft-wide highway sign is adjacent to a roadway, as shown in the figure. As a driver approaches the sign, the viewing angle θ changes.

(a) Express viewing angle θ as a function of the distance x between the driver and the sign.

(b) For what distance x is the viewing angle largest?

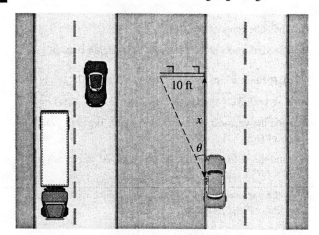

78. A 380-ft-tall building supports a 40-ft communications tower (see the figure). As a driver approaches the building, the viewing angle θ of the tower changes.

(a) Express the viewing angle θ as a function of the distance x between the driver and the building.

(b) At what distance from the building is the viewing angle θ as large as possible?

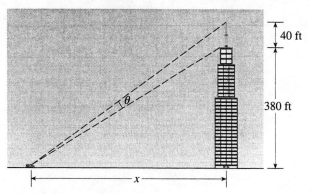

79–84 ■ A complex number is given.
(a) Graph the complex number in the complex plane.
(b) Find the modulus and argument.
(c) Write the number in trigonometric form.

79. $4 + 4i$

80. $-10i$

81. $5 + 3i$

82. $1 + \sqrt{3}\, i$

83. $-1 + i$

84. -20

85–88 ■ Find the indicated power.

85. $(1 - \sqrt{3}\, i)^4$

86. $(1 + i)^8$

87. $(\sqrt{3} + i)^{-4}$

88. $\left(\dfrac{1}{2} + \dfrac{\sqrt{3}}{2}i\right)^{20}$

89–92 ■ Find the indicated roots.

89. The square roots of $-16i$

90. The cube roots of $4 + 4\sqrt{3}\, i$

91. The sixth roots of 1 **92.** The eighth roots of i

93–94 ■ Find $|\mathbf{u}|$, $\mathbf{u} + \mathbf{v}$, $\mathbf{u} - \mathbf{v}$, $2\mathbf{u}$, and $3\mathbf{u} - 2\mathbf{v}$.

93. $\mathbf{u} = \langle -2, 3 \rangle$, $\mathbf{v} = \langle 8, 1 \rangle$ **94.** $\mathbf{u} = 2\mathbf{i} + \mathbf{j}$, $\mathbf{v} = \mathbf{i} - 2\mathbf{j}$

95. Find the vector $\mathbf{u}$ with initial point $P(0, 3)$ and terminal point $Q(3, -1)$.

96. Find the vector $\mathbf{u}$ having length $|\mathbf{u}| = 20$ and direction $\theta = 60°$.

97. If the vector $5\mathbf{i} - 8\mathbf{j}$ is placed in the plane with its initial point at $P(5, 6)$, find its terminal point.

98. Find the direction of the vector $2\mathbf{i} - 5\mathbf{j}$.

99. Two tugboats are pulling a barge, as shown. One pulls with a force of 2.0×10^4 lb in the direction N 50° E and the other with a force of 3.4×10^4 lb in the direction S 75° E.
(a) Find the resultant force on the barge as a vector.
(b) Find the magnitude and direction of the resultant force.

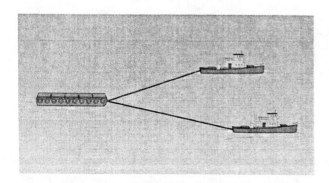

100. An airplane heads N 60° E at a speed of 600 mi/h relative to the air. A wind begins to blow in the direction N 30° W at 50 mi/h.
(a) Find the velocity of the airplane as a vector.
(b) Find the true speed and direction of the airplane.

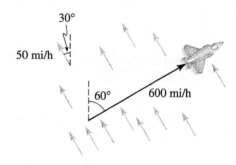

101–104 ■ Find $|\mathbf{u}|$, $\mathbf{u} \cdot \mathbf{u}$, and $\mathbf{u} \cdot \mathbf{v}$.

101. $\mathbf{u} = \langle 4, -3 \rangle$, $\mathbf{v} = \langle 9, -8 \rangle$

102. $\mathbf{u} = \langle 5, 12 \rangle$, $\mathbf{v} = \langle 10, -4 \rangle$

103. $\mathbf{u} = -2\mathbf{i} + 2\mathbf{j}$, $\mathbf{v} = \mathbf{i} + \mathbf{j}$

104. $\mathbf{u} = 10\mathbf{j}$, $\mathbf{v} = 5\mathbf{i} - 3\mathbf{j}$

105–108 ■ Are $\mathbf{u}$ and $\mathbf{v}$ orthogonal? If not, find the angle between them.

105. $\mathbf{u} = \langle -4, 2 \rangle$, $\mathbf{v} = \langle 3, 6 \rangle$

106. $\mathbf{u} = \langle 5, 3 \rangle$, $\mathbf{v} = \langle -2, 6 \rangle$

107. $\mathbf{u} = 2\mathbf{i} + \mathbf{j}$, $\mathbf{v} = \mathbf{i} + 3\mathbf{j}$

108. $\mathbf{u} = \mathbf{i} - \mathbf{j}$, $\mathbf{v} = \mathbf{i} + \mathbf{j}$

109–110 ■ The vectors $\mathbf{u}$ and $\mathbf{v}$ are given.
(a) Find the component of $\mathbf{u}$ along $\mathbf{v}$.
(b) Find $\text{proj}_{\mathbf{v}}\, \mathbf{u}$.
(c) Resolve $\mathbf{u}$ into the vectors $\mathbf{u}_1$ and $\mathbf{u}_2$, where $\mathbf{u}_1$ is parallel to $\mathbf{v}$ and $\mathbf{u}_2$ is perpendicular to $\mathbf{v}$.

109. $\mathbf{u} = \langle 3, 1 \rangle$, $\mathbf{v} = \langle 6, -1 \rangle$

110. $\mathbf{u} = \langle -8, 6 \rangle$, $\mathbf{v} = \langle 20, 20 \rangle$

111. Find the work done by the force $\mathbf{F} = 2\mathbf{i} + 9\mathbf{j}$ in moving an object from the point $(1, 1)$ to the point $(7, -1)$.

112. A force $\mathbf{F}$ with magnitude 250 lb moves an object in the direction of the vector $\mathbf{D}$ a distance of 20 ft. If the work done is 3800 ft-lb, find the angle between $\mathbf{F}$ and $\mathbf{D}$.

7 TEST

1. Verify each identity.

   (a) $\tan \theta \sin \theta + \cos \theta = \sec \theta$

   (b) $\dfrac{\tan x}{1 - \cos x} = \csc x(1 + \sec x)$

   (c) $\dfrac{2 \tan x}{1 + \tan^2 x} = \sin 2x$

2. Let $x = 2 \sin \theta$, $-\pi/2 < \theta < \pi/2$. Simplify the expression

$$\frac{x}{\sqrt{4 - x^2}}$$

3. Find the exact value of each expression.

   (a) $\sin 8° \cos 22° + \cos 8° \sin 22°$ (b) $\sin 75°$ (c) $\sin \dfrac{\pi}{12}$

4. For the angles α and β in the figures, find $\cos(\alpha + \beta)$.

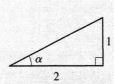

5. (a) Write $\sin 3x \cos 5x$ as a sum of trigonometric functions.
   (b) Write $\sin 2x - \sin 5x$ as a product of trigonometric functions.

6. If $\sin \theta = -\frac{4}{5}$ and θ is in quadrant III, find $\tan(\theta/2)$.

7. Graph $y = \sin x$ and $y = \sin^{-1}x$, and specify the domain of each function.

8. Express θ in each figure in terms of x.

   (a)

   (b)

9. Solve each trigonometric equation in the interval $[0, 2\pi)$.
   (a) $2 \cos^2 x + 5 \cos x + 2 = 0$ (b) $\sin 2x - \cos x = 0$

10. Find all solutions in the interval $[0, 2\pi)$, correct to five decimal places:

$$5 \cos 2x = 2$$

11. Find the exact value of $\cos\left(\tan^{-1}\frac{9}{40}\right)$.

12. Let $z = 1 + \sqrt{3}\, i$
   (a) Graph z in the complex plane.
   (b) Write z in trigonometric form.
   (c) Find the complex number z^9.

13. Let

$$z_1 = 4\left(\cos\frac{7\pi}{12} + i\sin\frac{7\pi}{12}\right)$$

$$z_2 = 2\left(\cos\frac{5\pi}{12} + i\sin\frac{5\pi}{12}\right)$$

Find $z_1 z_2$ and $\dfrac{z_1}{z_2}$.

14. Find the cube roots of $27i$, and sketch these roots in the complex plane.

15. Let $\mathbf{u}$ be the vector with initial point $P(3, -1)$ and terminal point $Q(-3, 9)$.
   (a) Express $\mathbf{u}$ in terms of $\mathbf{i}$ and $\mathbf{j}$.
   (b) Find the length of $\mathbf{u}$.

16. Let $\mathbf{u} = \langle 1, 3 \rangle$ and $\mathbf{v} = \langle -6, 2 \rangle$.
   (a) Find $\mathbf{u} - 3\mathbf{v}$.
   (b) Find $|\mathbf{u} + \mathbf{v}|$.
   (c) Find $\mathbf{u} \cdot \mathbf{v}$.
   (d) Are $\mathbf{u}$ and $\mathbf{v}$ perpendicular?

17. A river is flowing due east at 8 mi/h. A man heads his motorboat in a direction N 30° E in the river. The speed of the motorboat relative to the water is 12 mi/h.
   (a) Express the true velocity of the motorboat as a vector.
   (b) Find the true speed and direction of the motorboat.

18. Let $\mathbf{u} = 3\mathbf{i} + 2\mathbf{j}$ and $\mathbf{v} = 5\mathbf{i} - \mathbf{j}$.
   (a) Find the angle between $\mathbf{u}$ and $\mathbf{v}$.
   (b) Find the component of $\mathbf{u}$ along $\mathbf{v}$.
   (c) Find $\text{proj}_{\mathbf{v}}\, \mathbf{u}$.

19. Find the work done by the force $\mathbf{F} = 3\mathbf{i} - 5\mathbf{j}$ in moving an object from the point $(2, 2)$ to the point $(7, -13)$.

Focus on Problem Solving
Using Analogy

Often a difficult problem can be successfully tackled by **using analogy**. We first solve a similar but simpler problem. The simpler problem can reveal insights that give us a new way to attack the original problem. This problem-solving principle is particularly useful when we've hit a dead end in a problem or if we're having trouble getting started. Mathematicians frequently use this principle to guide them in the uncharted waters of modern mathematical research.

A Trigonometric Equation

How many solutions does the following equation have?

$$\sin x = \frac{x}{100}$$

Thinking about the Problem

There is no obvious algebraic technique for solving this equation, so let's try to solve it graphically, by graphing $y = \sin x$ and $y = x/100$ on the same axes. We should be able to count the solutions easily from the graph.

In Figure 1 we graph these functions over three complete periods of the sine function, that is, for $-3\pi \leq x \leq 3\pi$. The line $y = x/100$ has such a shallow slope that it is virtually indistinguishable from the *x*-axis in this graph, and it's obvious that if we extend the graph to the left and right, we will find many more solutions of the equation.

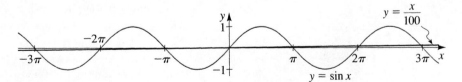

FIGURE 1

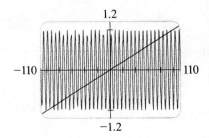

FIGURE 2

We'll use a graphing calculator to get a wider, more appropriate graph. Figure 2 shows the result when we graph $y = \sin x$ and $y = x/100$ in the viewing rectangle $[-110, 110]$ by $[-1.2, 1.2]$. The graph still doesn't tell us much, because it is such a mess—the graphing calculator doesn't have enough resolution to draw this many periods of the sine function accurately.

Solving a Simpler Problem

The graphs in Figures 1 and 2 didn't help us because the equation has too many solutions to count easily. If we change 100 to 10, then the line will be much less shallow. So, let's see if we can count the number of solutions of the equation

$$\sin x = \frac{x}{10}$$

The graph in Figure 3 shows that this equation has seven solutions. The figure captures all the solutions, because to the left and right of the portion shown the graph of $y = x/10$ lies below or above the graph of $y = \sin x$.

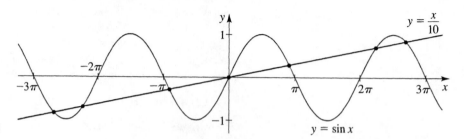

FIGURE 3

Examining the solutions more closely, we see that the graphs of $y = x/10$ and $y = \sin x$ intersect twice in each period of $y = \sin x$. This means that there are *two* solutions in each period. So to count the number of solutions we need only count the number of periods for which the two graphs intersect. From Figure 3 we see that there are *four* such periods: two for which $x \geq 0$ and two for which $x \leq 0$. Since the solution $x = 0$ occurs in both cases, the total number of solutions of the equation is

$$2 \cdot 4 - 1 = 7$$

■ Solving the Original Problem

We now use the insight we gained in solving the simpler equation to solve the original equation. When the slope is $1/100$, there will also be two solutions in each period. All we need to find is the number of periods in which the graphs of $y = x/100$ and $y = \sin x$ intersect. Since $-1 \leq \sin x \leq 1$, the graphs can intersect only when $-1 \leq x/100 \leq 1$ as well. Solving this inequality, we see that the graphs intersect only in the interval $-100 \leq x \leq 100$. How many complete periods of $y = \sin x$ occur in this interval? Since $100/2\pi \approx 16$, there are 16 periods between 0 and 100 and 16 periods between -100 and 0, for a total of 32 periods. So, the number of solutions of the original equation is

$$2 \cdot 32 - 1 = 63$$

As in the simpler case, we have subtracted 1 to avoid counting $x = 0$ twice.   ■

■ Problems

1. Find the number of solutions of the equation $\sin x = \dfrac{x}{1,000,000}$.

2. Find the number of solutions of the equation $\cos x = \dfrac{x^2}{400}$.

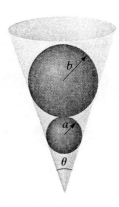

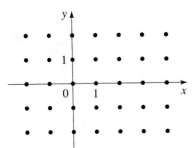

Lattice points in the plane

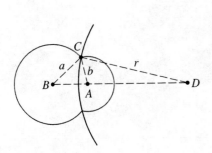

3. Three tangent circles of radius 10 cm are drawn as shown. All centers lie on the line *AB*. The tangent *AC* to the right-hand circle is drawn, intersecting the middle circle at *D* and *E*. Find the length of the segment *DE*.

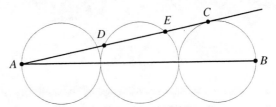

4. A ball of radius *a* is set inside a cone so that the surface of the cone is tangent to the ball. A larger ball of radius *b* fits inside the cone in such a way that it is tangent to both the ball of radius *a* and the sides of the cone. Express *b* in terms of *a* and the angle θ shown in the figure to the left.

5. Points (m, n) in the coordinate plane, both of whose coordinates are integers, are called *lattice points*. Show that it's impossible for any equilateral triangle to have each of its vertices at a lattice point. [*Hint:* See Section 7.2, Exercise 48(b).]

6. Find $\angle A + \angle B + \angle C$ in the figure.

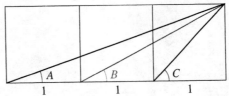

7. If $0 < \theta < \pi/2$ and $\sin 2\theta = a$, find $\sin \theta + \cos \theta$.

8. Show that $\pi/4 = \tan^{-1}\frac{1}{2} + \tan^{-1}\frac{1}{5} + \tan^{-1}\frac{1}{8}$.

   NOTE This identity was used by Zacharias Dase in 1844 to calculate the decimal expansion of π to 200 places.

9. When two bubbles cling together in midair, their common surface is part of a sphere whose center *D* lies on the line passing through the centers of the bubbles. Also, the angles *ACB* and *ACD* both have measure 60° (see the figure).
   (a) Show that the radius *r* of the common face is given by
$$r = \frac{ab}{a - b}$$
   (b) If the radii of the two bubbles are 4 cm and 3 cm, respectively, find the radius of the common face.
   (c) What shape does the common face take if the two bubbles have radii of the same length?

10. Solve the inequality $|\tan x| \le 1$.

11. Solve the equation $|\sin x| = \sin x + 2 \cos x$, $0 \le x \le 2\pi$.

12. Prove that $\log_2 5$ is irrational.

13. Evaluate $(\log_2 3)(\log_3 4)(\log_4 5) \cdots (\log_{31} 32)$.

14. Show that if $x > 0$ and $x \ne 1$, then
$$\frac{1}{\log_2 x} + \frac{1}{\log_3 x} + \frac{1}{\log_5 x} = \frac{1}{\log_{30} x}$$

8

Systems of Equations and Inequalities

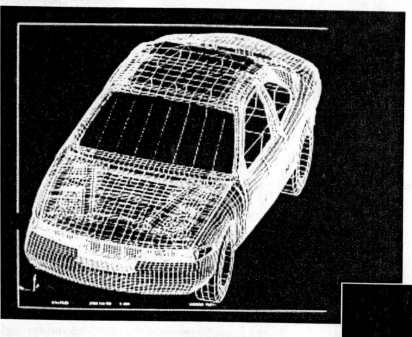

Systems of equations and inequalities are essential in modeling situations that involve many varying quantities. For instance, systems of equations are used in manipulating three-dimensional images on a computer screen; systems of inequalities are used to find the most efficient routing for a telephone call or for a data packet sent over the Internet.

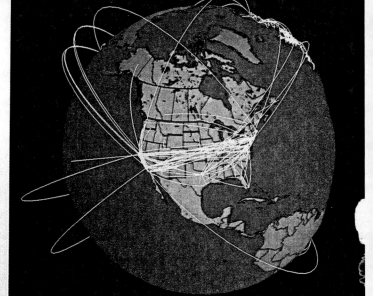

5. (a) $n(t) = 112,000e^{0.04t}$ (b) About 142,000   (c) 2008
7. (a) 20,000   (b) $n(t) = 20,000e^{0.1096t}$
(c) About 48,000   (d) 2010
9. (a) $n(t) = 8600e^{0.1508t}$ (b) About 11,600   (c) 4.6 h
11. (a) 2029   (b) 2049   **13.** 22.85 h
15. (a) $n(t) = 10e^{-0.0231t}$ (b) 1.6 g   (c) 70 yr
17. 18 yr   **19.** 149 h   **21.** 3560 yr
23. (a) 210°F   (b) 153°F   (c) 28 min
25. (a) 137°F   (b) 116 min
27. (a) 2.3   (b) 3.5   (c) 8.3
29. (a) 10^{-3} M   (b) 3.2×10^{-7} M
31. $4.8 \le \text{pH} \le 6.4$
33. $\log 20 \approx 1.3$ **35.** Twice as intense   **37.** 8.2
39. 6.3×10^{-3} W/m^2 **41.** (b) 106 dB

Chapter 4 Review ■ page 390

1. $\mathbb{R}, (0, \infty), y = 0$

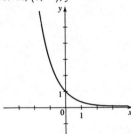

3. $\mathbb{R}, (-\infty, 5), y = 5$

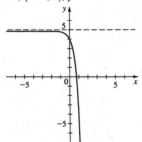

5. $(1, \infty), \mathbb{R}, x = 1$

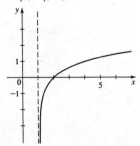

7. $(0, \infty), \mathbb{R}, x = 0$

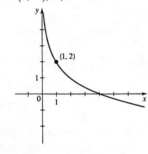

9. $\mathbb{R}, (-1, \infty), y = -1$

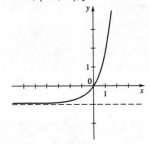

11. $(0, \infty), \mathbb{R}, x = 0$

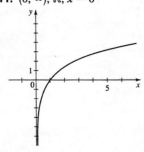

13. $\left(-\infty, \frac{1}{2}\right)$ **15.** $(-\infty, -2) \cup (2, \infty)$ **17.** $2^{10} = 1024$
19. $10^y = x$ **21.** $\log_2 64 = 6$ **23.** $\log 74 = x$ **25.** 7
27. 45   **29.** 6   **31.** -3 **33.** $\frac{1}{2}$ **35.** 2   **37.** 92   **39.** $\frac{2}{3}$
41. $\log A + 2 \log B + 3 \log C$
43. $\frac{1}{2}\left[\ln(x^2 - 1) - \ln(x^2 + 1)\right]$
45. $2 \log_5 x + \frac{3}{2} \log_5(1 - 5x) - \frac{1}{2} \log_5(x^3 - x)$
47. $\log 96$ **49.** $\log_2\left[\dfrac{(x - y)^{3/2}}{(x^2 + y^2)^2}\right]$ **51.** $\log\left(\dfrac{x^2 - 4}{\sqrt{x^2 + 4}}\right)$
53. -15 **55.** $\frac{1}{3}(5 - \log_5 26) \approx 0.99$
57. $\frac{4}{3} \ln 10 \approx 3.07$ **59.** 3   **61.** $-4, 2$ **63.** 0.430618
65. 2.303600

67.

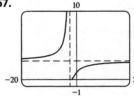

vertical asymptote
$x = -2$
horizontal asymptote
$y = 2.72$
no maximum or minimum

69.

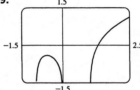

vertical asymptotes
$x = -1, x = 0, x = 1$
local maximum
$\approx (-0.58, -0.41)$

71. 2.42   **73.** $0.16 < x < 3.15$
75. Increasing on $(-\infty, 0]$ and $[1.10, \infty)$,
decreasing on $[0, 1.10]$
77. 1.953445   **79.** $\log_4 258$
81. (a) \$16,081.15   (b) \$16,178.18   (c) \$16,197.64
(d) \$16,198.31   **83.** (a) $n(t) = 30e^{0.15t}$ (b) 55   (c) 19 yr
85. (a) 9.97 mg   (b) 1.39×10^5 yr
87. (a) $n(t) = 150e^{-0.0004359t}$ (b) 97.0 mg   (c) 2520 yr
89. (a) $n(t) = 1500e^{0.1515t}$ (b) 7940   **91.** 7.9, basic
93. 8.0

Chapter 4 Test ■ page 393

1.

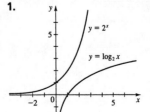

2.

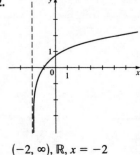

$(-2, \infty), \mathbb{R}, x = -2$

3. (a) $\frac{3}{2}$ **(b)** 3 **(c)** $\frac{2}{3}$ **(d)** 2

4. $\frac{1}{2}\left[\log(x+2) - 4\log x - \log(x^2+4)\right]$

5. $\ln\left(\dfrac{x\sqrt{3-x^4}}{(x^2+1)^2}\right)$ **6. (a)** 4.32 **(b)** 0.77 **(c)** 5.39 **(d)** 2

7. (a) $n(t) = 1000e^{2.07944t}$ **(b)** 22,627 **(c)** 1.3 h
(d)

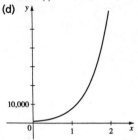

8. (a) $A(t) = 12{,}000\left(1 + \dfrac{0.056}{12}\right)^{12t}$

(b) \$14,195.06 **(c)** 9.249 yr

9. (a)

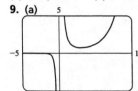

(b) $x = 0$, $y = 0$
(c) Local minimum $\approx (3.00, 0.74)$
(d) $(-\infty, 0) \cup [0.74, \infty)$
(e) $-0.85, 0.96, 9.92$

Focus on Modeling ■ page 403

1. (a)

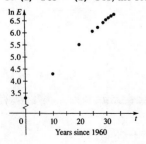

(b) $y = ab^t$, where $a = 4.041807 \times 10^{-16}$ and
$b = 1.021003194$, and y is the population in millions in
the year t. **(c)** 457.9 million **(d)** 221.2 million **(e)** No
3. (a) Yes **(b)** Yes, the scatter plot appears linear.

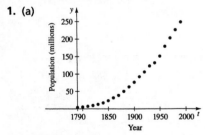

(c) $\ln E = 3.30161 \times 0.10769t$, where t is years since 1960 and
E is expenditure in billions of dollars.
(d) $E = 27.15633e^{0.10769t}$ **(e)** 1310.9 billion dollars
5. (a) $y = ab^t$, where $a = 301.813054$, $b = 0.819745$, and
t is the number of years since 1970
(b) $y = at^4 + bt^3 + ct^2 + dt + e$, where $a = -0.002430$,
$b = 0.135159$, $c = -2.014322$, $d = -4.055294$,
$e = 199.092227$, and t is the number of years since 1970
(c) From the graphs we see that the fourth-degree polynomial is
a better model.

(d) 202.8, 27.8; 184.0, 43.5

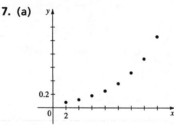

7. (a)

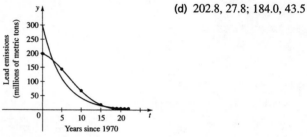

(b)

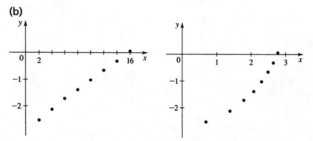

(c) Exponential Function
(d) $y = a \cdot b^x$ where $a = 0.057697$ and $b = 1.200236$
9. (a) $y = a + b \ln t$ where $a = -7154.888$, $b = 1016.007$,
and y is metric tons of coal produced in the year t
(b) 912 metric tons

CHAPTER 5

Section 5.1 ■ page 416

5. $P\left(\frac{4}{5}, \frac{3}{5}\right)$ **7.** $P\left(-\sqrt{5}/3, \frac{2}{3}\right)$ **9.** $P\left(-\sqrt{2}/3, \sqrt{7}/3\right)$
11. $t = \pi/4$, $(\sqrt{2}/2, \sqrt{2}/2)$; $t = \pi/2$, $(0, 1)$; $t = 3\pi/4$,
$(-\sqrt{2}/2, \sqrt{2}/2)$; $t = \pi$, $(-1, 0)$; $t = 5\pi/4$, $(-\sqrt{2}/2, -\sqrt{2}/2)$;
$t = 3\pi/2$, $(0, -1)$; $t = 7\pi/4$, $(\sqrt{2}/2, -\sqrt{2}/2)$; $t = 2\pi$, $(1, 0)$

13. $(0, 1)$ **15.** $\left(-\sqrt{3}/2, \frac{1}{2}\right)$ **17.** $\left(\frac{1}{2}, -\sqrt{3}/2\right)$
19. $\left(-\frac{1}{2}, \sqrt{3}/2\right)$ **21.** $(-\sqrt{2}/2, -\sqrt{2}/2)$
23. (a) $\left(-\frac{3}{5}, \frac{4}{5}\right)$ (b) $\left(\frac{3}{5}, -\frac{4}{5}\right)$ (c) $\left(-\frac{3}{5}, -\frac{4}{5}\right)$ (d) $\left(\frac{3}{5}, \frac{4}{5}\right)$
25. (a) $\pi/4$ (b) $\pi/3$ (c) $\pi/3$ (d) $\pi/6$
27. (a) $\pi/5$ (b) $\pi/6$ (c) $\pi/3$ (d) $\pi/6$
29. (a) $\pi/3$ (b) $\left(-\frac{1}{2}, \sqrt{3}/2\right)$ **31.** (a) $\pi/4$ (b) $(-\sqrt{2}/2, \sqrt{2}/2)$
33. (a) $\pi/3$ (b) $\left(-\frac{1}{2}, -\sqrt{3}/2\right)$
35. (a) $\pi/4$ (b) $(-\sqrt{2}/2, -\sqrt{2}/2)$
37. (a) $\pi/6$ (b) $\left(-\sqrt{3}/2, -\frac{1}{2}\right)$
39. (a) $\pi/3$ (b) $\left(\frac{1}{2}, \sqrt{3}/2\right)$
41. (a) $\pi/3$ (b) $\left(-\frac{1}{2}, -\sqrt{3}/2\right)$ **43.** $(0.5, 0.8)$
45. $(0.5, -0.9)$

Section 5.2 ■ page 426

1. $t = \pi/4$, $\sin t = \sqrt{2}/2$, $\cos t = \sqrt{2}/2$; $t = \pi/2$, $\sin t = 1$,
$\cos t = 0$; $t = 3\pi/4$, $\sin t = \sqrt{2}/2$, $\cos t = -\sqrt{2}/2$; $t = \pi$,
$\sin t = 0$, $\cos t = -1$; $t = 5\pi/4$, $\sin t = -\sqrt{2}/2$,
$\cos t = -\sqrt{2}/2$; $t = 3\pi/2$, $\sin t = -1$, $\cos t = 0$; $t = 7\pi/4$,
$\sin t = -\sqrt{2}/2$, $\cos t = \sqrt{2}/2$; $t = 2\pi$, $\sin t = 0$, $\cos t = 1$
3. (a) $-\sqrt{3}/2$ (b) $\frac{1}{2}$ **5.** (a) -1 (b) -1
7. (a) 1 (b) -1 **9.** (a) 0 (b) 0
11. (a) $\frac{1}{2}$ (b) 2 **13.** (a) $\frac{1}{2}$ (b) $\frac{1}{2}$
15. (a) $\sqrt{3}/3$ (b) $-\sqrt{3}/3$ **17.** (a) 2 (b) $-2\sqrt{3}/3$
19. (a) $\sqrt{2}/2$ (b) $\sqrt{2}$ **21.** (a) -1 (b) -1
23. $\sin 0 = 0$, $\cos 0 = 1$, $\tan 0 = 0$, $\sec 0 = 1$,
others undefined
25. $\sin \pi = 0$, $\cos \pi = -1$, $\tan \pi = 0$, $\sec \pi = -1$,
others undefined
27. $\frac{4}{5}, \frac{3}{5}, \frac{4}{3}$ **29.** $-\sqrt{11}/4, \sqrt{5}/4, -\sqrt{55}/5$ **31.** $\frac{9}{41}, \frac{40}{41}, \frac{9}{40}$
33. $-\frac{12}{13}, -\frac{5}{13}, \frac{12}{5}$ **35.** (a) 0.8 (b) 0.84147
37. (a) 0.9 (b) 0.93204 **39.** (a) 1 (b) 1.02964
41. (a) -0.6 (b) -0.57482 **43.** Negative
45. Negative   **47.** II   **49.** II
51. $\sin t = \sqrt{1 - \cos^2 t}$ **53.** $\tan t = (\sin t)/\sqrt{1 - \sin^2 t}$
55. $\sec t = -\sqrt{1 + \tan^2 t}$ **57.** $\tan t = \sqrt{\sec^2 t - 1}$
59. $\tan^2 t = (\sin^2 t)/(1 - \sin^2 t)$
61. $\cos t = -\frac{4}{5}$, $\tan t = -\frac{3}{4}$, $\csc t = \frac{5}{3}$, $\sec t = -\frac{5}{4}$,
$\cot t = -\frac{4}{3}$
63. $\sin t = -2\sqrt{2}/3$, $\cos t = \frac{1}{3}$, $\tan t = -2\sqrt{2}$, $\csc t = -\frac{3}{4}\sqrt{2}$,
$\cot t = -\sqrt{2}/4$
65. $\sin t = -\frac{3}{5}$, $\cos t = \frac{4}{5}$, $\csc t = -\frac{5}{3}$, $\sec t = \frac{5}{4}$,
$\cot t = -\frac{4}{3}$
67. $\cos t = -\sqrt{15}/4$, $\tan t = \sqrt{15}/15$, $\csc t = -4$,
$\sec t = -4\sqrt{15}/15$, $\cot t = \sqrt{15}$
69. Odd   **71.** Odd   **73.** Even   **75.** Neither

Section 5.3 ■ page 439

1.
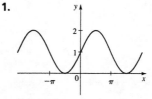

3.
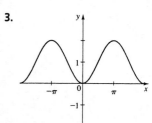

5.
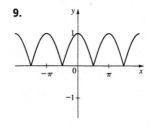

7.
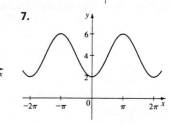

9.
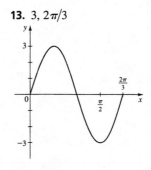

11. $1, \frac{\pi}{2}$
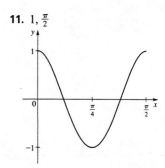

13. $3, 2\pi/3$
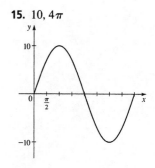

15. $10, 4\pi$
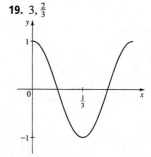

17. $1, 6\pi$
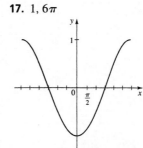

19. $3, \frac{2}{3}$

21. $1, 2\pi, \pi/2$

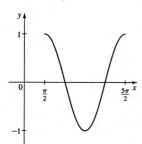

23. $2, 2\pi, \pi/6$

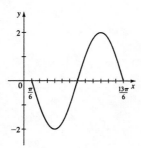

25. $5, 2\pi/3, \pi/12$

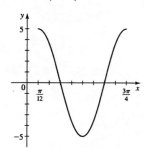

27. $2, 3\pi, \pi/4$

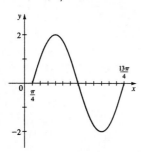

29. $3, 2, -\frac{1}{2}$

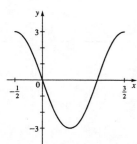

31. $\frac{1}{2}, \pi, \pi/6$

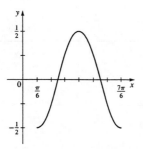

33. $1, 2\pi/3, -\pi/3$

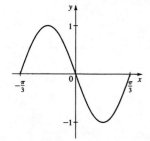

35. (a) $4, 2\pi, 0$ (b) $y = 4 \sin x$
37. (a) $3, 4\pi, 0$ (b) $y = 3 \sin \frac{1}{2}x$
39. (a) $\frac{1}{2}, \pi, -\pi/3$ (b) $y = -\frac{1}{2} \cos 2(x + \pi/3)$

41.

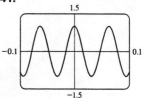

43.

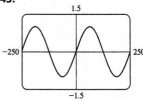

45.

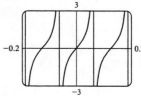

47.

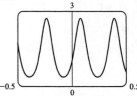

49. (a) 20 s   (b) 6 ft   **51.** (a) $\frac{1}{80}$ min   (b) 80

(c)

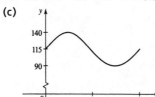

(d) 140/90; it is higher
than normal

53.

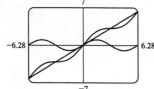

55.

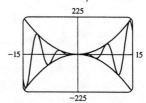

$y = x^2 \sin x$ is a sine
curve that lies between
the graphs of $y = x^2$ and
$y = -x^2$

57.

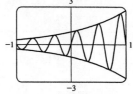

$y = e^x \sin 5\pi x$ is a sine curve
that lies between the graphs
of $y = e^x$ and $y = -e^x$

59.

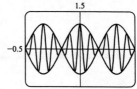

$y = \cos 3\pi x \cos 21\pi x$ is
a cosine curve that lies
between the graphs of
$y = \cos 3\pi x$ and
$y = -\cos 3\pi x$

61. Maximum value 1.76 when $x \approx 0.94$, minimum value -1.76 when $x \approx -0.94$ (The same maximum and minimum values occur at infinitely many other values of x.)

63. Maximum value 3.00 when $x \approx 1.57$, minimum value -1.00 when $x \approx -1.57$ (The same maximum and minimum values occur at infinitely many other values of x.)

65. 1.16   **67.** 0.34, 2.80

69. (a) Odd   (b) $0, \pm 2\pi, \pm 4\pi, \pm 6\pi, \ldots$

(c)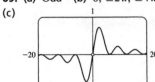

(d) $f(x)$ approaches 0

(e) $f(x)$ approaches 0

Section 5.4 ■ page 451

1. π

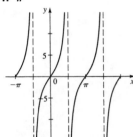

3. π

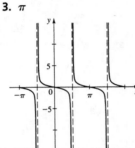

5. π

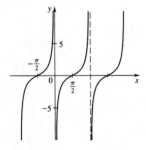

7. 2π

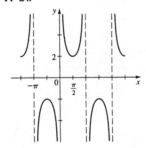

9. 2π

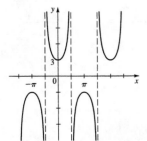

11. π

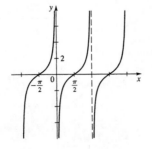

13. 2π

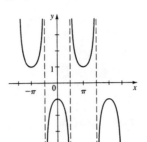

15. π

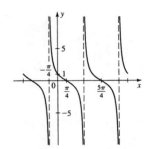

17. 2π

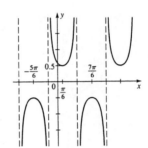

19. $\pi/2$

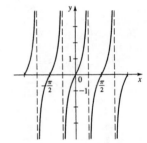

21. 1

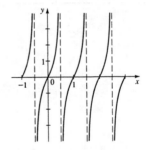

23. π

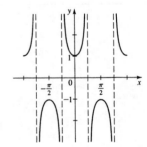

25. π

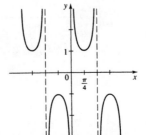

27. $\pi/3$

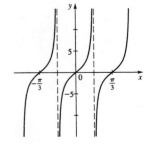

29. $2\pi/3$

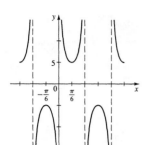

31. $\pi/2$

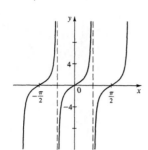

45. $\pi/2$

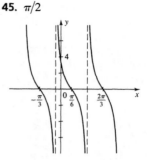

33. $\pi/2$

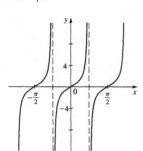

35. $\pi/2$

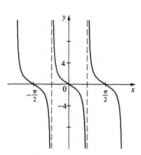

Chapter 5 Review ■ **page 452**

1. (b) $\frac{1}{2}, -\sqrt{3}/2, -\sqrt{3}/3$ **3.** (a) $\pi/3$ (b) $(-\frac{1}{2}, \sqrt{3}/2)$
(c) $\sin t = \sqrt{3}/2$, $\cos t = -\frac{1}{2}$, $\tan t = -\sqrt{3}$, $\csc t = 2\sqrt{3}/3$,
$\sec t = -2$, $\cot t = -\sqrt{3}/3$ **5.** (a) $\pi/4$ (b) $(-\sqrt{2}/2, -\sqrt{2}/2)$
(c) $\sin t = -\sqrt{2}/2$, $\cos t = -\sqrt{2}/2$, $\tan t = 1$, $\csc t = -\sqrt{2}$,
$\sec t = -\sqrt{2}$, $\cot t = 1$ **7.** (a) $\sqrt{2}/2$ (b) $-\sqrt{2}/2$
9. (a) 0.89121 (b) 0.45360 **11.** (a) 0 (b) Undefined
13. (a) Undefined (b) 0 **15.** (a) $-\sqrt{3}/3$ (b) $-\sqrt{3}$
17. $(\sin t)/(1 - \sin^2 t)$ **19.** $(\sin t)/\sqrt{1 - \sin^2 t}$
21. $\tan t = -\frac{5}{12}$, $\csc t = \frac{13}{5}$, $\sec t = -\frac{13}{12}$, $\cot t = -\frac{12}{5}$
23. $\sin t = 2\sqrt{5}/5$, $\cos t = -\sqrt{5}/5$, $\tan t = -2$,
$\sec t = -\sqrt{5}$
25. $(16 - \sqrt{17})/4$ **27.** 3
29. (a) $10, 4\pi, 0$ **31.** (a) $1, 4\pi, 0$
(b) (b)

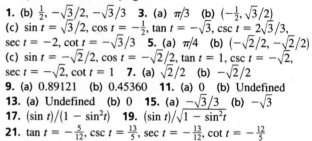

33. (a) $3, \pi, 1$ **35.** (a) $1, 4, -\frac{1}{3}$
(b) (b)

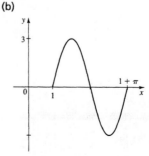
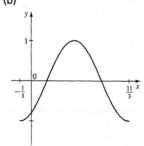

37. 2

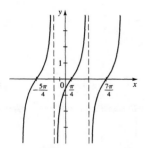

39. $2\pi/3$

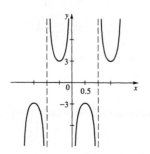

41. $3\pi/2$

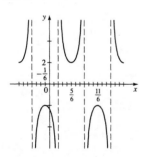

43. 2

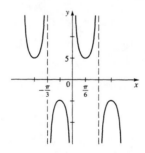

37. $y = 5 \sin 4x$

39. $y = \frac{1}{2} \sin 2\pi\left(x + \frac{1}{3}\right)$

41. π

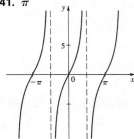

43. π

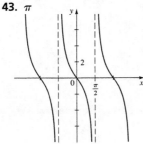

45. π

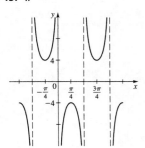

47. 2π

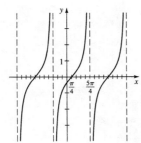

49. (a)

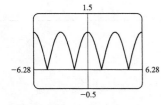

(b) Period π
(c) Even

51. (a)

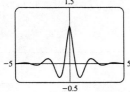

(b) Not periodic
(c) Neither

53. (a)

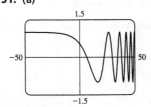

(b) Not periodic
(c) Even

55.

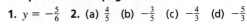

$y = x \sin x$ is a sine function whose graph lies between those of $y = x$ and $y = -x$

57.

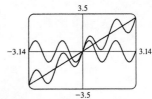

The graphs are related by graphical addition.

59. $1.76, -1.76$ **61.** $0.30, 2.84$

63. (a) Odd (b) $0, \pm\pi, \pm2\pi, \ldots$

(c)

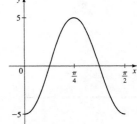

(d) $f(x)$ approaches 0
(e) $f(x)$ approaches 0

Chapter 5 Test ■ page 454

1. $y = -\frac{5}{6}$ **2.** (a) $\frac{4}{5}$ (b) $-\frac{3}{5}$ (c) $-\frac{4}{3}$ (d) $-\frac{5}{3}$

3. (a) $-\frac{1}{2}$ (b) $-\sqrt{2}/2$ (c) $\sqrt{3}$ (d) -1

4. $\tan t = -(\sin t)/\sqrt{1 - \sin^2 t}$ **5.** $-\frac{2}{15}$

6. (a) $5, \pi/2, 0$ (b)

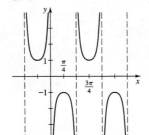

7. (a) $2, 4\pi, \pi/3$ (b)

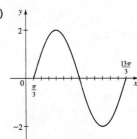

8. π

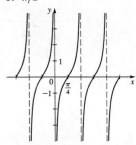

9. $\pi/2$

10. $y = 2 \sin 2(x + \pi/3)$

11. (a)

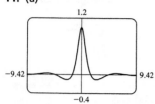

(b) Even

(c) Minimum value -0.11
when $x \approx \pm 2.54$,
maximum value 1
when $x = 0$

Focus on Modeling ■ page 466

1. (a) $2, 2\pi/3, 3/(2\pi)$ **(b)**

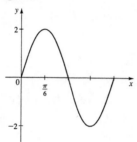

3. (a) $\frac{1}{4}, 4\pi/3, 3/(4\pi)$ **(b)**

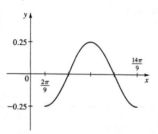

5. (a) 10 m/min

(b)

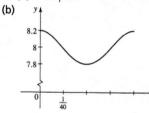

(c) 0.4 m

7. (a) 8900   **(b)** about 3.14 yr   **9.** $d(t) = 5 \sin 5\pi t$

11. $y = 21 \sin\left(\dfrac{\pi}{6} t\right)$

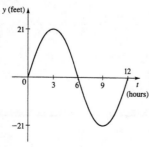

13. $y = 5 \cos 2\pi t$ **15.** $y = 11 + 10 \sin\left(\dfrac{\pi t}{10}\right)$

17. $y = 3.8 + 0.2 \sin\left(\dfrac{\pi}{5} t\right)$ **19.** $E(t) = 155 \cos 120\pi t$

21. (a) 45V   **(b)** 40   **(c)** 40   **(d)** $V(t) = 45 \cos 80\pi t$

23. (a)

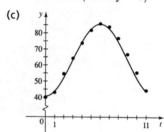

(b) $y = 22.9 \cos 0.52(t - 6) + 62.9$ where y is temperature (°F) and t is months (January $= 0$)

(c)

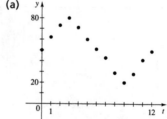

(d) $y = 23.4 \sin (0.48t - 1.36) + 62.2$

25. (a)

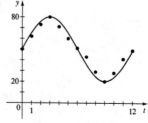

(b) $y = 30 \sin 0.52t + 50$ where y is the owl population in year t

(c)

(d) $y = 25.8 \sin (0.52t - 0.02) + 50.6$

27. $f(t) = e^{-0.9t} \sin \pi t$ **29.** $c = \frac{1}{3} \ln 4 \approx 0.46$

CHAPTER 6

Section 6.1 ■ page 480

1. $\pi/5 \approx 0.628$ rad   **3.** $-8\pi/3 \approx -8.378$ rad   **5.** $\pi/3 \approx$ 1.047 rad   **7.** $-3\pi/4 \approx -2.356$ rad   **9.** $135°$ **11.** $150°$
13. $-270/\pi \approx 85.9°$ **15.** $-15°$ **17.** $410°, 770°, -310°,$ $-670°$ **19.** $11\pi/4, 19\pi/4, -5\pi/4, -13\pi/4$ **21.** $7\pi/4,$ $15\pi/4, -9\pi/4, -17\pi/4$ **23.** Yes   **25.** Yes   **27.** Yes
29. $13°$ **31.** $30°$ **33.** $280°$ **35.** $5\pi/6$ **37.** π **39.** $\pi/4$
41. $55\pi/9 \approx 19.2$ **43.** 4 **45.** 4 mi   **47.** 2 rad $\approx 114.6°$
49. $36/\pi \approx 11.459$ m   **51.** $330\pi \approx 1037$ mi
53. 1.6 million mi   **55.** 1.15 mi   **57.** 50 m^2 **59.** 4 m
61. 6 cm^2 **63.** $32\pi/15$ ft/s ≈ 6.7 ft/s
65. (a) 2000π rad/min   (b) $50\pi/3$ ft/s ≈ 52.4 ft/s
67. 39.3 mi/h   **69.** 2.1 m/s

Section 6.2 ■ page 489

1. $\sin \theta = \frac{4}{5}, \cos \theta = \frac{3}{5}, \tan \theta = \frac{4}{3}, \csc \theta = \frac{5}{4}, \sec \theta = \frac{5}{3},$ $\cot \theta = \frac{3}{4}$ **3.** $\sin \theta = \frac{40}{41}, \cos \theta = \frac{9}{41}, \tan \theta = \frac{40}{9}$ $\csc \theta = \frac{41}{40}, \sec \theta = \frac{41}{9}, \cot \theta = \frac{9}{40}$ **5.** $\sin \theta = 2\sqrt{13}/13,$ $\cos \theta = 3\sqrt{13}/13, \tan \theta = \frac{2}{3}, \csc \theta = \sqrt{13}/2, \sec \theta = \sqrt{13}/3,$ $\cot \theta = \frac{3}{2}$ **7.** (a) $3\sqrt{34}/34, 3\sqrt{34}/34$ (b) $\frac{3}{5}, \frac{3}{5}$
(c) $\sqrt{34}/5, \sqrt{34}/5$ **9.** $\frac{25}{2}$ **11.** $13\sqrt{3}/2$ **13.** 16.51658
15. $x = 28 \cos \theta, y = 28 \sin \theta$
17. $\cos \theta = \frac{4}{5}, \tan \theta = \frac{3}{4}, \csc \theta = \frac{5}{3}, \sec \theta = \frac{5}{4}, \cot \theta = \frac{4}{3}$

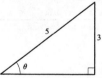

19. $\sin \theta = \sqrt{2}/2, \cos \theta = \sqrt{2}/2,$
$\tan \theta = 1, \csc \theta = \sqrt{2},$
$\sec \theta = \sqrt{2}$

21. $\sin \theta = \sqrt{45}/7, \cos \theta = \frac{2}{7}, \tan \theta = \sqrt{45}/2, \csc \theta = 7\sqrt{45}/45,$ $\cot \theta = 2\sqrt{45}/45$ **23.** $(1 + \sqrt{3})/2$ **25.** 1 **27.** $\frac{1}{2}$
29.   **31.**

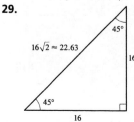

Section 6.3 ■ page 501

1. (a) $30°$ (b) $60°$ (c) $60°$ **3.** (a) $\pi/4$ (b) $\pi/6$ (c) $\pi/3$
5. (a) $\pi/5$ (b) $\pi - \frac{11}{5} \approx 0.94$ (c) $3\pi/7$ **7.** $\frac{1}{2}$ **9.** $-\sqrt{2}/2$
11. $-\sqrt{3}$ **13.** 1 **15.** $-\sqrt{3}/2$ **17.** $\sqrt{3}/3$ **19.** $\sqrt{3}/2$
21. -1 **23.** $\frac{1}{2}$ **25.** 2 **27.** -1 **29.** undefined
31. III   **33.** IV   **35.** $\tan \theta = -\sqrt{1 - \cos^2\theta}/\cos \theta$
37. $\cos \theta = \sqrt{1 - \sin^2\theta}$ **39.** $\sec \theta = -\sqrt{1 + \tan^2\theta}$
41. $\cos \theta = -\frac{4}{5}, \tan \theta = -\frac{3}{4}, \csc \theta = \frac{5}{3}, \sec \theta = -\frac{5}{4},$ $\cot \theta = -\frac{4}{3}$
43. $\sin \theta = -\frac{3}{5}, \cos \theta = \frac{4}{5}, \csc \theta = -\frac{5}{3}, \sec \theta = \frac{5}{4},$ $\cot \theta = -\frac{4}{3}$
45. $\sin \theta = \frac{1}{2}, \cos \theta = \sqrt{3}/2, \tan \theta = \sqrt{3}/3,$ $\sec \theta = 2\sqrt{3}/3, \cot \theta = \sqrt{3}$
47. $\sin \theta = 3\sqrt{5}/7, \tan \theta = -3\sqrt{5}/2, \csc \theta = 7\sqrt{5}/15,$ $\sec \theta = -\frac{7}{2}, \cot \theta = -2\sqrt{5}/15$
49. (a) $\sqrt{3}/2, \sqrt{3}$ (b) $\frac{1}{2}, \sqrt{3}/4$ (c) $\frac{3}{4}, 0.88967$
51. 19.1 **53.** $66.1°$

55. (a)

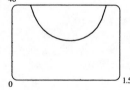

(b) 21.07
57. (a) $A(\theta) = 400 \sin \theta \cos \theta$
(b)

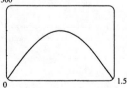

(c) width = depth ≈ 14.14 in.

Section 6.4 ■ page 510

1. 318.8 **3.** 24.8 **5.** $44°$ **7.** $\angle C = 114°, a \approx 51, b \approx 24$

33. $\sin \theta \approx 0.45, \cos \theta \approx 0.89, \tan \theta \approx 0.50, \csc \theta \approx 2.24,$ $\sec \theta \approx 1.12, \cot \theta \approx 2.00$
35. 1026 ft   **37.** (a) 2100 mi   (b) No   **39.** 19 ft
41. $38.7°$ **43.** 345 ft   **45.** 415 ft, 152 ft
47. 2570 ft   **49.** 5808 ft   **51.** 91.7 million mi
53. 3960 mi   **55.** 230.9   **57.** 63.7
59. $a = \sin \theta, b = \tan \theta, c = \sec \theta, d = \cos \theta$

9. $\angle C = 62°$, $a \approx 200$, $b \approx 242$

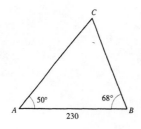

11. $\angle B = 85°$, $a \approx 5$, $c \approx 9$

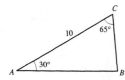

13. $\angle A = 100°$, $a \approx 89$, $c \approx 71$

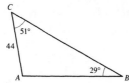

15. $\angle B \approx 30°$, $\angle C \approx 40°$, $c \approx 19$ **17.** No solution
19. $\angle A_1 \approx 125°$, $\angle C_1 \approx 30°$, $a_1 \approx 49$;
$\angle A_2 \approx 5°$, $\angle C_2 \approx 150°$, $a_2 \approx 5.6$
21. No solution   **23.** 219 ft
25. (a) 1018 mi   (b) 1017 mi   **27.** 155 m
29. (a) $d \dfrac{\sin \alpha}{\sin(\beta - \alpha)}$ (c) 2350 ft   **31.** 48.2°

Section 6.5 ■ page 518

1. 28.9   **3.** 47   **5.** 29.89°   **7.** 15
9. $\angle A \approx 39.4°$, $\angle B \approx 20.6°$, $c \approx 24.6$
11. $\angle A \approx 48°$, $\angle B \approx 79°$, $c \approx 3.2$
13. $\angle A \approx 50°$, $\angle B \approx 73°$, $\angle C \approx 57°$
15. $\angle A_1 \approx 83.6°$, $\angle C_1 \approx 56.4°$, $a_1 \approx 193$;
$\angle A_2 \approx 16.4°$, $\angle C_2 \approx 123.6$, $a_2 \approx 54.9$
17. No such triangle   **19.** 2   **21.** 25.4   **23.** 84.6°   **25.** 24.3
27. 2.30 mi   **29.** 23.1 mi   **31.** 2179 mi   **33.** (a) 62.6 mi
(b) S 18.2° E   **35.** 96°   **37.** 211 ft   **39.** 3835 ft
41. 3.85 cm² **43.** 14.3 m   **45.** $165,554

Chapter 6 Review ■ page 522

1. (a) $\pi/3$ (b) $11\pi/6$ (c) $-3\pi/4$ (d) $-\pi/2$
3. (a) 450°   (b) $-30°$ (c) 405°   (d) $(558/\pi)° \approx 177.6°$
5. 8 m   **7.** 82 ft   **9.** 0.619 rad $\approx 35.4°$
11. 18,151 ft²   **13.** (a) 300π rad/min ≈ 942.5 rad/min
(b) 7539.8 in./min = 628.3 ft/min   **15.** $\sin \theta = 5/\sqrt{74}$,
$\cos \theta = 7/\sqrt{74}$, $\tan \theta = \frac{5}{7}$, $\csc \theta = \sqrt{74}/5$, $\sec \theta = \sqrt{74}/7$,
$\cot \theta = \frac{7}{5}$ **17.** $x \approx 3.83$, $y \approx 3.21$
19. $x \approx 2.92$, $y \approx 3.11$
21.

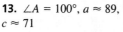

23. $a = \cot \theta$, $b = \csc \theta$
25. 48 m   **27.** 1076 mi
29. $-\sqrt{2}/2$ **31.** 1

33. $-\sqrt{3}/3$ **35.** $-\sqrt{2}/2$ **37.** $2\sqrt{3}/3$ **39.** $-\sqrt{3}$
41. $\sin \theta = \frac{12}{13}$, $\cos \theta = -\frac{5}{13}$, $\tan \theta = -\frac{12}{5}$, $\csc \theta = \frac{13}{12}$,
$\sec \theta = -\frac{13}{5}$, $\cot \theta = -\frac{5}{12}$
43. 60°   **45.** $\tan \theta = -\sqrt{1 - \cos^2 \theta}/\cos \theta$
47. $\tan^2 \theta = \sin^2 \theta/(1 - \sin^2 \theta)$
49. $\sin \theta = \sqrt{7}/4$, $\cos \theta = \frac{3}{4}$, $\csc \theta = 4\sqrt{7}/7$,
$\cot \theta = 3\sqrt{7}/7$
51. $\cos \theta = -\frac{4}{5}$, $\tan \theta = -\frac{3}{4}$, $\csc \theta = \frac{5}{3}$, $\sec \theta = -\frac{5}{4}$,
$\cot \theta = -\frac{4}{3}$
53. $-\sqrt{5}/5$ **55.** 1   **57.** 5.32   **59.** 148.07   **61.** 77.82
63. 77.3 mi   **65.** 3.9 mi   **67.** 119.2 m   **69.** 14.98

Chapter 6 Test ■ page 526

1. $5\pi/3$, $-\pi/10$ **2.** 150°, 137.5°
3. (a) 400π rad/min ≈ 1256.6 rad/min   (b) 31,416 ft/min
4. (a) $\sqrt{2}/2$ (b) $\sqrt{3}/3$ (c) 2   (d) 1
5. $(26 + 6\sqrt{13})/39$ **6.** $a = 24 \sin \theta$, $b = 24 \cos \theta$
7. $(4 - 3\sqrt{2})/4$ **8.** $-\frac{13}{12}$ **9.** $\tan \theta = -\sqrt{\sec^2 \theta - 1}$
10. 19.6 ft   **11.** 9.1   **12.** 250.5   **13.** 8.4   **14.** 19.5
15. (a) 15.3 m²   (b) 24.3 m   **16.** (a) 129.9°   (b) 44.9
17. 554 ft

Focus on Problem Solving ■ page 530

1. Tetrahedron 4, 6, 4; octahedron 8, 12, 6; cube 6, 12, 8;
dodecahedron 12, 30, 20; icosahedron 20, 30, 12
3. Hexagons   **5.** $P + 2\pi$ **7.** $2\left(\dfrac{\pi}{3} - \dfrac{\sqrt{3}}{4}\right) \approx 1.2$
9. 0   **11.** $\sqrt{a^2 + (b + c)^2}$
15. (a) $13 = 2^2 + 3^2$, $41 = 4^2 + 5^2$
(c) $533 = 2^2 + 23^2 = 7^2 + 22^2$

CHAPTER 7

Section 7.1 ■ page 540

1. $\cos t$ **3.** $\sec x$ **5.** -1 **7.** $\csc u$ **9.** 1   **11.** $\cos y$
13. $\sin^2 x$ **15.** $\sec x$ **17.** $2 \sec u$ **19.** $\cos^2 x$
21. $\cos \theta$ **23.** LHS $= \sin \theta \dfrac{\cos \theta}{\sin \theta} =$ RHS
25. LHS $= \cos u \dfrac{1}{\cos u} = \cot u =$ RHS
27. LHS $= \dfrac{\sin y}{\cos y} \sin y = \dfrac{1 - \cos^2 y}{\cos y} = \sec y - \cos y =$ RHS
29. LHS $= \sin B + \cos B \dfrac{\cos B}{\sin B}$
$= \dfrac{\sin^2 B + \cos^2 B}{\sin B} = \dfrac{1}{\sin B} =$ RHS

31. LHS $= -\dfrac{\cos \alpha}{\sin \alpha} \cos \alpha - \sin \alpha = \dfrac{-\cos^2\alpha - \sin^2\alpha}{\sin \alpha}$

$= \dfrac{-1}{\sin \alpha} = $ RHS

33. LHS $= \dfrac{\sin \theta}{\cos \theta} + \dfrac{\cos \theta}{\sin \theta} = \dfrac{\sin^2 \theta + \cos^2 \theta}{\cos \theta \sin \theta}$

$= \dfrac{1}{\cos \theta \sin \theta} = $ RHS

35. LHS $= 1 - \cos^2\beta = \sin^2\beta = $ RHS

37. LHS $= \dfrac{(\sin x + \cos x)^2}{(\sin x + \cos x)(\sin x - \cos x)} = \dfrac{\sin x + \cos x}{\sin x - \cos x}$

$= \dfrac{(\sin x + \cos x)(\sin x - \cos x)}{(\sin x - \cos x)(\sin x - \cos x)} = $ RHS

39. LHS $= \dfrac{\dfrac{1}{\cos t} - \cos t}{\dfrac{1}{\cos t}} \cdot \dfrac{\cos t}{\cos t} = \dfrac{1 - \cos^2 t}{1} = $ RHS

41. LHS $= \dfrac{1}{\cos^2 y} = \sec^2 y = $ RHS

43. LHS $= \cot x \cos x + \cot x - \csc x \cos x - \csc x$

$= \dfrac{\cos^2 x}{\sin x} + \dfrac{\cos x}{\sin x} - \dfrac{\cos x}{\sin x} - \dfrac{1}{\sin x} = \dfrac{\cos^2 x - 1}{\sin x}$

$= \dfrac{-\sin^2 x}{\sin x} = $ RHS

45. LHS $= \sin^2 x\left(1 + \dfrac{\cos^2 x}{\sin^2 x}\right) = \sin^2 x + \cos^2 x = $ RHS

47. LHS $= 2(1 - \sin^2 x) - 1 = 2 - 2 \sin^2 x - 1 = $ RHS

49. LHS $= \dfrac{1 - \cos \alpha}{\sin \alpha} \cdot \dfrac{1 + \cos \alpha}{1 + \cos \alpha} = \dfrac{1 - \cos^2 \alpha}{\sin \alpha(1 + \cos \alpha)}$

$= \dfrac{\sin^2\alpha}{\sin \alpha(1 + \cos \alpha)} = $ RHS

51. LHS $= \dfrac{\sin x - 1}{\sin x + 1} \cdot \dfrac{\sin x + 1}{\sin x + 1} = \dfrac{\sin^2 x - 1}{(\sin x + 1)^2} = $ RHS

53. LHS $= \dfrac{\sin^2 t + 2 \sin t \cos t + \cos^2 t}{\sin t \cos t}$

$= \dfrac{\sin^2 t + \cos^2 t}{\sin t \cos t} + \dfrac{2 \sin t \cos t}{\sin t \cos t} = \dfrac{1}{\sin t \cos t} + 2$

$= $ RHS

55. LHS $= \dfrac{1 + \dfrac{\sin^2 u}{\cos^2 u}}{1 - \dfrac{\sin^2 u}{\cos^2 u}} \cdot \dfrac{\cos^2 u}{\cos^2 u} = \dfrac{\cos^2 u + \sin^2 u}{\cos^2 u - \sin^2 u} = $ RHS

57. LHS $= \dfrac{\sec x}{\sec x - \tan x} \cdot \dfrac{\sec x + \tan x}{\sec x + \tan x}$

$= \dfrac{\sec x(\sec x + \tan x)}{\sec^2 x - \tan^2 x} = $ RHS

59. LHS $= (\sec v - \tan v) \cdot \dfrac{\sec v + \tan v}{\sec v + \tan v}$

$= \dfrac{\sec^2 v - \tan^2 v}{\sec v + \tan v} = $ RHS

61. LHS $= \dfrac{\sin x + \cos x}{\dfrac{1}{\cos x} + \dfrac{1}{\sin x}} = \dfrac{\sin x + \cos x}{\dfrac{\sin x + \cos x}{\cos x \sin x}}$

$= (\sin x + \cos x)\dfrac{\cos x \sin x}{\sin x + \cos x} = $ RHS

63. LHS $= \dfrac{\dfrac{1}{\sin x} - \dfrac{\cos x}{\sin x}}{\dfrac{1}{\cos x} - 1} \cdot \dfrac{\sin x \cos x}{\sin x \cos x} = \dfrac{\cos x(1 - \cos x)}{\sin x(1 - \cos x)}$

$= \dfrac{\cos x}{\sin x} = $ RHS

65. LHS $= \dfrac{\sin^2 u}{\cos^2 u} - \dfrac{\sin^2 u \cos^2 u}{\cos^2 u} = \dfrac{\sin^2 u}{\cos^2 u}(1 - \cos^2 u) = $ RHS

67. LHS $= (\sec^2 x - \tan^2 x)(\sec^2 x + \tan^2 x) = $ RHS

69. RHS $= \dfrac{\sin \theta - \dfrac{1}{\sin \theta}}{\cos \theta - \dfrac{\cos \theta}{\sin \theta}} = \dfrac{\dfrac{\sin^2 \theta - 1}{\sin \theta}}{\dfrac{\cos \theta \sin \theta - \cos \theta}{\sin \theta}}$

$= \dfrac{\cos^2\theta}{\cos \theta(\sin \theta - 1)} = $ LHS

71. LHS $= \dfrac{-\sin^2 t + \tan^2 t}{\sin^2 t} = -1 + \dfrac{\sin^2 t}{\cos^2 t} \cdot \dfrac{1}{\sin^2 t}$

$= -1 + \sec^2 t = $ RHS

73. LHS $= \dfrac{\sec x - \tan x + \sec x + \tan x}{(\sec x + \tan x)(\sec x - \tan x)}$

$= \dfrac{2 \sec x}{\sec^2 x - \tan^2 x} = $ RHS

75. LHS $= \tan^2 x + 2 \tan x \cot x + \cot^2 x = \tan^2 x + 2 + \cot^2 x$

$= (\tan^2 x + 1) + (\cot^2 x + 1) = $ RHS

77. LHS $= \dfrac{\dfrac{1}{\cos u} - 1}{\dfrac{1}{\cos u} + 1} \cdot \dfrac{\cos u}{\cos u} = $ RHS

79. LHS $= \dfrac{(\sin x + \cos x)(\sin^2 x - \sin x \cos x + \cos^2 x)}{\sin x + \cos x}$

$= \sin^2 x - \sin x \cos x + \cos^2 x = $ RHS

81. LHS $= \dfrac{1 + \sin x}{1 - \sin x} \cdot \dfrac{1 + \sin x}{1 + \sin x} = \dfrac{(1 + \sin x)^2}{1 - \sin^2 x}$

$= \dfrac{(1 + \sin x)^2}{\cos^2 x} = \left(\dfrac{1 + \sin x}{\cos x}\right)^2 = $ RHS

83. LHS $= \left(\dfrac{\sin x}{\cos x} + \dfrac{\cos x}{\sin x}\right)^4 = \left(\dfrac{\sin^2 x + \cos^2 x}{\sin x \cos x}\right)^4$

$= \left(\dfrac{1}{\sin x \cos x}\right)^4 = $ RHS

85. $\tan \theta$ **87.** $\tan \theta$ **89.** $3 \cos \theta$

91.

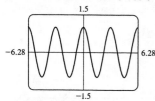

Yes

93.

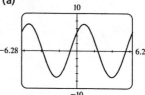

No

Section 7.2 ■ page 548

1. $\dfrac{\sqrt{6} + \sqrt{2}}{4}$ **3.** $\dfrac{\sqrt{6} - \sqrt{2}}{4}$ **5.** $2 + \sqrt{3}$ **7.** $\dfrac{-\sqrt{6} - \sqrt{2}}{4}$

9. $\dfrac{\sqrt{6} + \sqrt{2}}{4}$ **11.** $\sqrt{2}/2$ **13.** $1/2$ **15.** $\sqrt{3}$

17. LHS $= \dfrac{\sin\left(\frac{\pi}{2} - u\right)}{\cos\left(\frac{\pi}{2} - u\right)} = \dfrac{\sin \frac{\pi}{2} \cos u - \cos \frac{\pi}{2} \sin u}{\cos \frac{\pi}{2} \cos u + \sin \frac{\pi}{2} \sin u}$

$= \dfrac{\cos u}{\sin u} = $ RHS

19. LHS $= \dfrac{1}{\cos\left(\frac{\pi}{2} - u\right)} = \dfrac{1}{\cos \frac{\pi}{2} \cos u + \sin \frac{\pi}{2} \sin u}$

$= \dfrac{1}{\sin u} = $ RHS

21. LHS $= \sin x \cos \frac{\pi}{2} - \cos x \sin \frac{\pi}{2} = $ RHS
23. LHS $= \sin x \cos \pi - \cos x \sin \pi = $ RHS

25. LHS $= \dfrac{\tan x - \tan \pi}{1 + \tan x \tan \pi} = $ RHS

27. LHS $=$

$\cos x \cos \frac{\pi}{6} - \sin x \sin \frac{\pi}{6} + \sin x \cos \frac{\pi}{3} - \cos x \sin \frac{\pi}{3}$
$= \frac{\sqrt{3}}{2} \cos x - \frac{1}{2} \sin x + \frac{1}{2} \sin x - \frac{\sqrt{3}}{2} \cos x = $ RHS

29. LHS $= \sin x \cos y + \cos x \sin y$
$- (\sin x \cos y - \cos x \sin y) = $ RHS

31. LHS $= \dfrac{1}{\tan(x - y)} = \dfrac{1 + \tan x \tan y}{\tan x - \tan y}$

$= \dfrac{1 + \frac{1}{\cot x}\frac{1}{\cot y}}{\frac{1}{\cot x} - \frac{1}{\cot y}} \cdot \dfrac{\cot x \cot y}{\cot x \cot y} = $ RHS

33. LHS $= \dfrac{\sin x}{\cos x} - \dfrac{\sin y}{\cos y} = \dfrac{\sin x \cos y - \cos x \sin y}{\cos x \cos y} = $ RHS

35. LHS $=$

$\dfrac{\sin x \cos y + \cos x \sin y - (\sin x \cos y - \cos x \sin y)}{\cos x \cos y - \sin x \sin y + \cos x \cos y + \sin x \sin y}$

$= \dfrac{2 \cos x \sin y}{2 \cos x \cos y} = $ RHS

37. LHS $= \sin((x + y) + z)$
$= \sin(x + y) \cos z + \cos(x + y) \sin z$
$= \cos z \left[\sin x \cos y + \cos x \sin y\right]$
$\quad + \sin z \left[\cos x \cos y - \sin x \sin y\right] = $ RHS

39. $2 \sin\left(x + \dfrac{5\pi}{6}\right)$ **41.** $5\sqrt{2} \sin\left(2x + \dfrac{7\pi}{4}\right)$

43. $f(x) = \sqrt{2} \sin\left(x + \dfrac{\pi}{4}\right)$

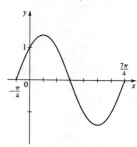

47. $\tan \gamma = \dfrac{17}{6}$

49. (a)

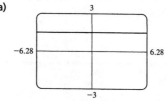

$\sin^2\left(x + \dfrac{\pi}{4}\right) + \sin^2\left(x - \dfrac{\pi}{4}\right) = 1$

51. (a)

(b) $k = 5\sqrt{2}$,
$\theta = \pi/4$

Section 7.3 ■ page 557

1. $\dfrac{120}{169}, \dfrac{119}{169}, \dfrac{120}{119}$ **3.** $-\dfrac{24}{25}, \dfrac{7}{25}, -\dfrac{24}{7}$ **5.** $\dfrac{24}{25}, \dfrac{7}{25}, \dfrac{24}{7}$

7. $-\dfrac{3}{5}, \dfrac{4}{5}, -\dfrac{3}{4}$ **9.** $\dfrac{1}{2}\left(\dfrac{3}{4} - \cos 2x + \dfrac{1}{4} \cos 4x\right)$

11. $\dfrac{1}{32}\left(\dfrac{3}{4} - \cos 4x + \dfrac{1}{4} \cos 8x\right)$

13. $\dfrac{1}{16}(1 - \cos 2x - \cos 4x + \cos 2x \cos 4x)$

15. $\dfrac{1}{2}\sqrt{2 - \sqrt{3}}$ **17.** $\dfrac{1}{2}\sqrt{2 + \sqrt{2}}$ **19.** $\sqrt{2} - 1$

21. $\dfrac{1}{2}\sqrt{2 - \sqrt{3}}$ **23.** (a) $\sin 36°$ (b) $\sin 6\theta$

25. (a) $\cos 68°$ (b) $\cos 10\theta$ **27.** (a) $\tan 4°$ (b) $\tan 2\theta$

29. $\sqrt{10}/10,\ 3\sqrt{10}/10,\ \frac{1}{3}$

31. $\sqrt{(3+2\sqrt{2})/6},\ \sqrt{(3-2\sqrt{2})/6},\ 3+2\sqrt{2}$

33. $\sqrt{6}/6,\ -\sqrt{30}/6,\ -\sqrt{5}/5$

35. $\frac{1}{2}(\sin 5x - \sin x)$ **37.** $\frac{1}{2}(\sin 5x + \sin 3x)$

39. $\frac{3}{2}(\cos 11x + \cos 3x)$ **41.** $2\sin 4x \cos x$

43. $2\sin 5x \sin x$ **45.** $-2\cos\frac{9}{2}x \sin\frac{5}{2}x$

47. $(\sqrt{2}+\sqrt{3})/2$ **49.** $\frac{1}{4}(\sqrt{2}-1)$ **51.** $\sqrt{2}/2$

53. LHS $= \cos(2 \cdot 5x) =$ RHS

55. LHS $= \sin^2 x + 2\sin x \cos x + \cos^2 x = 1 + 2\sin x \cos x$
$=$ RHS

57. LHS $= \dfrac{(2\sin 2x \cos 2x)}{\sin x} = \dfrac{2(2\sin x \cos x)(\cos 2x)}{\sin x}$
$=$ RHS

59. LHS $= \dfrac{2(\tan x - \cot x)}{(\tan x + \cot x)(\tan x - \cot x)} = \dfrac{2}{\tan x + \cot x}$

$= \dfrac{2}{\frac{\sin x}{\cos x} + \frac{\cos x}{\sin x}} \cdot \dfrac{\sin x \cos x}{\sin x \cos x} = \dfrac{2\sin x \cos x}{\sin^2 x + \cos^2 x}$

$= 2\sin x \cos x =$ RHS

61. LHS $= \tan(2x + x) = \dfrac{\tan 2x + \tan x}{1 - \tan 2x \tan x}$

$= \dfrac{\frac{2\tan x}{1-\tan^2 x} + \tan x}{1 - \frac{2\tan x}{1-\tan^2 x}\tan x}$

$= \dfrac{2\tan x + \tan x(1-\tan^2 x)}{1 - \tan^2 x - 2\tan x \tan x} =$ RHS

63. LHS $= (\cos^2 x + \sin^2 x)(\cos^2 x - \sin^2 x)$
$= \cos^2 x - \sin^2 x =$ RHS

65. LHS $= \dfrac{2\sin 3x \cos 2x}{2\cos 3x \cos 2x} = \dfrac{\sin 3x}{\cos 3x} =$ RHS

67. LHS $= \dfrac{2\sin 5x \cos 5x}{2\sin 5x \cos 4x} =$ RHS

69. LHS $= \dfrac{2\sin\left(\frac{x+y}{2}\right)\cos\left(\frac{x-y}{2}\right)}{2\cos\left(\frac{x+y}{2}\right)\cos\left(\frac{x-y}{2}\right)}$

$= \dfrac{\sin\left(\frac{x+y}{2}\right)}{\cos\left(\frac{x+y}{2}\right)} =$ RHS

73. LHS $=$

$\dfrac{(\sin x + \sin 5x) + (\sin 2x + \sin 4x) + \sin 3x}{(\cos x + \cos 5x) + (\cos 2x + \cos 4x) + \cos 3x}$

$= \dfrac{2\sin 3x \cos 2x + 2\sin 3x \cos x + \sin 3x}{2\cos 3x \cos 2x + 2\cos 3x \cos x + \cos 3x}$

$= \dfrac{\sin 3x(2\cos 2x + 2\cos x + 1)}{\cos 3x(2\cos 2x + 2\cos x + 1)} =$ RHS

75. (a)
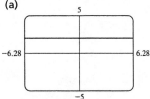

$\dfrac{\sin 3x}{\sin x} - \dfrac{\cos 3x}{\cos x} = 2$

77. (a)
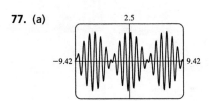

(c)
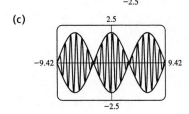

The graph of $y = f(x)$ lies between the two other graphs.

83. (a) $P(t) = 8t^4 - 8t^2 + 1$
(b) $Q(t) = 16t^5 - 20t^3 + 5t$

Section 7.4 ■ page 567

1. (a) $\pi/6$ (b) $\pi/3$ (c) Not defined

3. (a) $\pi/4$ (b) $\pi/4$ (c) $-\pi/4$

5. (a) $\pi/2$ (b) 0   (c) π

7. (a) $\pi/6$ (b) $-\pi/6$ (c) Not defined

9. (a) 0.13889   (b) 2.75876   **11.** (a) 0.88998

(b) Not defined   **13.** $\frac{1}{4}$ **15.** 5   **17.** $\pi/3$ **19.** $-\pi/6$

21. $-\pi/3$ **23.** $\sqrt{3}/3$ **25.** $\frac{1}{2}$ **27.** $\pi/3$ **29.** $\frac{4}{5}$

31. $\frac{12}{13}$ **33.** $\frac{13}{5}$ **35.** $\sqrt{5}/5$ **37.** $\frac{24}{25}$ **39.** 1

41. $\sqrt{1-x^2}$ **43.** $x/\sqrt{1-x^2}$ **45.** $\dfrac{1-x^2}{1+x^2}$ **47.** 0

49. (a) $h = 2\tan\theta$ (b) $\theta = \tan^{-1}\left(\frac{h}{2}\right)$

51. (a) $\theta = \sin^{-1}\left(\frac{h}{680}\right)$ (b) $\theta = 0.826$ rad

53. (a)
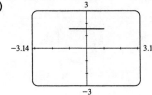

Conjecture: $y = \pi/2$ for $-1 \leqslant x \leqslant 1$

55. (a) 0.28   (b) $(-3 + \sqrt{17})/4$

Section 7.5 ■ page 579

1. $\dfrac{\pi}{2} + 2k\pi$ **3.** $\dfrac{\pi}{3} + 2k\pi, \dfrac{5\pi}{3} + 2k\pi$

5. $\dfrac{4\pi}{3} + 2k\pi, \dfrac{5\pi}{3} + 2k\pi$

7. $\dfrac{\pi}{3} + 2k\pi, \dfrac{2\pi}{3} + 2k\pi, \dfrac{4\pi}{3} + 2k\pi, \dfrac{5\pi}{3} + 2k\pi$

9. $\dfrac{(2k+1)\pi}{4}$ **11.** $\dfrac{\pi}{2} + k\pi, \dfrac{7\pi}{6} + 2k\pi, \dfrac{11\pi}{6} + 2k\pi$

13. $-\dfrac{\pi}{3} + k\pi$ **15.** $\dfrac{\pi}{2} + k\pi$

17. $\dfrac{\pi}{3} + 2k\pi, \dfrac{5\pi}{3} + 2k\pi$ **19.** $\dfrac{3\pi}{2} + 2k\pi$

21. No solution   **23.** $\dfrac{7\pi}{18} + \dfrac{2k\pi}{3}, \dfrac{11\pi}{18} + \dfrac{2k\pi}{3}$

25. $\dfrac{1}{4}\left(\dfrac{\pi}{3} + 2k\pi\right), \dfrac{1}{4}\left(-\dfrac{\pi}{3} + 2k\pi\right)$ **27.** $\dfrac{1}{2}\left(\dfrac{\pi}{6} + k\pi\right)$

29. $4k\pi$ **31.** $4\left(\dfrac{2\pi}{3} + k\pi\right)$ **33.** $\dfrac{k\pi}{3}$

35. $\dfrac{\pi}{6} + 2k\pi, \dfrac{2\pi}{3} + 2k\pi, \dfrac{5\pi}{6} + 2k\pi, \dfrac{4\pi}{3} + 2k\pi$

37. $\dfrac{\pi}{8} + \dfrac{k\pi}{2}, \dfrac{3\pi}{8} + \dfrac{k\pi}{2}$ **39.** $\dfrac{\pi}{9}, \dfrac{5\pi}{9}, \dfrac{7\pi}{9}, \dfrac{11\pi}{9}, \dfrac{13\pi}{9}, \dfrac{17\pi}{9}$

41. $\dfrac{\pi}{6}, \dfrac{3\pi}{4}, \dfrac{5\pi}{6}, \dfrac{7\pi}{4}$ **43.** $\dfrac{\pi}{3}, \dfrac{2\pi}{3}, \dfrac{4\pi}{3}, \dfrac{5\pi}{3}$

45. $0, \dfrac{2\pi}{3}, \dfrac{4\pi}{3}$ **47.** (a) $1.15928 + 2k\pi, 5.12391 + 2k\pi$

(b) $1.15928, 5.12391$

49. (a) $1.36944 + 2k\pi, 4.91375 + 2k\pi$

(b) $1.36944, 4.91375$

51. (a) $0.46365 + k\pi, 2.67795 + k\pi$

(b) $0.46365, 2.67795, 3.60524, 5.81954$

53. (a) $0.33984 + 2k\pi, 2.80176 + 2k\pi$

(b) $0.33984, 2.80176$

55. $((2k+1)\pi, -2)$ **57.** $\left(\dfrac{\pi}{3} + k\pi, \sqrt{3}\right)$

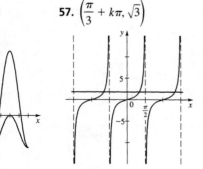

59. $0.94721°$ or $89.05279°$ **61.** $44.95°$ or $135.05°$

63. $\dfrac{\pi}{8}, \dfrac{3\pi}{8}, \dfrac{5\pi}{8}, \dfrac{7\pi}{8}, \dfrac{9\pi}{8}, \dfrac{11\pi}{8}, \dfrac{13\pi}{8}, \dfrac{15\pi}{8}$

65. $\dfrac{\pi}{9}, \dfrac{2\pi}{9}, \dfrac{7\pi}{9}, \dfrac{8\pi}{9}, \dfrac{13\pi}{9}, \dfrac{14\pi}{9}$

67. $\dfrac{\pi}{2}, \dfrac{7\pi}{6}, \dfrac{3\pi}{2}, \dfrac{11\pi}{6}$ **69.** 0   **71.** $\dfrac{k\pi}{2}$

73. $\dfrac{\pi}{9} + \dfrac{2k\pi}{3}, \dfrac{\pi}{2} + k\pi, \dfrac{5\pi}{9} + \dfrac{2k\pi}{3}$

75. $0, \pm0.95$ **77.** 1.92 **79.** ±0.71

Section 7.6 ■ page 589

1. 4

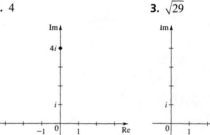

3. $\sqrt{29}$

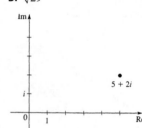

5. 2

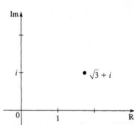

7. 1

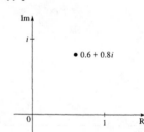

9.

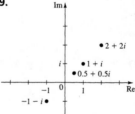

11.

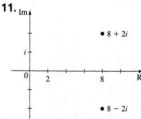

13.

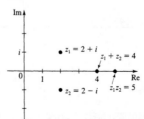

15.

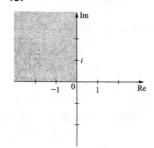

17.

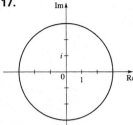

19.

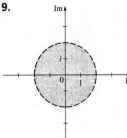

21.

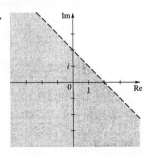

23. $\sqrt{2}\left(\cos\dfrac{\pi}{4} + i\sin\dfrac{\pi}{4}\right)$ **25.** $2\left(\cos\dfrac{7\pi}{4} + i\sin\dfrac{7\pi}{4}\right)$

27. $4\left(\cos\dfrac{11\pi}{6} + i\sin\dfrac{11\pi}{6}\right)$ **29.** $3\left(\cos\dfrac{3\pi}{2} + i\sin\dfrac{3\pi}{2}\right)$

31. $5\sqrt{2}\left(\cos\dfrac{\pi}{4} + i\sin\dfrac{\pi}{4}\right)$ **33.** $8\left(\cos\dfrac{11\pi}{6} + i\sin\dfrac{11\pi}{6}\right)$

35. $20(\cos\pi + i\sin\pi)$

37. $5\left[\cos\left(\tan^{-1}\frac{4}{3}\right) + i\sin\left(\tan^{-1}\frac{4}{3}\right)\right]$

39. $3\sqrt{2}\left(\cos\dfrac{3\pi}{4} + i\sin\dfrac{3\pi}{4}\right)$ **41.** $8\left(\cos\dfrac{\pi}{6} + i\sin\dfrac{\pi}{6}\right)$

43. $\sqrt{5}\left[\cos\left(\tan^{-1}\frac{1}{2}\right) + i\sin\left(\tan^{-1}\frac{1}{2}\right)\right]$

45. $2\left(\cos\dfrac{\pi}{4} + i\sin\dfrac{\pi}{4}\right)$

47. $z_1 z_2 = \cos\dfrac{4\pi}{3} + i\sin\dfrac{4\pi}{3}$

$\dfrac{z_1}{z_2} = \cos\dfrac{2\pi}{3} + i\sin\dfrac{2\pi}{3}$

49. $z_1 z_2 = 15\left(\cos\dfrac{3\pi}{2} + i\sin\dfrac{3\pi}{2}\right)$

$\dfrac{z_1}{z_2} = \dfrac{3}{5}\left(\cos\dfrac{7\pi}{6} - i\sin\dfrac{7\pi}{6}\right)$

51. $z_1 z_2 = 8(\cos 150° + i\sin 150°)$

$\dfrac{z_1}{z_2} = 2(\cos 90° + i\sin 90°)$

53. $z_1 z_2 = 100(\cos 350° + i\sin 350°)$

$\dfrac{z_1}{z_2} = \frac{4}{25}(\cos 50° + i\sin 50°)$

55. $z_1 = 2\left(\cos\dfrac{\pi}{6} + i\sin\dfrac{\pi}{6}\right)$

$z_2 = 2\left(\cos\dfrac{\pi}{3} + i\sin\dfrac{\pi}{3}\right)$

$z_1 z_2 = 4\left(\cos\dfrac{\pi}{2} + i\sin\dfrac{\pi}{2}\right)$

$\dfrac{z_1}{z_2} = \cos\dfrac{\pi}{6} - i\sin\dfrac{\pi}{6}$

$\dfrac{1}{z_1} = \dfrac{1}{2}\left(\cos\dfrac{\pi}{6} - i\sin\dfrac{\pi}{6}\right)$

57. $z_1 = 4\left(\cos\dfrac{11\pi}{6} + i\sin\dfrac{11\pi}{6}\right)$

$z_2 = \sqrt{2}\left(\cos\dfrac{3\pi}{4} + i\sin\dfrac{3\pi}{4}\right)$

$z_1 z_2 = 4\sqrt{2}\left(\cos\dfrac{7\pi}{12} + i\sin\dfrac{7\pi}{12}\right)$

$\dfrac{z_1}{z_2} = 2\sqrt{2}\left(\cos\dfrac{13\pi}{12} + i\sin\dfrac{13\pi}{12}\right)$

$\dfrac{1}{z_1} = \dfrac{1}{4}\left(\cos\dfrac{11\pi}{6} - i\sin\dfrac{11\pi}{6}\right)$

59. $z_1 = 5\sqrt{2}\left(\cos\dfrac{\pi}{4} + i\sin\dfrac{\pi}{4}\right)$

$z_2 = 4(\cos 0 + i\sin 0)$

$z_1 z_2 = 20\sqrt{2}\left(\cos\dfrac{\pi}{4} + i\sin\dfrac{\pi}{4}\right)$

$\dfrac{z_1}{z_2} = \dfrac{5\sqrt{2}}{4}\left(\cos\dfrac{\pi}{4} + i\sin\dfrac{\pi}{4}\right)$

$\dfrac{1}{z_1} = \dfrac{\sqrt{2}}{10}\left(\cos\dfrac{\pi}{4} - i\sin\dfrac{\pi}{4}\right)$

61. $z_1 = 20(\cos\pi + i\sin\pi)$

$z_2 = 2\left(\cos\dfrac{\pi}{6} + i\sin\dfrac{\pi}{6}\right)$

$z_2 z_2 = 40\left(\cos\dfrac{7\pi}{6} + i\sin\dfrac{7\pi}{6}\right)$

$\dfrac{z_1}{z_2} = 10\left(\cos\dfrac{5\pi}{6} + i\sin\dfrac{5\pi}{6}\right)$

$\dfrac{1}{z_1} = \frac{1}{20}(\cos\pi - i\sin\pi)$

63. -1024 **65.** $512(-\sqrt{3} + i)$ **67.** -1

69. 4096 **71.** $8(-1 + i)$ **73.** $\frac{1}{2048}(-\sqrt{3} - i)$

75. $2\sqrt{2}\left(\cos\dfrac{\pi}{12} + i\sin\dfrac{\pi}{12}\right),$

$2\sqrt{2}\left(\cos\dfrac{13\pi}{12} + i\sin\dfrac{13\pi}{12}\right)$

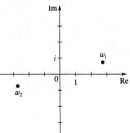

77. $3\left(\cos\dfrac{3\pi}{8} + i\sin\dfrac{3\pi}{8}\right)$, $3\left(\cos\dfrac{7\pi}{8} + i\sin\dfrac{7\pi}{8}\right)$,

$3\left(\cos\dfrac{11\pi}{8} + i\sin\dfrac{11\pi}{8}\right)$, $3\left(\cos\dfrac{15\pi}{8} + i\sin\dfrac{15\pi}{8}\right)$

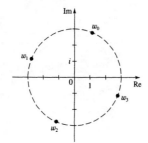

79. ± 1, $\pm i$, $\pm\dfrac{\sqrt{2}}{2} \pm \dfrac{\sqrt{2}}{2}i$

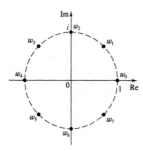

81. $\dfrac{\sqrt{3}}{2} + \dfrac{1}{2}i$, $-\dfrac{\sqrt{3}}{2} + \dfrac{1}{2}i$, $-i$

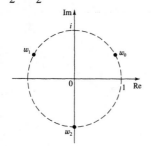

83. $\pm\dfrac{\sqrt{2}}{2} \pm \dfrac{\sqrt{2}}{2}i$

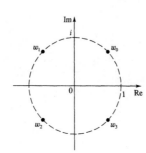

85. $\pm\dfrac{\sqrt{2}}{2} \pm \dfrac{\sqrt{2}}{2}i$

87. $2\left(\cos\dfrac{\pi}{18} + i\sin\dfrac{\pi}{18}\right)$, $2\left(\cos\dfrac{13\pi}{18} + i\sin\dfrac{13\pi}{18}\right)$,

$2\left(\cos\dfrac{25\pi}{18} + i\sin\dfrac{25\pi}{18}\right)$

89. $2^{1/6}\left(\cos\dfrac{5\pi}{12} + i\sin\dfrac{5\pi}{12}\right)$, $2^{1/6}\left(\cos\dfrac{13\pi}{12} + i\sin\dfrac{13\pi}{12}\right)$,

$2^{1/6}\left(\cos\dfrac{21\pi}{12} + i\sin\dfrac{21\pi}{12}\right)$

Section 7.7 ■ page 599

1.

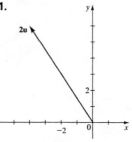

3.

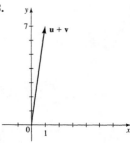

5.

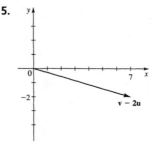

7. $\langle 3, 3\rangle$ **9.** $\langle 3, -1\rangle$ **11.** $\langle 5, 7\rangle$ **13.** $\langle -4, -3\rangle$
15. $\langle 0, 2\rangle$ **17.** $\langle 4, 14\rangle, \langle -9, -3\rangle, \langle 5, 8\rangle, \langle -6, 17\rangle$
19. $\langle 0, -2\rangle, \langle 6, 0\rangle, \langle -2, -1\rangle, \langle 8, -3\rangle$
21. $4i, -9i + 6j, 5i - 2j, -6i + 8j$
23. $\sqrt{5}, \sqrt{13}, 2\sqrt{5}, \frac{1}{2}\sqrt{13}, \sqrt{26}, \sqrt{10}, \sqrt{5} - \sqrt{13}$
25. $\sqrt{101}, 2\sqrt{2}, 2\sqrt{101}, \sqrt{2}, \sqrt{73}, \sqrt{145}, \sqrt{101} - 2\sqrt{2}$
27. $20\sqrt{3}i + 20j$ **29.** $-\dfrac{\sqrt{2}}{2}i - \dfrac{\sqrt{2}}{2}j$
31. $4\cos 10°i + 4\sin 10°j \approx 3.94i + 0.69j$
33. $15\sqrt{3}, -15$ **35.** $5, 53.13°$ **37.** $13, 157.38°$
39. $2, 60°$ **41.** $2i - 3j$ **43.** (a) $40j$ (b) $425i$
(c) $425i + 40j$ (d) 427 mi/h, N 84.6° E
45. 794 mi/h, N 26.6° W   **47.** (a) $10i$ (b) $10i + 17.32j$
(c) $20i + 17.32j$ (d) 26.5 mi/h, N 49.1° E
49. (a) $22.8i + 7.4j$ (b) 7.4 mi/h, 22.8 mi/h
51. (a) $\langle 5, -3\rangle$ (b) $\langle -5, 3\rangle$ **53.** (a) $-4j$ (b) $4j$
55. (a) $\langle -7.57, 10.61\rangle$ (b) $\langle 7.57, -10.61\rangle$
57. $T_1 \approx -56.5i + 67.4j, T_2 \approx 56.5i + 32.6j$

Section 7.8 ■ page 609

1. (a) 2 (b) 45° **3.** (a) 13 (b) 56° **5.** (a) -1
(b) 97° **7.** (a) $5\sqrt{3}$ (b) 30° **9.** Yes **11.** No
13. Yes **15.** 9 **17.** -5 **19.** $-\frac{12}{5}$ **21.** -24
23. (a) $\langle 1, 1 \rangle$ (b) $\mathbf{u}_1 = \langle 1, 1 \rangle$, $\mathbf{u}_2 = \langle -3, 3 \rangle$
25. (a) $\langle -\frac{1}{2}, \frac{3}{2} \rangle$ (b) $\mathbf{u}_1 = \langle -\frac{1}{2}, \frac{3}{2} \rangle$, $\mathbf{u}_2 = \langle \frac{3}{2}, \frac{1}{2} \rangle$
27. (a) $\langle -\frac{18}{5}, \frac{24}{5} \rangle$ (b) $\mathbf{u}_1 = \langle -\frac{18}{5}, \frac{24}{5} \rangle$, $\mathbf{u}_2 = \langle \frac{28}{5}, \frac{21}{5} \rangle$
29. -28 **31.** 25 **33.** 16 ft-lb **35.** 8660 ft-lb
37. 1164 lb **39.** 23.6°

Chapter 7 Review ■ page 612

1. LHS $= \sin\theta \left(\dfrac{\cos\theta}{\sin\theta} + \dfrac{\sin\theta}{\cos\theta} \right) = \cos\theta + \dfrac{\sin^2\theta}{\cos\theta}$
$= \dfrac{\cos^2\theta + \sin^2\theta}{\cos\theta} = $ RHS

3. LHS $= (1 - \sin^2 x)\csc x - \csc x = \csc x - \sin^2 x \csc x - \csc x$
$= -\sin^2 x \dfrac{1}{\sin x} = $ RHS

5. LHS $= \dfrac{\cos^2 x}{\sin^2 x} - \dfrac{\tan^2 x}{\sin^2 x} = \cot^2 x - \dfrac{1}{\cos^2 x} = $ RHS

7. LHS $= \dfrac{\cos x}{\frac{1}{\cos x}(1 - \sin x)} = \dfrac{\cos x}{\frac{1}{\cos x} - \frac{\sin x}{\cos x}} = $ RHS

9. LHS $= \sin^2 x \dfrac{\cos^2 x}{\sin^2 x} + \cos^2 x \dfrac{\sin^2 x}{\cos^2 x} = \cos^2 x + \sin^2 x = $ RHS

11. LHS $= \dfrac{2\sin x \cos x}{1 + 2\cos^2 x - 1} = \dfrac{2\sin x \cos x}{2\cos^2 x} = \dfrac{2\sin x}{2\cos x} = $ RHS

13. LHS $= \dfrac{1 - \cos x}{\sin x} = \dfrac{1}{\sin x} - \dfrac{\cos x}{\sin x} = $ RHS

15. LHS $= \frac{1}{2}[\cos((x+y)-(x-y)) - \cos((x+y)+(x-y))]$
$= \frac{1}{2}(\cos 2y - \cos 2x) = \frac{1}{2}[1 - 2\sin^2 y - (1 - 2\sin^2 x)]$
$= \frac{1}{2}(2\sin^2 x - 2\sin^2 y) = $ RHS

17. LHS $= 1 + \dfrac{\sin x}{\cos x} \cdot \dfrac{1 - \cos x}{\sin x} = 1 + \dfrac{1 - \cos x}{\cos x}$
$= 1 + \dfrac{1}{\cos x} - 1 = $ RHS

19. LHS $= \cos^2 \frac{x}{2} - 2\sin \frac{x}{2}\cos \frac{x}{2} + \sin^2 \frac{x}{2} = 1 - \sin\left(2 \cdot \frac{x}{2}\right) = $ RHS

21. LHS $= \dfrac{2\sin x \cos x}{\sin x} - \dfrac{2\cos^2 x - 1}{\cos x}$
$= 2\cos x - 2\cos x + \dfrac{1}{\cos x} = $ RHS

23. LHS $= \dfrac{\tan x + \tan \frac{\pi}{4}}{1 - \tan x \tan \frac{\pi}{4}} = $ RHS

25. (a) 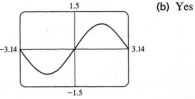 (b) Yes

27. (a) 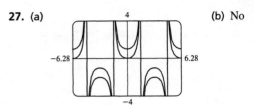 (b) No

29. (a) 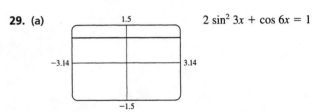 $2\sin^2 3x + \cos 6x = 1$

31. $0, \pi$ **33.** $\dfrac{\pi}{6}, \dfrac{5\pi}{6}$ **35.** $\dfrac{\pi}{3}, \dfrac{5\pi}{3}$ **37.** $\dfrac{2\pi}{3}, \dfrac{4\pi}{3}$

39. $\dfrac{\pi}{3}, \dfrac{2\pi}{3}, \dfrac{3\pi}{4}, \dfrac{4\pi}{3}, \dfrac{5\pi}{3}, \dfrac{7\pi}{4}$

41. $\dfrac{\pi}{6}, \dfrac{\pi}{2}, \dfrac{5\pi}{6}, \dfrac{7\pi}{6}, \dfrac{3\pi}{2}, \dfrac{11\pi}{6}$ **43.** $\dfrac{\pi}{6}$ **45.** 1.18

49. $\frac{1}{2}\sqrt{2 + \sqrt{3}}$ **51.** $\sqrt{2} - 1$ **53.** $\sqrt{2}/2$

55. $\sqrt{2}/2$ **57.** $\dfrac{\sqrt{2} + \sqrt{3}}{4}$ **59.** $2\dfrac{\sqrt{10} + 1}{9}$

61. $\frac{2}{3}(\sqrt{2} + \sqrt{5})$ **63.** $\sqrt{(3 + 2\sqrt{2})/6}$ **65.** $\pi/3$
67. $\frac{1}{2}$ **69.** $2/\sqrt{21}$ **71.** $\frac{7}{9}$ **73.** $x/\sqrt{1 + x^2}$

75. $\theta = \cos^{-1} \dfrac{x}{3}$ **77.** (a) $\theta = \tan^{-1}\left(\dfrac{10}{x}\right)$ (b) none

79. (a)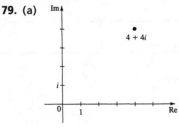

(b) $4\sqrt{2}, \dfrac{\pi}{4}$ (c) $4\sqrt{2}\left(\cos \dfrac{\pi}{4} + i\sin \dfrac{\pi}{4}\right)$

81. (a)

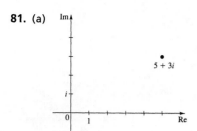

(b) $\sqrt{34}$, $\tan^{-1}\left(\frac{3}{5}\right)$ **(c)** $\sqrt{34}\left[\cos\left(\tan^{-1}\frac{3}{5}\right) + i\sin\left(\tan^{-1}\frac{3}{5}\right)\right]$

83. (a)

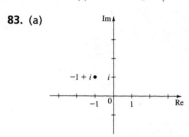

(b) $\sqrt{2}, \dfrac{3\pi}{4}$ **(c)** $\sqrt{2}\left(\cos\dfrac{3\pi}{4} + i\sin\dfrac{3\pi}{4}\right)$

85. $8(-1 + i\sqrt{3})$ **87.** $-\frac{1}{32}(1 + i\sqrt{3})$

89. $\pm 2\sqrt{2}(1 - i)$ **91.** $\pm 1, \pm\frac{1}{2} \pm \dfrac{\sqrt{3}}{2}i$

93. $\sqrt{13}, \langle 6, 4\rangle, \langle -10, 2\rangle, \langle -4, 6\rangle, \langle -22, 7\rangle$

95. $3\mathbf{i} - 4\mathbf{j}$ **97.** $(10, -2)$ **99. (a)** $(4.8\mathbf{i} + 0.4\mathbf{j}) \times 10^4$

(b) 4.8×10^4 lb, N 85.2° E   **101.** 5, 25, 60

103. $2\sqrt{2}, 8, 0$ **105.** Yes   **107.** No, 45°

109. (a) $17\sqrt{37}/37$ **(b)** $\left\langle\frac{102}{37}, -\frac{17}{37}\right\rangle$ **(c)** $\mathbf{u}_1 = \left\langle\frac{102}{37}, -\frac{17}{37}\right\rangle$,

$\mathbf{u}_2 = \left\langle\frac{9}{37}, \frac{54}{37}\right\rangle$ **111.** -6

Chapter 7 Test ■ page 615

1. (a) LHS $= \dfrac{\sin\theta}{\cos\theta}\sin\theta + \cos\theta = \dfrac{\sin^2\theta + \cos^2\theta}{\cos\theta}$ = RHS

(b) LHS $= \dfrac{\tan x}{1 - \cos x} \cdot \dfrac{1 + \cos x}{1 + \cos x} = \dfrac{\tan x(1 + \cos x)}{1 - \cos^2 x}$

$= \dfrac{\frac{\sin x}{\cos x}(1 + \cos x)}{\sin^2 x} = \dfrac{1}{\sin x} \cdot \dfrac{1 + \cos x}{\cos x}$ = RHS

(c) LHS $= \dfrac{2\tan x}{\sec^2 x} = \dfrac{2\sin x}{\cos x} \cdot \cos^2 x = 2\sin x\cos x$ = RHS

2. $\tan\theta$ **3. (a)** $\frac{1}{2}$ **(b)** $\dfrac{\sqrt{2} + \sqrt{6}}{4}$ **(c)** $\frac{1}{2}\sqrt{2 - \sqrt{3}}$

4. $(10 - 2\sqrt{5})/15$

5. (a) $\frac{1}{2}(\sin 8x - \sin 2x)$ **(b)** $-2\cos\frac{7}{2}x\sin\frac{3}{2}x$ **6.** -2

7.

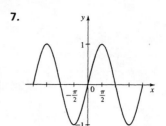

Domain $\mathbb{R}$ Domain $[-1, 1]$

8. (a) $\theta = \tan^{-1}\dfrac{x}{4}$ **(b)** $\theta\cos^{-1}\dfrac{3}{x}$ **9. (a)** $\dfrac{2\pi}{3}, \dfrac{4\pi}{3}$

(b) $\dfrac{\pi}{6}, \dfrac{\pi}{2}, \dfrac{5\pi}{6}, \dfrac{3\pi}{2}$ **10.** 0.57964, 2.56195, 3.72123, 5.70355

11. $\frac{40}{41}$

12. (a)

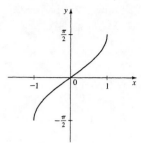

(b) $2\left(\cos\dfrac{\pi}{3} + i\sin\dfrac{\pi}{3}\right)$ **(c)** -512

13. $-8, \sqrt{3} + i$

14. $-3i, 3\left(\pm\dfrac{\sqrt{3}}{2} + \dfrac{1}{2}i\right)$

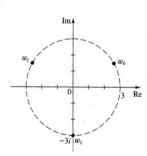

15. (a) $-6\mathbf{i} + 10\mathbf{j}$ **(b)** $2\sqrt{34}$

16. (a) $\langle 19, -3\rangle$ **(b)** $5\sqrt{2}$ **(c)** 0   **(d)** Yes

17. (a) $14\mathbf{i} + 6\sqrt{3}\mathbf{j}$ **(b)** 17.4 mi/h, N 53.4° E

18. (a) 45°   **(b)** $\sqrt{26}/2$ **(c)** $\dfrac{5}{2}\mathbf{i} - \dfrac{1}{2}\mathbf{j}$ **19.** 90

Focus on Problem Solving ■ page 618

1. 636,619   **3.** 16 cm   **7.** $\sqrt{1 + a}$ **9. (b)** 12 cm

(c) A flat disk   **11.** $\dfrac{\pi}{2}, \dfrac{5\pi}{4}, \dfrac{7\pi}{4}$ **13.** 5

SEQUENCES AND SERIES

Arithmetic

$$a, a + d, a + 2d, a + 3d, a + 4d, \ldots$$

$$a_n = a + (n - 1)d$$

$$S_n = \sum_{k=1}^{n} a_k = \frac{n}{2}[2a + (n - 1)d] = n\left(\frac{a + a_n}{2}\right)$$

Geometric

$$a, ar, ar^2, ar^3, ar^4, \ldots \qquad a_n = ar^{n-1}$$

$$S_n = \sum_{k=1}^{n} a_k = a\frac{1 - r^n}{1 - r}$$

If $|r| < 1$, then the sum of an infinite geometric series is

$$S = \frac{a}{1 - r}$$

THE BINOMIAL THEOREM

$$(a + b)^n = \binom{n}{0}a^n + \binom{n}{1}a^{n-1}b + \cdots + \binom{n}{n-1}ab^{n-1} + \binom{n}{n}b^n$$

FINANCE

Compound interest

$$A = P\left(1 + \frac{r}{n}\right)^{nt}$$

where A is the amount after t years, P is the principal, r is the interest rate, and the interest is compounded n times per year.

Amount of an annuity

$$A_f = R\frac{(1 + i)^n - 1}{i}$$

where A_f is the final amount, i is the interest rate per time period, and there are n payments of size R.

Present value of an annuity

$$A_p = R\frac{1 - (1 + i)^{-n}}{i}$$

where A_p is the present value, i is the interest rate per time period, and there are n payments of size R.

Installment buying

$$R = \frac{iA_p}{1 - (1 + i)^{-n}}$$

where R is the size of each payment, i is the interest rate per time period, A_p is the amount of the loan, and n is the number of payments.

COUNTING

Fundamental Counting Principle

Suppose that two events occur in order. If the first can occur in m ways and the second can occur in n ways (after the first has occurred), then the two events can occur in order in $m \times n$ ways.

The number of **permutations** of n objects taken r at a time is

$$P(n, r) = \frac{n!}{(n - r)!}$$

The number of **combinations** of n objects taken r at a time is

$$C(n, r) = \frac{n!}{r!\,(n - r)!}$$

The number of **subsets** of a set with n elements is 2^n.

The number of **distinct permutations** of n elements, with n_i elements of the ith kind (where $n_1 + n_2 + \cdots + n_k = n$), is

$$\frac{n!}{n_1!\,n_2!\cdots n_k!}$$

PROBABILITY

If S is a sample space consisting of equally likely outcomes, and E is an event in S, then the probability of E is

$$P(E) = \frac{n(E)}{n(S)} = \frac{\text{number of elements in } E}{\text{number of elements in } S}$$

Complement of an event:

$$P(E') = 1 - P(E)$$

Union of two events:

$$P(E \cup F) = P(E) + P(F) - P(E \cap F)$$

Intersection of two independent events:

$$P(E \cap F) = P(E)P(F)$$

If a game gives payoffs of $a_1, a_2, \ldots, a_n$ with probabilities $p_1, p_2, \ldots, p_n$, respectively, then the **expected value** is

$$E = a_1p_1 + a_2p_2 + \cdots + a_np_n$$

ANGLE MEASUREMENT

π radians $= 180°$

$1° = \dfrac{\pi}{180}$ rad $\qquad$ 1 rad $= \dfrac{180°}{\pi}$

$s = r\theta \qquad A = \tfrac{1}{2}r^2\theta \quad (\theta \text{ in radians})$

To convert from degrees to radians, multiply by $\dfrac{\pi}{180}$.

To convert from radians to degrees, multiply by $\dfrac{180}{\pi}$.

TRIGONOMETRIC FUNCTIONS OF REAL NUMBERS

$\sin t = y \qquad\qquad \csc t = \dfrac{1}{y}$

$\cos t = x \qquad\qquad \sec t = \dfrac{1}{x}$

$\tan t = \dfrac{y}{x} \qquad\qquad \cot t = \dfrac{x}{y}$

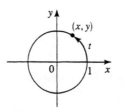

TRIGONOMETRIC FUNCTIONS OF ANGLES

$\sin \theta = \dfrac{y}{r} \qquad\qquad \csc \theta = \dfrac{r}{y}$

$\cos \theta = \dfrac{x}{r} \qquad\qquad \sec \theta = \dfrac{r}{x}$

$\tan \theta = \dfrac{y}{x} \qquad\qquad \cot \theta = \dfrac{x}{y}$

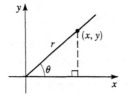

RIGHT ANGLE TRIGONOMETRY

$\sin \theta = \dfrac{\text{opp}}{\text{hyp}} \qquad\qquad \csc \theta = \dfrac{\text{hyp}}{\text{opp}}$

$\cos \theta = \dfrac{\text{adj}}{\text{hyp}} \qquad\qquad \sec \theta = \dfrac{\text{hyp}}{\text{adj}}$

$\tan \theta = \dfrac{\text{opp}}{\text{adj}} \qquad\qquad \cot \theta = \dfrac{\text{adj}}{\text{opp}}$

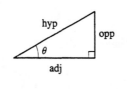

SPECIAL VALUES OF THE TRIGONOMETRIC FUNCTIONS

θ	radians	$\sin \theta$	$\cos \theta$	$\tan \theta$
0°	0	0	1	0
30°	$\pi/6$	$1/2$	$\sqrt{3}/2$	$\sqrt{3}/3$
45°	$\pi/4$	$\sqrt{2}/2$	$\sqrt{2}/2$	1
60°	$\pi/3$	$\sqrt{3}/2$	$1/2$	$\sqrt{3}$
90°	$\pi/2$	1	0	—
180°	π	0	−1	0
270°	$3\pi/2$	−1	0	—

SPECIAL TRIANGLES

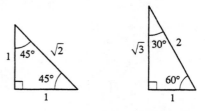

GRAPHS OF THE TRIGONOMETRIC FUNCTIONS

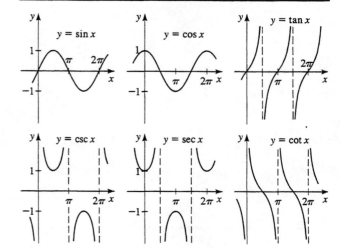

SINE AND COSINE CURVES

$y = a \sin k(x - b) \quad (k > 0) \qquad y = a \cos k(x - b) \quad (k > 0)$

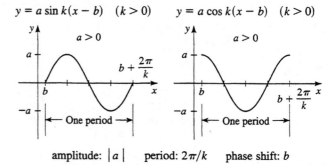

amplitude: $|a|$ $\qquad$ period: $2\pi/k$ $\qquad$ phase shift: b

GRAPHS OF THE INVERSE TRIGONOMETRIC FUNCTIONS

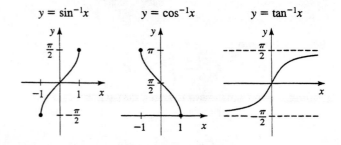